적중100

영어 기출 문제집

중3

시사 | 박준언

Best Collection

구성과 특징

교과서의 주요 학습 내용을 중심으로 학습 영역별 특성에 맞춰 단계별로 다양한 학습 기회를 제공하여
단원별 학습능력 평가는 물론 중간 및 기말고사 시험 등에 완벽하게 대비할 수 있도록 내용을 구성

Words & Expressions

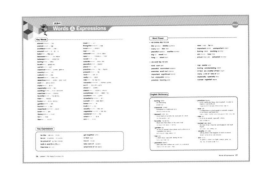

Step1	Key Words 단원별 핵심 단어 설명 및 풀이
	Key Expression 단원별 핵심 숙어 및 관용어 설명
	Word Power 반대 또는 비슷한 뜻 단어 배우기
	English Dictionary 영어로 배우는 영어 단어
Step2	실력평가 단원별 수시평가 대비 주관식, 객관식 문제풀이
Step3	서술형 대비 학업성취도 및 수행능력평가 대비 서술형 문제풀이

Conversation

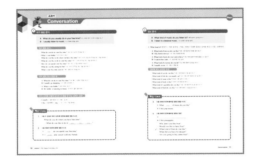

Step1	핵심 의사소통 소통에 필요한 주요 표현 방법 요약
	핵심 Check 기본적인 표현 방법 및 활용능력 확인
Step2	대화문 익히기 교과서 대화문 심층 분석 및 확인
Step3	교과서 확인학습 빈칸 채우기를 통한 문장 완성 능력 확인
Step4	기본평가 시험대비 기초 학습 능력 평가
Step5	실력평가 단원별 수시평가 대비 주관식, 객관식 문제풀이
Step6	서술형 대비 학업성취도 및 수행능력평가 대비 서술형 문제풀이

Grammar

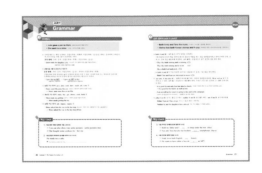

Step1	주요 문법 단원별 주요 문법 사항과 예문을 알기 쉽게 설명
	핵심 Check 기본 문법사항에 대한 이해 여부 확인
Step2	기본평가 시험대비 기초 학습 능력 평가
Step3	실력평가 단원별 수시평가 대비 주관식, 객관식 문제풀이
Step4	서술형 대비 학업성취도 및 수행능력평가 대비 서술형 문제풀이

Reading

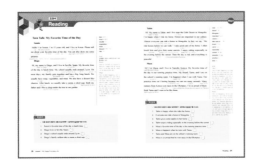

Step1	구문 분석 단원별로 제시된 문장에 대한 구문별 분석과 내용 설명
	확인문제 문장에 대한 기본적인 이해와 인지능력 확인
Step2	확인학습A 빈칸 채우기를 통한 문장 완성 능력 확인
Step3	확인학습B 제시된 우리말을 영어로 완성하여 작문 능력 키우기
Step4	실력평가 단원별 수시평가 대비 주관식, 객관식 문제풀이
Step5	서술형 대비 학업성취도 및 수행능력평가 대비 서술형 문제풀이
	교과서 구석구석 교과서에 나오는 기타 문장까지 완벽 학습

Composition

|영역별 핵심문제|

단어 및 어휘, 대화문, 문법, 독해 등 각 영역별 기출문제의 출제 유형을 분석하여 실전에 대비하고 연습할 수 있도록 문제를 배열

|단원별 예상문제|

기출문제를 분석한 후 새로운 시험 출제 경향을 더하여 새롭게 출제될 수 있는 문제를 포함하여 시험에 완벽하게 대비할 수 있도록 준비

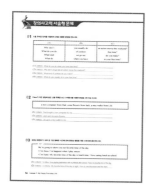

|서술형 실전 및 창의사고력 문제|

학교 시험에서 점차 늘어나는 서술형 시험에 집중 대비하고 고득점을 취득하는데 만전을 기하기 위한 학습 코너

|단원별 모의고사|

영역별, 단계별 학습을 모두 마친 후 실전 연습을 위한 모의고사

교과서 파헤치기

- **단어Test1~3** 영어 단어 우리말 쓰기, 우리말을 영어 단어로 쓰기, 영영풀이에 해당하는 단어와 우리말 쓰기
- **대화문Test1~2** 대화문 빈칸 완성 및 전체 대화문 쓰기
- **본문Test1~5** 빈칸 완성, 우리말 쓰기, 문장 배열연습, 영어 작문하기 복습 등 단계별 반복 학습을 통해 교과서 지문에 대한 완벽한 습득
- **구석구석지문Test1~2** 지문 빈칸 완성 및 전문 영어로 쓰기

Contents

Lesson **3**

Future Dreams, Future Jobs

의사소통 기능

- 확실성 정도 표현하기
  I'm quite sure you could become a great soccer player.
- 의견 표현하기
  It seems to me that you belong to the realistic type.

언어 형식

- It is[was] ~ that 강조 구문
  It is the growth ring in a fish **that** interests me.
- have+목적어+과거분사
  It's my responsibility to **have each song played** the same way every time.

Words & Expressions

Key Words

- **among** [əmʌ́ŋ] 전 ~ 중에서
- **analyst** [ǽnəlist] 명 분석가
- **analyze** [ǽnəlàiz] 동 분석하다
- **animator** [ǽnəmèitər] 명 만화 영화 제작자
- **attend** [əténd] 동 출석하다, 참석하다
- **audition** [ɔːdíʃən] 동 오디션을 보다
- **banker** [bǽŋkər] 명 은행가, 은행원
- **bank teller** 은행 창구 직원
- **brush** [brʌʃ] 명 붓, 솔
- **calm** [kɑːm] 동 진정시키다, 평온하게 하다
- **cast** [kæst] 명 출연자들
- **clear** [kliər] 형 명백한, 투명한
- **conduct** [kəndʌ́kt] 동 지휘하다, 처신하다
- **create** [kriéit] 동 창조하다
- **creature** [kríːtʃər] 명 생물, 생명체
- **data** [déitə] 명 자료
- **detail** [ditéil] 명 세부, 세목
- **developer** [divéləpər] 명 개발자
- **dish** [diʃ] 명 요리
- **engineer** [èndʒiníər] 명 기술자
- **enough** [inʌ́f] 부 충분히 형 충분한
- **figure** [fígjər] 명 인물, 형상, 사람 모양의 장난감
- **fix** [fiks] 동 고치다
- **florist** [flɔ́ːrist] 명 플로리스트, 화초 연구가
- **gardener** [gáːrdnər] 명 정원사
- **greenery** [gríːnəri] 명 화초, 푸른 잎
- **guide** [gaid] 동 안내하다
- **hairdresser** [héərdrèsər] 명 미용사
- **handle** [hǽndl] 동 다루다
- **highly** [háili] 부 매우, 대단히
- **historian** [histɔ́ːriən] 명 역사가, 역사학자
- **include** [inklúːd] 동 포함하다
- **information** [ìnfərméiʃən] 명 정보
- **lawyer** [lɔ́ːjər] 명 변호사
- **lead** [liːd] 동 이끌다, 인도하다
- **machine** [məʃíːn] 명 기계
- **mail carrier** 우편집배원
- **microphone** [máikrəfòun] 명 마이크
- **office worker** 회사원
- **orchestra** [ɔ́ːrkəstrə] 명 오케스트라, 관현악단
- **performance** [pərfɔ́ːrməns] 명 공연
- **personality** [pə̀ːrsənǽləti] 명 성격
- **poet** [póuit] 명 시인
- **police station** 경찰서
- **popular culture** 대중 문화
- **realistic** [rìːəlístik] 형 현실적인
- **recommend** [rèkəménd] 동 추천하다
- **record** [rékɔːrd] 명 기록 [rikɔ́ːrd] 동 녹화하다, 기록하다
- **reduce** [ridjúːs] 동 줄이다, 완화하다
- **report** [ripɔ́ːrt] 명 보고서
- **reporter** [ripɔ́ːrtər] 명 기자, 리포터
- **resource** [ríːsɔːrs] 명 자원
- **responsibility** [rispὰnsəbíləti] 명 책임
- **run** [rʌn] 동 실행하다
- **seem** [siːm] 동 ~인 것 같다
- **select** [silékt] 동 선택하다, 고르다
- **social worker** 사회복지사
- **someday** [sʌ́mdei] 부 언젠가
- **specialist** [spéʃəlist] 명 전문가
- **stethoscope** [stéθəskòup] 명 청진기
- **strength** [streŋkθ] 명 힘, 강점
- **tour guide** 관광 가이드
- **traditional** [trədíʃənl] 형 전통의, 전통적인
- **type** [taip] 명 유형
- **veterinarian** [vètərənέəriən] 명 수의사
- **weakness** [wíːknis] 명 약함, 약점

Key Expressions

- **be happy with** ~ ~에 만족하다
- **be interested in** ~ ~에 관심이 있다
- **belong to** (단체, 조직에) 소속하다, 속하다
- **by - ing** ~함으로써
- **care for** ~을 보살피다
- **come true** 실현되다
- **dream of** ~ ~을 꿈꾸다
- **I'm sure that** ~ ~을 확신하다
- **It seems that** ~ ~처럼 보이다, ~일 것 같다
- **make the best use of** ~을 최대한 활용하다

Word Power

※ 서로 비슷한 뜻을 가진 어휘

□ **run** : **operate** (실행하다, 작동시키다)
□ **fix** : **repair** (고치다)
□ **handle** : **deal with** (다루다)
□ **select** : **choose** (고르다, 선택하다)

□ **highly** : **greatly** (매우, 대단히)
□ **include** : **involve** (포함하다)
□ **guide** : **lead** (안내하다, 이끌다)
□ **recommend** : **propose** (추천하다)

※ 서로 반대되는 뜻을 가진 어휘

□ **weakness** (약함, 약점) ↔ **strength** (강함, 강점)
□ **include** (포함하다) ↔ **exclude** (제외하다)
□ **clear** (분명한) ↔ **unclear** (불확실한)

□ **increase** (증가하다) ↔ **decrease** (감소하다)
□ **construct** (건설하다) ↔ **destroy** (파괴하다)
□ **lead** (이끌다) ↔ **follow** (따르다)

English Dictionary

□ **analyst** 분석가
→ someone whose job is to analyze and examine something
어떤 것을 분석하고 조사하는 일을 하는 사람

□ **analyze** 분석하다
→ to study or examine something in detail, in order to discover more about it
어떤 것에 대해 더 많은 것을 발견하기 위해 자세히 연구하거나 조사하다

□ **audition** 오디션을 보다
→ to give a short performance in order to show that you are suitable for a part in a film, play, show, etc.
영화, 연극, 쇼 등의 어떤 한 역할에 적합하다는 것을 보여주기 위해 짧은 공연을 하다

□ **bank teller** 은행 창구 직원
→ a person whose job is to pay out and take in money in a bank
은행에서 돈을 지급하고 수납하는 것이 직업인 사람

□ **belong to** 소속하다, 속하다
→ to be a member of an organization
조직의 일원이 되다

□ **care for** 보살피다
→ to protect someone or something and provide the things they need, especially someone who is young, old or ill
누군가나 무언가를 보호하고 특히 어리거나, 늙거나, 병든 사람을 위해서 그들이 필요로 하는 것들을 제공해 주다

□ **cast** 출연자
→ the actors in a film, play, or show
영화, 연극, 또는 쇼에 나오는 배우들

□ **collect** 모으다
→ to take things and put them together
물건을 가져가서 한데 모으다

□ **data** 자료
→ facts or information that can be analysed
분석될 수 있는 사실이나 정보

□ **developer** 개발자
→ a person or company that creates new products, especially computer products such as software
특히 소프트웨어와 같은 컴퓨터 제품을 신제품으로 만드는 사람 또는 회사

□ **greenery** 푸른 잎, 화초
→ green plants or branches, especially when cut and used as decoration
특히 잘려서 장식으로 사용되는 녹색 식물이나 가지

□ **include** 포함하다
→ to contain something as a part of something else, or to make something part of something else
무언가를 다른 것의 일부로 포함하거나 다른 것의 일부로 만들다

□ **lead** 이끌다
→ to bring a person or thing to a state or place
사람이나 사물을 어떤 상태나 장소로 데려오다[가져오다]

□ **make the best use of** 최대한 활용하다
→ to use something as much as you can
당신이 할 수 있는 만큼 많이 무언가를 사용하다

□ **personality** 성격
→ the type of person you are, shown by the way you behave, feel, and think
당신이 어떤 사람인지, 행동하고 느끼고 생각하는 방식으로 보여지는 것

□ **responsibility** 책임
→ your job or duty to deal with something or someone
어떤 것 또는 어떤 사람을 처리해야 할 일이나 의무

□ **resource** 자원
→ a useful or valuable possession or quality of a country, organization, or person
국가, 조직 또는 개인의 유용하거나 가치 있는 소유물 또는 자질

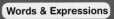
중요
01 다음 문장의 빈칸에 공통으로 들어갈 말로 가장 알맞은 것은?

> • Ted and I _____ the same school.
> • My parents are out of town to _____ the wedding.

① record ② develop
③ create ④ attend
⑤ select

서답형
02 다음 글의 빈칸에 들어갈 알맞은 말을 쓰시오.

> A _____ is someone who creates beautiful things with flowers.

[03~04] 다음 설명에 해당하는 단어를 고르시오.

03
> to be a member of an organization

① reduce ② belong to
③ make up ④ come true
⑤ make the best use of

중요
04
> a useful or valuable possession or quality of a country, organization, or person

① source ② personality
③ resource ④ cast
⑤ developer

서답형
05 다음 우리말에 맞게 빈칸에 알맞은 단어를 쓰시오.

> 나는 내 팀의 강점과 약점을 보여 주기 위해서 그 자료들을 분석합니다.

➡ I _____ the data to show my team's _____s and _____es.

06 다음 빈칸에 공통으로 들어갈 말로 가장 알맞은 것은?

> (A) Children's pictures _____ the walls of the classroom.
> (B) It is a lot of fun to _____ your house with beautiful flowers.

① include ② increase
③ select ④ care for
⑤ decorate

서답형
07 다음 짝지어진 단어의 관계가 같도록 빈칸에 알맞은 말을 쓰시오.

> fix : _____ = deal with : handle

중요
08 다음 빈칸에 들어갈 말로 알맞게 짝지어진 것은?

> As a director of a musical theater, I do a lot of things. I _____ the actors and I look for good, strong voices. After selecting the _____, I teach them the songs for each scene. Then, I put the cast and orchestra together for practice.

① lead – gardener ② conduct – cast
③ record – actor ④ audition – cast
⑤ analyze – analyst

01 다음 빈칸에 들어갈 말을 〈보기〉에서 찾아 쓰시오.

┤ 보기 ├
among   field   reduce   belong to   calm

(1) She helps them _____ stress and _____ themselves.
(2) What are you most interested in _____ the things on this list?
(3) Most people _____ one of six personality types. Realistic is one of the types.
(4) I am an ocean scientist. Ocean science is a big _____ .

02 다음 글의 밑줄 친 우리말에 해당하는 말을 쓰시오. (주어진 단어를 활용하여 쓰시오.)

I am happy when I create (A)다채로운 무언가를 with fresh flowers and greenery. If you like plants and the arts, I (B)강력히 추천합니다(high) you become a florist.

➡ (A) _____
   (B) _____

03 다음 우리말과 같은 표현이 되도록 문장의 빈칸을 채우시오.

(1) 나는 스포츠 데이터 분석가입니다.
➡ I am a sport data _____ .
(2) 나의 일은 녹화된 경기를 보고 자료를 수집하기 위해 컴퓨터 프로그램을 실행하는 것입니다.
➡ My job is to watch _____ games and run a computer program to collect data.

(3) 공연 동안에, 나는 오케스트라 석에 있고 지휘를 합니다.
➡ _____ the _____, I am in the orchestra area and conduct.

04 영영풀이에 해당하는 단어를 〈보기〉에서 찾아 첫 번째 빈칸에 쓰고, 두 번째 빈칸에는 우리말 뜻을 쓰시오.

┤ 보기 ├
greenery   collect   personality

(1) _____: to take things and put them together: _____
(2) _____: the type of person you are, shown by the way you behave, feel, and think: _____
(3) _____: green plants or branches, especially when cut and used as decoration: _____

05 빈칸에 공통으로 들어갈 단어를 쓰시오.

• To _____ an orchestra, you have to be able to hear the music in your head.
• The police officers _____ a school violence prevention campaign in Incheon four times a year.

Conversation

1 확실성 정도 표현하기

> ### I'm quite sure you could become a great soccer player.
> 나는 네가 훌륭한 축구선수가 될 수 있을 거라고 꽤 확신한다.

■ 'I'm sure (that) ~.'은 '나는 ~을 확신해.'라는 의미로 that절의 내용에 대해 자신의 확신을 나타내며, 'I'm (quite/fairly/absolutely) sure[certain] ~.'으로 표현할 수 있다.

■ 확실성 정도 표현하기(긍정)
  • I was quite sure (that) you would be a successful fashion designer.
    나는 네가 성공적인 디자이너가 될 거라고 꽤 확신했다.
  • I have no doubt that you will become a great soccer player.
    나는 네가 훌륭한 축구선수가 될 것이라고 의심하지 않는다.

■ 확실성 정도 표현하기(부정)
  • I'm not sure you will become a great soccer player.
    나는 네가 훌륭한 축구선수가 될 수 있을 거라고 확신하지 않는다.

■ 상대방에게 확신 여부를 물을 때는 '확실해?'를 의미하는 'Are you sure?'를 쓴다.
  • A: Where is Kevin? Kevin은 어디에 있니?
    B: He's on the left. 그는 왼쪽에 있어.
    A: Are you sure? 확실해?
    B: Yes, I am. 응. 그래.

핵심 Check

1. 다음 대화의 빈칸에 들어갈 말로 알맞은 것을 <u>모두</u> 고르시오.

   A: I'm interested in art. Which job would be right for me?

   A: _____ a designer could be a good job for you.

   ① I'm fairly certain that
   ② I have no doubt that
   ③ I wonder whether
   ④ I'm quite sure that
   ⑤ Make sure that

② 의견 표현하기

> **It seems to me that you belong to the realistic type.** 너는 현실적인 타입에 속하는 것 같다.

■ 'It seems to me that ~.'은 '~인 것 같다'라는 의미로 자신의 의견이나 생각을 나타내는 표현이다. 'It seems to me ~'와 유사한 표현으로 'In my opinion, ~', 'I think ~', 'I believe ~', 'In my view, ~', 'For me, ~' 등이 있다.

■ 의견을 표현하는 방법
내 생각에, 너는 현실적인 타입에 속하는 것 같다.
= I think that you belong to the realistic type.
= In my view, you belong to the realistic type.
= In my opinion, you belong to the realistic type.

- **A:** What do you think about bringing cell phones to school? 너는 휴대전화를 학교에 가져오는 것에 대해 어떻게 생각하니?
  B: In my opinion, it is helpful in case of an emergency. 내 생각에, 그것은 응급상황인 경우에 도움이 돼.

- **A:** What do you think about a water saving movement? 물 절약 운동에 대해서 어떻게 생각해?
  B: It seems to me that it is important to save water. 물을 절약하는 것은 중요한 것 같아.

✎ 핵심 Check

2. 다음 대화의 빈칸에 들어갈 말로 <u>어색한</u> 것은?

   A: I want to be a fashion designer. What would help me become one?
   B: _____ going to fashion shows would be helpful.

① In my opinion,
② It seems to me that
③ In my view,
④ For me,
⑤ You have to believe that

Listen & Speak 1 A-1

B: Anne, ❶I'm planning to visit the police station to see my uncle. He is a police officer.

G: Oh, I want to become a police officer someday.

B: ❷You do? Me, too. ❸I have dreamed of becoming a police officer since I was ten.

G: Can I come with you, Matt? I want to meet your uncle and ask him something.

B: Sure. What are you going to ask?

G: I want to ask him ❹what I need to do to become a police officer.

B: I see. ❺I'm sure he would like to meet you.

B: Anne, 나는 우리 삼촌을 보러 경찰서에 갈 예정이야. 그는 경찰관이거든.
G: 오, 나는 언젠가 경찰관이 되고 싶어.
B: 그래? 나도야. 나는 10살 때부터 경찰관이 되는 것을 꿈꿔 왔어.
G: 내가 너와 함께 갈 수 있을까, Matt? 나 너희 삼촌을 만나서 몇 가지 물어보고 싶어.
B: 물론이지. 무엇을 물어볼 거니?
G: 나는 경찰관이 되기 위해 내가 무엇을 해야 하는지 물어보고 싶어.
B: 알겠어. 나는 그가 널 만나고 싶어할 거라고 확신해.

❶ 'be planning to+동사원형'은 미래의 계획을 말할 때 사용하는 표현으로 '~할 예정이다'로 해석한다. to see는 부사적 용법의 목적으로 '~하기 위해'라는 뜻이다.
❷ do는 want to become a police officer를 대신하는 대동사다.
❸ 'since+주어+과거동사'는 '~한 이후로'의 의미로 현재완료와 주로 사용된다. 'dreamed of(전치사)+동명사(V-ing)' 형태를 사용한다.
❹ ask의 직접목적어 자리에 사용된 간접의문문으로 '의문사+주어+동사'의 어순을 취한다.
❺ 'I'm sure (that) ~.'은 '나는 ~을 확신해.'라는 의미로 확실성의 정도를 표현하는 말이다.

Check(√) True or False

(1) Anne wants to be a police officer.　　　　　　　　　　　T ☐　F ☐

(2) Matt has dreamed of becoming a police officer since he was ten.　T ☐　F ☐

Listen & Speak 2 A-1

G: I'm glad to meet you, Mr. Han. Could you please tell me what you do?

M: Okay. I guide travelers to different places in China and give them information about ❶where they should visit.

G: What else do you do?

M: I tell them about popular culture and traditional food in China.

G: ❷It seems to me knowing a lot about China is very important. Are you happy with your job?

M: Yes. I really love my job.

G: 만나 뵙게 되어 반갑습니다, Mr. Han. 당신이 어떤 일을 하시는지 말해 주실 수 있나요?
M: 그래. 나는 중국에 있는 다양한 장소로 여행객들을 안내하고 그들이 방문해야 할 곳에 대한 정보를 제공해.
G: 그 외에 또 어떤 일을 하시나요?
M: 나는 그들에게 중국의 대중문화와 전통 음식에 대해 말해 줘.
G: 중국에 대해 많이 아는 것이 매우 중요한 것 같네요. 당신의 직업에 만족하시나요?
M: 응. 나는 내 직업을 정말 사랑해.

❶ 전치사 about의 목적어 자리에 사용된 간접의문문이다.
❷ 'It seems to me that ~.'은 '~인 것 같다'라는 의미로 자신의 의견이나 생각을 나타내는 표현이다.

Check(√) True or False

(3) Mr. Han must be a tour guide.　　　　　　　　　　　T ☐　F ☐

(4) The girl isn't interested in Han's occupation.　　　　　T ☐　F ☐

Listen & Speak 1 A-2

M: What's wrong, Jisu?

G: I want to be an animator, but my drawing skill is not ❶good enough.

M: Hmm... ❷Being an animator is not just about being a good artist.

G: What should I do to become an animator?

M: Read a lot of books to make good stories and practice drawing every day.

G: Okay, I'll do so.

M: ❸I'm quite sure that you can be a good animator if you try hard.

G: Thank you very much.

M: 무슨 문제 있니, 지수야?

G: 저는 만화 영화 제작자가 되고 싶은데, 그리기 실력이 좋은 편이 아니에요.

M: 음... 만화 영화 제작자가 되는 것은 단순히 그림을 잘 그린다고 되는 것만은 아니란다.

G: 만화 영화 제작자가 되기 위해서 제가 무엇을 해야 하나요?

M: 좋은 이야기를 만들기 위해 책을 많이 읽고, 그림 그리는 것을 매일 연습하렴.

G: 알겠어요. 그렇게 할게요.

M: 나는 네가 열심히 노력하면 훌륭한 만화 영화 제작자가 될 수 있다고 아주 확신해.

G: 정말 감사해요.

❶ enough는 부사로 형용사 뒤에서 수식을 한다.
❷ Being은 동명사 주어로 단수 취급하고, 전치사 about 뒤에도 동명사 being을 사용한다.
❸ '나는 ~을 아주 확신해.'라는 의미로 that절의 내용에 대한 자신의 확신을 나타내는 표현이다.

Check(√) True or False

(5) Jisu is very good at drawing.   T ☐ F ☐

(6) The man advised Jisu to read lots of books and practice drawing every day.   T ☐ F ☐

Listen & Speak 2 A-2

B: Did you finish the report about your role model?

G: Yes, I did. I wrote about my role model, Ms. Shin. ❶I want to be like her.

B: ❷What does she do?

G: ❸She teaches people how to stretch. She also ❹helps them reduce stress and calm themselves.

B: Good. ❺It seems that she helps to keep both their mind and body healthy.

G: Yes, and I think it's great.

B: 네 롤 모델에 관한 기사 다 썼니?

G: 응, 다 썼어. 나는 나의 롤 모델인 신 씨에 관해 썼어. 나는 그녀처럼 되고 싶어.

B: 그녀는 무슨 일을 하니?

G: 그녀는 사람들에게 스트레칭하는 방법을 가르쳐. 그녀는 또한 그들이 스트레스를 완화하여 평온해지도록 도와 줘.

B: 좋구나. 그녀가 사람들의 몸과 마음을 둘 다 건강하게 유지하도록 돕는 것 같아.

G: 맞아, 그리고 나는 그것이 훌륭하다고 생각해.

❶ want는 to부정사를 목적어로 취하는 동사이고, 'be like'는 '~처럼 되다'는 의미로 이때의 like는 전치사이다.
❷ 직업을 묻는 표현이다.
❸ 'teach+간접목적어+직접목적어(how to stretch)' 구문이다.
❹ 'help+목적어+목적보어(동사원형/to부정사)' 구문으로 '…가 ~하도록 돕다'라는 뜻이다.
❺ 'It seems that+주어+동사 ~'는 '~처럼 보이다, ~인 것 같다'는 의미로 '주어+seem(s) to부정사'로 문장을 전환할 수 있다. help는 to부정사와 동사원형을 목적어로 가질 수 있다.

Check(√) True or False

(7) The girl wants to be like Ms. Shin.   T ☐ F ☐

(8) Ms. Shin helps people cure their disease.   T ☐ F ☐

Listen & Speak 1 B

- **A:** I'm interested in technology. ❶Which job would be right for me?
- **B:** ❷I'm quite sure that an app developer could be a good job for you.
- **A:** I'm interested in writing. Which job would be right for me?
- **B:** I'm quite sure that a writer could be a good job for you.

❶ which는 명사를 수식하는 의문형용사로 '어느, 어떤'의 의미다.
❷ an app developer: 앱 개발자

Listen & Speak 2 B

- **A:** I want to be a radio program writer. What would ❶help me become one?
- **B:** ❷It seems to me writing your own stories would be helpful.
- **A:** I want to be a social worker. What would help me become one?
- **B:** It seems to me reading books to kids at a hospital would be helpful.

❶ help+목적어+동사원형: 목적어가 ～하는 것을 돕다 one=a writer
❷ It seems to me (that) ... 구문이다. writing은 동명사로 would be의 주어이다.

Real Life Talk

Bora: ❶What are you most interested in among the things on this list?

Jessie: I'm most interested in ❷working outside and playing sports.

Bora: Well, ❸it seems to me that you belong to the realistic type.

Jessie: What do you mean?

Bora: Most people belong to ❹one of six personality types. Realistic is one of the types.

Jessie: Oh, that's interesting. ❺What kind of jobs do they recommend for realistic types?

Bora: A farmer, a police officer, a soccer player, and so on.

Jessie: Oh, I have always wanted to be a soccer player.

Bora: That's good. ❻I'm quite sure you could become a great soccer player.

❶ be interested in ～: ～에 관심이 있다. most는 최상급으로 '가장'의 의미다.
❷ 전치사 in 다음에 동명사 'working ～ and playing ～'이 온다.
❸ belong to는 '～에 속하다'는 의미로 수동태를 사용하지 않는다.
❹ 'one of+복수명사'는 '～ 중 하나'라는 의미이다.
❺ 'What kind of 명사 ～?'는 '어떤 종류의 ～?라는 의미이다.
❻ 확실성의 정도를 표현하는 말이다.

Wrap Up 1

B: Hello, what are you doing, Sumi?

G: I'm looking for a good recipe on the Internet. I need it for my family dinner today.

B: That is nice. Do you cook often?

G: Yes, ❶I try to cook every weekend. I want to be a chef someday.

B: What are you doing ❷to make your dream come true?

G: I'm ❸taking a cooking class. I try to think of new and creative dishes.

B: ❹I'm quite sure you could be a good chef.

❶ try+to부정사: ～하려고 애쓰다[노력하다], try+V-ing: 시험 삼아 ～해 보다
❷ to make는 부사적 용법의 목적으로 '～하기 위해서'라는 뜻이다. 여기서 make는 사역동사로 '목적어(your dream)+동사원형(come)' 형태를 취한다.
❸ 'take a class'는 '수업을 듣다'는 뜻이다.
❹ 'I'm quite sure ～'는 확실성의 정도를 표현하는 말이다.

● 다음 우리말과 일치하도록 빈칸에 알맞은 말을 쓰시오.

Listen & Speak 1 A

1. B: Anne, I'm _____ to visit the _____ _____ to see my uncle. He is a police _____.

   G: Oh, I want _____ _____ a police officer _____.

   B: You _____? Me, too. I have _____ of _____ a police officer _____ I was ten.

   G: Can I come _____ you, Matt? I want to meet your uncle and _____ him _____.

   B: Sure. What are you _____ to ask?

   G: I want to ask him _____ I need _____ _____ to become a police officer.

   B: I see. I'm _____ he _____ _____ _____ meet you.

2. M: What's _____, Jisu?

   G: I want to be an _____, but my _____ skill is not good _____.

   M: Hmm... _____ an animator is not just about _____ good _____.

   G: What should I do to become an _____?

   M: Read _____ _____ _____ books to make good stories and _____ _____ every day.

   G: Okay, I'll do so.

   M: I'm _____ _____ _____ you can be a good animator _____ you try hard.

   G: Thank you very much.

Listen & Speak 1 B

● A: I'm _____ in _____. _____ job would be _____ for me?

   B: I'm quite _____ that an app _____ could be a good job for you.

● A: I'm interested _____ _____. _____ _____ would _____ _____ me?

   B: I'm _____ _____ that a writer could _____ _____ _____ _____ you.

해석

1. B: Anne, 나는 우리 삼촌을 보러 경찰서에 갈 예정이야. 그는 경찰관이거든.
   G: 오, 나는 언젠가 경찰관이 되고 싶어.
   B: 그래? 나도야. 나는 10살 때부터 경찰관이 되는 것을 꿈꿔왔어.
   G: 내가 너와 함께 갈 수 있을까, Matt? 나 너희 삼촌을 만나서 몇 가지 물어보고 싶어.
   B: 물론이지. 무엇을 물어 볼 거니?
   G: 나는 경찰관이 되기 위해 내가 무엇을 해야 하는지 물어보고 싶어.
   B: 알겠어. 나는 그가 널 만나고 싶어할 거라고 확신해.

2. M: 무슨 문제 있니, 지수야?
   G: 저는 만화 영화 제작자가 되고 싶은데, 그리기 실력이 좋은 편이 아니에요.
   M: 음... 만화 영화 제작자가 되는 것은 단순히 그림을 잘 그린다고 되는 것만은 아니란다.
   G: 만화 영화 제작자가 되기 위해서 제가 무엇을 해야 하나요?
   M: 좋은 이야기를 만들기 위해 책을 많이 읽고, 그림 그리는 것을 매일 연습하렴.
   G: 알겠어요. 그렇게 할게요.
   M: 나는 네가 열심히 노력하면 훌륭한 만화 영화 제작자가 될 수 있다고 아주 확신해.
   G: 정말 감사해요.

● A: 나는 기술에 관심이 있어. 어떤 직업이 나에게 맞을까?
   B: 나는 앱 개발자가 너에게 좋은 직업이 될 수 있을 거라고 아주 확신해.
● A: 나는 쓰기에 관심이 있어. 어떤 직업이 나에게 맞을까?
   B: 나는 작가가 너에게 좋은 직업이 될 수 있을 거라고 아주 확신해.

Listen & Speak 2 A

1. **G:** I'm _____ to meet you, Mr. Han. Could you please tell me
   _____ _____ _____ ?

   M: Okay. I _____ travelers to different places in China and give
   them _____ about where they should _____.

   G: What _____ do you do?

   M: I tell them about _____ _____ and _____ food in China.

   G: _____ _____ to me _____ a lot about China is very
   important. Are you _____ _____ your job?

   M: Yes. I really love my job.

2. **B:** Did you finish the report about your _____ _____ ?

   G: Yes, I did. I wrote about my role model, Ms. Shin. I want to
   _____ _____ her.

   B: What _____ she _____ ?

   G: She teaches people _____ _____ _____. She also helps
   them _____ stress and _____ _____.

   B: Good. _____ _____ _____ she helps _____ _____
   _____ their mind _____ body healthy.

   G: Yes, and I think it's great.

Listen & Speak 2 B

- **A:** I want to be a radio _____ _____. What would help me
  _____ one?

  B: It seems to me _____ your own stories would be _____.

- **A:** I want to be a _____ _____. What would _____ _____ _____
  _____ one?

  B: It _____ to me _____ _____ _____ _____ at a
  hospital would _____ _____.

Real Life Talk

Bora: What are you _____ _____ in _____ the things on this
list?

Jessie: I'm most interested in _____ outside and playing sports.

해석

1. **G:** 만나 뵙게 되어 반갑습니다, Mr. Han. 당신이 어떤 일을 하시는지 말해 주실 수 있나요?
   M: 그래. 나는 중국에 있는 다양한 장소로 여행객들을 안내하고 그들이 방문해야 할 곳에 대한 정보를 제공해.
   G: 그 외에 또 어떤 일을 하시나요?
   M: 나는 그들에게 중국의 대중문화와 전통 음식에 대해 말해 줘.
   G: 중국에 대해 많이 아는 것이 매우 중요한 것 같네요. 당신의 직업에 만족하시나요?
   M: 응. 나는 내 직업을 정말 사랑해.

2. **B:** 네 롤 모델에 관한 기사 다 썼니?
   G: 응, 다 썼어. 나는 나의 롤 모델인 신 씨에 관해 썼어. 나는 그녀처럼 되고 싶어.
   B: 그녀는 무슨 일을 하니?
   G: 그녀는 사람들에게 스트레칭하는 방법을 가르쳐. 그녀는 또한 그들이 스트레스를 완화하여 평온해지도록 도와 줘.
   B: 좋네. 그녀가 그들의 몸과 마음을 둘 다 건강하게 유지하도록 돕는 것 같아.
   G: 맞아, 그리고 나는 그것이 훌륭하다고 생각해.

- **A:** 나는 라디오 방송 작가가 되고 싶어. 내가 그것이 되는 데 뭐가 도움이 될까?
  B: 너 자신만의 이야기를 쓰는 것이 도움이 될 것 같아.
- **A:** 나는 사회복지사가 되고 싶어. 내가 그것이 되는 데 뭐가 도움이 될까?
  B: 병원에서 아이들에게 책을 읽어 주는 것이 도움이 될 것 같아.

보라: 너는 이 목록에 있는 것들 중에서 무엇에 가장 관심이 있니?
Jessie: 나는 밖에서 일하는 것과 스포츠 하는 것에 가장 관심이 있어.

Bora: Well, _____ _____ _____ _____ you _____ _____ the _____ type.

Jessie: What do you _____?

Bora: Most people _____ _____ one of six _____ _____. _____ is one of the _____.

Jessie: Oh, that's _____. _____ _____ _____ jobs do they _____ for realistic types?

Bora: A farmer, a police officer, a soccer player, _____ _____ _____.

Jessie: Oh, I have always wanted _____ _____ a soccer player.

Bora: That's good. _____ _____ _____ you could become a great soccer player.

보라: 음, 내 생각에 너는 현실적인 타입에 속하는 것 같아.
Jessie: 무슨 의미야?
보라: 대부분의 사람들은 여섯 가지 성격 유형 중 한 가지에 속해. 현실적인 타입도 그중 하나야.
Jessie: 오, 재미있다. 현실적인 타입의 사람들에게 그들이 추천하는 직업은 뭐야?
보라: 농부, 경찰관, 축구 선수 같은 거야.
Jessie: 오, 나는 항상 축구 선수가 되고 싶어 해 왔어.
보라: 멋지다. 나는 네가 훌륭한 축구 선수가 될 수 있을 거라고 아주 확신해.

Communication Task Step 2

A: I have _____ _____, _____ _____, 1 I, and _____ _____.

B: It _____ _____ me that you _____ _____ Type S.

C: Yes. _____ _____ are _____ for Type S are teacher, nurse, librarian or counselor.

A: Cool. I _____ _____ _____ to be a teacher.

D: That _____ great. I'm _____ _____ _____ _____ _____ be a good teacher.

A: 나는 S가 3개, A가 2개, I가 1개, E가 1개 있어.
B: 너는 S 타입에 속해 있는 것 같아.
C: 응. S 타입에게 추천되는 직업은 선생님, 간호사, 사서, 상담사야.
A: 멋지다. 나는 항상 선생님이 되고 싶었어.
D: 그거 멋지네. 나는 네가 좋은 선생님이 될 수 있다고 아주 확신해.

Wrap Up 1

B: Hello, what are you _____, Sumi?

G: I'm looking for a good _____ on the Internet. I need it for my family dinner today.

B: That is nice. Do you _____ often?

G: Yes, I try _____ _____ every weekend. I want to be a _____ someday.

B: What are you doing to _____ your dream come true?

G: I'm _____ a cooking class. I try _____ _____ _____ _____ new and _____ dishes.

B: _____ _____ _____ you could be a good chef.

B: 안녕, 뭐 하고 있니, 수미야?
G: 나는 인터넷으로 좋은 요리법을 찾아보고 있어. 나는 오늘 우리 가족의 저녁 식사를 위해 그것이 필요해.
B: 그거 멋지네. 너는 요리를 자주 하니?
G: 응, 나는 매주 주말에 요리를 하려고 노력해. 나는 언젠가 요리사가 되고 싶어.
B: 네 꿈을 이루기 위해서 무엇을 하고 있니?
G: 나는 요리 수업을 듣고 있어. 새롭고 창의적인 요리를 생각해 내기 위해 노력해.
B: 나는 네가 좋은 요리사가 될 것이라고 아주 확신해.

01 우리말 해석에 맞도록 문장의 빈칸에 알맞은 말을 쓰시오.

• 너는 현실적인 타입에 속하는 것 같다.

➡ _____ _____ to me _____ you belong to the realistic type.

02 다음 대화의 빈칸에 들어갈 말로 알맞은 것은?

A: I'm interested in art. Which job would be right for me?
B: _____ a designer could be a good job for you.

① I question whether
② You may think that
③ I'm quite sure that
④ I'm very annoyed that
⑤ You should think

03 다음 대화의 빈칸에 들어갈 말로 가장 알맞은 것은?

A: I want to be a radio program writer. What would help me become one?
B: _____

① It seems to me going to fashion shows would be helpful.
② It seems that she helps to keep both their mind and body healthy.
③ I'm quite sure that you could be a radio program writer.
④ It seems to me you are a cook.
⑤ It seems to me writing your own stories would be helpful.

다음 대화의 밑줄 친 말의 의도로 알맞은 것은?

A: Jihun is good at painting.
B: Yes, he is. <u>I'm sure he will be a great painter.</u>

① 관심 표현하기   ② 확실성 정도 표현하기
③ 의견 표현하기   ④ 동의 표현하기
⑤ 반복 요청하기

[01~02] 다음 대화를 읽고 물음에 답하시오.

B: Anne, I'm (a)planning to visit the police station to see my uncle. He is a police officer.

G: Oh, I want (b)to become a police officer someday.

B: You do? Me, too. I have dreamed of (c)become a police officer since I was ten.

G: Can I come with you, Matt? I want to meet your uncle and ask him something.

B: Sure. What are you going to ask?

G: I want to ask him (d)what I need to do to become a police officer.

B: I see. (e)I'm sure he would like to meet you.

01 위 대화의 밑줄 친 (a)~(e) 중, 어법상 어색한 것은?

① (a)   ② (b)   ③ (c)   ④ (d)   ⑤ (e)

02 위 대화의 내용으로 알 수 없는 것은?

① Matt is going to meet his uncle this weekend.

② Anne wants to become a police officer.

③ Matt has wanted to be a police officer since he was ten.

④ Anne wants to ask Matt's uncle something.

⑤ Anne and Matt are going to go to the police station.

03 주어진 문장에 이어질 대화의 순서로 알맞은 것은?

A: I'm interested in animals. Which job is right for me?

(A) That's a person who works at a pet hair salon. He or she designs different hairstyles for pets.

(B) What is a pet hairdresser?

(C) I think a pet hairdresser can be a good job for you.

(D) That sounds nice.

① (B)–(A)–(C)–(D)   ② (B)–(C)–(A)–(D)

③ (C)–(A)–(D)–(B)   ④ (C)–(B)–(A)–(D)

⑤ (D)–(B)–(C)–(A)

04 다음 대화의 빈칸에 들어갈 말로 알맞은 것을 고르시오.

A: I want to be a fashion designer.

_____

B: It seems to me going to fashion shows would be helpful.

① Can I get your advice on fashion shows?

② Do you think I could be a fashion designer?

③ What would help me become one?

④ What would you like to do at fashion shows?

⑤ What do I like to be?

05 다음 대화의 밑줄 친 문장과 같은 의미가 되도록 주어진 단어를 이용하여 세 단어로 쓰시오.

A: It seems to me he is a cook.

B: That's right.

➡ _____, he is a cook. (opinion)

06 다음 두 사람의 대화가 어색한 것은?

① A: Can you imagine what jobs there will be in the future?
B: It seems to me that there will be space travel planners.

② A: Why are you applying to be a self-driving car mechanic?
B: I am interested in new technologies and cars.

③ A: Hello, what are you doing, Sumi?
B: I'm looking for a good recipe on the Internet.

④ A: What are you doing to make your dream come true?
B: I'm taking a cooking class.

⑤ A: I'm interested in technology. Which job would be right for me?
B: I'm quite sure that you could become a great soccer player.

07 서답형
다음 대화의 밑줄 친 우리말에 맞게 주어진 어구를 이용하여 영어로 쓰시오. (단어 2개를 추가하고, 어형 변화 필수)

> M: What's wrong, Jisu?
> G: I want to be an animator, but my drawing skill is not good enough.
> M: Hmm... 만화 영화 제작자가 되는 것은 단순히 그림을 잘 그린다고 되는 것만은 아니란다.

> be / an animator / not just / about / a good artist.

➡ _____

08 다음 대화의 밑줄 친 부분의 의도로 알맞은 것은?

> A: I want to be a radio program writer. What would help me become one?
> B: It seems to me writing your own stories would be helpful.

① 조언 구하기 ② 의견 표현하기
③ 확신 표현하기 ④ 궁금증 표현하기
⑤ 가능성 묻기

[09~10] 다음 대화를 읽고 물음에 답하시오.

> Bora: What are you most interested in among the things on this list?
> Jessie: I'm most interested in working (a)outside and playing sports.
> Bora: Well, it seems to me that you (b)belong to the realistic type.
> Jessie: What do you mean?
> Bora: Most people belong to one of six personality types. (c)Realistic is one of the types.
> Jessie: Oh, that's interesting. What kind of jobs do they (d)recommend for realistic types?
> Bora: A farmer, a police officer, a soccer player, and so on.
> Jessie: Oh, I have always wanted to be a soccer player.
> Bora: That's good. (e)I'm not sure you could become a great soccer player.

09 위 대화의 밑줄 (a)~(e) 중 어색한 것은?

① (a) ② (b) ③ (c) ④ (d) ⑤ (e)

10 위 대화를 읽고 답할 수 없는 것은?

① What is Jessie most interested in among the things on the list?
② What personality type does Jessie belong to?
③ What kind of job does Bora suggest to Jessie?
④ What has Jessie always wanted to be?
⑤ What jobs do they recommend for the realistic type?

[01~02] 다음 대화를 읽고 물음에 답하시오.

B: Anne, I'm planning to visit the police station to see my uncle. He is a police officer.

G: Oh, I want to become a police officer someday.

B: You do? Me, too. (A)나는 10살 때부터 경찰관이 되는 것을 꿈꿔왔어.

G: Can I come with you, Matt? I want to meet your uncle and ask him something.

B: Sure. What are you going to ask?

G: I want to ask him what I need to do to become a police officer.

B: I see. (B)_____

01 위 대화의 우리말 (A)에 맞게 주어진 어구를 알맞은 순서로 배열하시오. (부사절을 문장 뒤에 쓸 것.)

I / have / ten / becoming / a police officer / of / since / was / dreamed / I

➡ _____

_____

2 위 대화의 빈칸 (B)에 들어갈 말을 주어진 〈조건〉에 맞게 쓰시오.

┤ 조건 ├
• 삼촌이 Anne을 만나길 바라실 거라는 확실성 정도를 표현하는 말을 쓸 것.
• 대명사와 would like to를 사용할 것.

➡ _____

03 다음 대화의 빈칸에 들어갈 말로 자연스러운 것을 〈보기〉에서 찾아 문장을 쓰시오.

G: I'm glad to meet you, Mr. Han. (A)_____

M: Okay. I guide travelers to different places in China and give them information about where they should visit.

G: (B)_____

M: I tell them about popular culture and traditional food in China.

G: (C)_____
Are you happy with your job?

M: Yes. I really love my job.

┤ 보기 ├
• What else do you do?
• It seems to me knowing a lot about China is very important.
• Could you please tell me what you do?

4 다음 대화의 빈칸에 주어진 〈조건〉에 맞게 영어로 쓰시오.

┤ 조건 ├
(A) 동사 'do'를 사용하여 직업을 묻는 말을 쓸 것.
(B) 'seem'을 사용하여 의견을 표현하는 말을 쓸 것.

B: Did you finish the report about your role model?

G: Yes, I did. I wrote about my role model, Ms. Shin. I want to be like her.

B: (A)_____

G: She teaches people how to stretch. She also helps them reduce stress and calm themselves.

B: Good. (B)_____ she helps to keep both their mind and body healthy.

G: Yes, and I think it's great.

Grammar

1 It is[was] ～ that 강조구문

> • **It** is a puppy **that** I want to get for my birthday gift.
> 내가 생일 선물로 받고 싶은 것은 바로 강아지이다.
> • **It** was at the concert **that** Jane met Sean for the first time.
> Jane이 처음으로 Sean을 만난 것은 바로 콘서트에서였다.

■ It+be동사+[명사]+that+불완전한 문장: 주어나 목적어인 명사를 강조한다.

  • **Steve** invented **the machine**.
    → It was **Steve** that invented the machine. 그 기계를 발명한 것은 바로 Steve였다.
    → It was **the machine** that Steve invented. Steve가 발명한 것은 바로 그 기계였다.

■ It+be동사+[부사(구/절)]+that+완전한 문장: 부사(구/절)를 강조한다.

  • I met her at the party.
    → It was **at the party** that I met her.
      내가 그녀를 만난 것은 바로 파티에서였다.

■ 'It is[was] ～ that' 강조구문에서 강조하는 대상이 명사일 경우, that을 관계대명사 who 또는 which 등으로 대체할 수 있다.

  • Dr. King took care of my ants.
    → **It was** Dr. King **that[who]** took care of my ants. 나의 개미들을 돌봤던 이는 바로 King 박사였다.
    → **It was** my ants **that[which]** Dr. King took care of. King 박사가 돌봤던 것은 바로 나의 개미들이었다.

핵심 Check

1. 괄호 안에서 알맞은 것을 고르시오.

   (1) It was Susan's car (who / which) Rooney bought last week.

   (2) It was at the theater (that / which) Mom met Daddy for the first time.

② have+목적어+목적보어

The orchestra practices hard to **have** each song **played** the same way every time.
그 오케스트라는 각각의 곡이 항상 같은 방식으로 연주되도록 하기 위해 열심히 연습한다.

Brian **had** his electric scooter **repaired** at the shop. Brian은 가게에서 그의 전기 스쿠터를 수리시켰다.

- have/has/had+목적어+목적보어: have는 '~하게 시키다, ~하게 하다'는 의미의 사역동사로 목적어의 능동/수동 여부에 따라 목적보어 자리에 원형동사 또는 과거분사가 온다.

  - The researchers **had** students **fill** the questionnaire.
    연구진들은 학생들이 그 질문지에 답하도록 시켰다. (능동: 동사원형)
  - The researchers **had** the questionnaire **filled** by students.
    연구진들은 그 질문지가 학생들에 의해 답변되도록 시켰다. (수동: 과거분사)
  - Please **have** Mr. Trump **come** in. Trump씨가 들어오게 해주세요. (능동)
  - Get out of my place, or I'll **have** you **arrested**.
    내 집에서 나가시오. 그렇지 않으면 당신이 체포되도록 하겠소. (수동)

- have/has/had+목적어+목적보어(과거분사): 좋지 않은 일의 경우, '~ 당하다'의 뜻으로 해석한다.

  - He **had** his bag **stolen** by a thief. 그는 도둑에게 가방을 도난당했다.
  - Karl **had** his hat **blown** off by the wind. 바람에 Karl의 모자가 날아갔다.
  - Sally **had** her ankle **broken** in a car accident. Sally는 자동차 사고로 발목이 부러졌다.

- 그 밖의 5형식 표현 동사들

  - Her teacher **made** her **read** that book. 그녀의 선생님은 그녀에게 그 책을 읽게 했다.
    → She **was made to read** that book by her teacher.
  - I could not **make** people **understand** me in Spanish. 나는 스페인어로 사람들에게 내 말을 이해시킬 수 없었다.
    → I could not **make** myself **understood** in Spanish (by people).
  - Jane **heard** the chairman **call** her name. Jane은 의장이 그녀의 이름을 부르는 것을 들었다.
    → Jane **heard** her name **called** by the chairman.
    → The chairman **was heard to call** Jane's name. 의장이 Jane의 이름을 부르는 것이 들렸다.
  - She **got** her son **to fix** the door. 그녀는 그녀의 아들이 문을 고치도록 시켰다.
    → She **got** the door **fixed** by her son.

핵심 Check

2. 다음 우리말에 맞게 괄호 안의 단어를 바르게 배열하시오.

(1) Peter는 여러 번 다리가 부러졌다. (legs, had, times, Peter, several, broken, his)

➡ _____

(2) 나는 이번 토요일에 머리를 깎을 것이다. (hair, will, have, this, cut, I, Saturday, my)

➡ _____

01 다음 문장에서 어법상 <u>어색한</u> 부분을 바르게 고쳐 쓰시오.

(1) The researchers had the girl watched the other student.

_____ ➡ _____

(2) I got my knee injure in a soccer game.

_____ ➡ _____

(3) It was last Friday which they lost their puppy.

_____ ➡ _____

(4) It is my uncle that encourage me to study.

_____ ➡ _____

02 다음 중 어법상 <u>바르지 않은</u> 것은?

① It was two years ago that Christine wrote that novel.

② It was in May that the baby saw the fireworks for the first time.

③ It was James who broke window yesterday.

④ It was the taxi that Frank proposed to Nancy.

⑤ It is when people praise her talent that the actress feels happy.

03 다음 빈칸에 들어갈 말로 알맞은 것은?

Mom _____ me take out the garbage.

① told   ② set   ③ asked

④ had   ⑤ got

04 다음 문장의 밑줄 친 부분을 강조하여 문장을 다시 쓰시오.

Barbara has always wanted to buy <u>those books</u>.

➡ _____

01 다음 문장의 밑줄 친 단어들 중 'It is[was] ~ that' 구문으로 강조할 수 없는 단어는?

> Jonathan wrote a touching story about
> ① ②
> a sick baby yesterday afternoon at the cafe.
> ③ ④ ⑤

02 다음 중 밑줄 친 부분의 쓰임이 나머지와 다른 것은?

① It was the lamp that Shelly broke this morning.

② It is my youngest sister that I always take care of.

③ It is his plan that you should join his soccer club.

④ It was at the mall that Lisa bought the stationery.

⑤ It was Minsu that met the mayor at the park last week.

03 다음 중 어법상 어색한 문장은?

① The workers hired yesterday had her house paint.

② Will you let her go like this?

③ Tom had his hair cut by a barber last Saturday.

④ She'll make my dream come true.

⑤ Aunt Mary always helped me to do my homework when I lived with her.

04 다음 중 어법상 어색한 문장은?

① Tylor's daddy had him drive his truck yesterday.

② My mother allowed me to buy the smartphone yesterday.

③ Sarah Conner had her car fix by the mechanic.

④ The crowd let the little girl play the piano on the street.

⑤ Walking a little fast helps you to relieve some stress from your daily lives.

서답형
05 다음 대화의 문맥에 맞게, 괄호 안에 주어진 단어를 강조하는 'It is[was] ~ that' 구문의 문장을 영작하시오. (7 단어)

> Mom: Did you tear the letter in two?
> Jinwoo: No, _____.
> (Poppy)

서답형
06 다음 〈보기〉의 문장 중 어법상 어색한 것들을 모두 골라 기호를 쓰고, 고치시오.

> ┤ 보기 ├
> ⓐ Those pictures behind you make me think of my golden days.
> ⓑ The director of the film ordered the actress gain 10 kilograms.
> ⓒ Let his son to take your laptop to his school for just a few days.
> ⓓ Mariah helped the new singer performing on the debut stage.
> ⓔ The teacher of Korean literature had Abdullah memorize the poems written by Yun Dongju.
> ⓕ No one could get the addict stops using drugs.

➡ _____
_____

[07~08] 다음 중 'It ~ that'의 쓰임이 나머지 넷과 <u>다른</u> 것은?

07 ① It is my twin sister that you see in this picture.

② It was 30 years ago that Mr. Miles came to govern the region.

③ It is certain that she fell in love with the stranger at first sight.

④ It was in the street that Laura bought the fruit which made them sick.

⑤ It was the skirt that Christine's aunt made on her birthday.

08 중요 ① It is the trumpet that Michelle usually enjoys playing in her free time.

② It was no wonder that Frank got accepted to Harvard University.

③ It was in the warehouse that the secret meeting was held.

④ It was Comet Halley that we happened to see last night.

⑤ It was only a minute ago that the train carrying her family left for LA.

09 중요 다음 중 어법상 <u>어색한</u> 문장은?

① He would not have his mind change by his son's accident.

② The storm made all the items on the shelves fall onto the floor.

③ My grandfather had my daddy take care of the old pine trees in his garden.

④ The fire fighters let everyone inside the building leave at once.

⑤ The Highclass Academy makes its students practice English so hard.

10 다음 문장의 빈칸 (A)~(D)에 들어갈 말로 가장 적절한 것은?

• The guards at the front gate had the guest (A)_____ the mansion. (enter)

• The general ordered our soldiers (B)_____ back a few meters. (step)

• The webtoons Sarah watches every day make her (C)_____. (smile)

• All of my classmates are expecting Haon (D)_____ Highschool Rapper. (win)

	(A)	(B)	(C)	(D)
①	to enter	to step	smile	win
②	to enter	step	to smile	win
③	enter	step	smile	to win
④	enter	to step	to smile	win
⑤	enter	to step	smile	to win

11 중요 다음 중 어법상 옳은 문장은?

① The manager of the hotel had the cleaning crew to wash the floor.

② Dayna's teacher always tells her eat vegetables.

③ The principal let the students to use the computers to prepare for the game.

④ Father always allows me to take pictures with his high-end camera.

⑤ I asked the P.E. teacher help me with the basketball practice.

12 서답형 다음 우리말을 괄호 안의 조건에 맞게 영작하시오.

• Laura는 Tom에게 그녀의 남편이 세탁기를 수리하는 것을 돕도록 시켰다.

(to, had, husband, the washing machine, repair 사용, 총 11단어로 할 것.)

➡ _____

_____

서답형

13 다음 대화가 자연스럽도록 주어진 단어를 모두 활용하여 문장을 완성하시오. (단어들 중 1 단어만 변형할 것.)

> **Father:** Has anyone done something to my plants? I think someone must have watered them too much.
>
> **Daughter:** _____
>
> _____ .
>
> (James / responsible / care / for / it / plants / take / is / is / of / who)

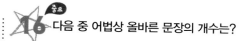

중요

14 다음 중 밑줄 친 that의 쓰임이 나머지와 다른 하나는?

① It was in this cake that Michael hid the ring for his proposal.

② It was his bike that Julie's little brothers broke yesterday.

③ It was in 2015 that Leo won the Academy Award of Best Actor.

④ It was her pet kitty that woke Jessy up this morning.

⑤ It was her belief that ghosts were following her anywhere she went.

15 다음 중 밑줄 친 that을 다른 단어로 대체하여 바꿔 쓸 수 없는 문장은?

① It was the robot arm that carried out the difficult task.

② It is true that the team eventually reached the top of the mountain.

③ It was the suspect that met the police officer the other night.

④ It is he that solved the problem.

⑤ It was Mike that found this book in her room.

중요

16 다음 중 어법상 올바른 문장의 개수는?

ⓐ The famous actor living next door had the refrigerator fix by a repairman.

ⓑ Bill's sisters asked him clean their desks.

ⓒ A lot of crowd watched the boys dancing on the street to the sound of K-pop music.

ⓓ It was soft that Susan bought a scarf.

ⓔ The police officer helped an old lady to cross the street with no traffic signal.

ⓕ Lisa got her son pick up the delivery box.

ⓖ It was my dog that bit her leg.

ⓗ Sean must get this work do on time.

① 1개　② 2개　③ 3개　④ 4개　⑤ 5개

17 다음 우리말을 바르게 영작한 것을 모두 고르시오.

> • 그 가수는 콘서트에서 팬들에게 자신의 사진을 찍도록 했다.

① The singer ordered her fans to take pictures of themselves at the concert.

② The singer let her pictures be taken her fans at the concert.

③ The singer had her fans take pictures of her at the concert.

④ The singer had her fans to take pictures of her at the concert.

⑤ The singer had her pictures taken by her fans at the concert.

서답형

18 다음 문장에서 어법상 어색한 부분을 하나만 찾아서 고치시오.

> • The soccer player had his leg break and got a scar on his forehead during the match.

➡ _____

01 다음 문장을 밑줄 친 부분을 강조하여, 각각 It으로 시작하는 문장으로 바꾸어 쓰시오.

> • <u>John</u> is going to buy <u>the masks</u> <u>at a</u>
>   (A)   (B)
> <u>party</u> <u>this Friday</u>.
>   (C)   (D)

➡ (A) _____

_____

(B) _____

_____

(C) _____

_____

(D) _____

_____

03 다음 각 문장에서 어법상 어색한 부분을 모두 찾아 바르게 고치시오. 단, 강조 구문 자체가 어색할 경우, 전체를 다시 쓰시오.

(1) It is the Hongdae street that the band gives a street performance.

➡ _____

(2) It was carefully that he rescued the injured.

➡ _____

(3) It was chairman of the council who Bush was.

➡ _____

(4) It was the playground that the boy was injured severely.

➡ _____

(5) It is her mistake who she doesn't recognize.

➡ _____

02 다음 그림을 보고, 우리말에 맞게 괄호 안의 단어를 배열하여 빈칸을 채우시오.

> • As my daddy _____
>   pancakes, I was standing with a ladle.
>   (help, make, to, him, have, me, 변형 가능)
>   아빠가 내게 아빠를 도와 팬케이크를 만들도록 시키셔서, 나는 국자를 들고 서 있었다.

04 〈보기〉의 단어들 중 가장 적절한 것을 골라 다음 문장의 빈칸에 써 넣으시오. (어형 변화 가능하며, 각 단어는 1회만 사용할 것)

> ┤ 보기 ├
> look / cry / come / clean / go

(1) Mom had Karl _____ his room.

(2) They felt some smoke _____ out of the conference hall.

(3) Shelly heard a baby _____ out loud.

(4) Her boss let Joen _____ scuba diving.

(5) That diet will allow you _____ slim.

05 다음 주어진 문장과 뜻이 같도록 빈칸을 알맞게 채우되, it을 반드시 사용하시오.

> • March 14, 1879 is the day Einstein was born on.

➡ It was _____ born.

06 다음 각 문장에서 어법상 어색한 단어를 한 개씩 찾아 올바르게 고치시오.

(1) The customs officers at the airport had the baggage check while a passenger was passing through.

  ➡ _____

(2) The host of the show got the singer sing that song again.

  ➡ _____

(3) Her father allowed Gabrielle meet the young boy to find out who he was.

  ➡ _____

(4) Will you let the boys playing here?

  ➡ _____

(5) Susan was broke her legs during the practice of the ballet movement.

  ➡ _____

(6) Those make-ups made you looks more healthy and alive.

  ➡ _____

07 다음 〈보기〉와 같이 두 문장이 같은 의미가 되도록 주어진 단어를 활용하여 제시된 글자 수에 맞게 쓰시오. (어형 변화 가능)

> ─┤ 보기 ├─
>
> Please tell the kids not to make noise here. (make, quiet / 5 단어)
> → Make them be quiet here.

(1) The teacher said to Susan, "Clear all the mess on your desk." (have, clean, Susan / 7 단어)

  ➡ _____

(2) His father looked a lot younger when he put the tie on. (make, much / 8 단어)

  ➡ _____

(3) Please don't stop the girl from watching the film. (allow, enjoy / 6 단어)

  ➡ _____

08 다음 문장을 읽고, 각 질문에 'It is[was] ~ that' 강조 구문을 사용하여 답하시오. 답할 수 없는 질문은 '답변 불가'라고 쓰시오.

> • Alicia had John's phone repaired at the repair shop two weeks ago.

(1) Who repaired John's phone?

  ➡ _____

(2) Who got John's phone repaired?

  ➡ _____

(3) When did Alicia have John's phone repaired?

  ➡ _____
  _____

(4) How many weeks did it take to repair John's phone?

  ➡ _____

(5) Where was John's phone repaired two weeks ago?

  ➡ _____
  _____

Reading

The World of Wonderful Jobs

Florist

Hi, I am Tom. A florist is someone who creates beautiful things with
주격 관계대명사

flowers. To become a florist, you need to know many things about
to부정사의 부사적 용법 중 목적(~하기 위해서)

flowers. I attended a high school for florists and gardeners. It was at
attended at(×)

this school that I learned how to grow and care for different types of
It was ~ that 강조 구문(at this school 강조)   ~하는 방법   =look after

flowers. These days, florists can do a lot of different things. I design
=many

movie sets sometimes and I decorate shops with flowers. I am happy

when I create something colorful with fresh flowers and greenery. If
부정대명사는 형용사의 수식을 뒤에서 받음

you like plants and the arts, I highly recommend you become a florist.
recommend (that) you (should) become a florist

Sport Data Analyst

I am Emma. I am a sport data analyst. It sounds like a difficult job,
~처럼 들리다(sound like+명사)

doesn't it? In fact, it is a lot of fun. I work for a baseball team.
부가의문문   =great

My job is to watch recorded games and run a computer program to
보어   to watch와 병렬 (to) run

collect data. Then, I analyze the data to show my team's strengths and
to부정사의 부사적 용법 중 목적(~하기 위해서)

weaknesses. If the team understands their strengths and weaknesses,

they can do better next time. Since I was young, I have been a big fan
다음번에는   ~이었을 때부터   현재완료: 계속

of baseball. Now, in my work, I watch baseball games all the time.
항상

This is a perfect job for me because watching baseball games is my
이유를 이끄는 접속사(~이기 때문에)   동명사 주어 단수 취급

hobby!

wonderful: 놀라운, 경이로운
attend: 참석하다. (~에) 다니다
care for: ~을 보살피다
these days: 요즈음
movie set: 영화 촬영장
decorate: 장식하다. 꾸미다
greenery: 화초
recorded: 녹화된
in fact: 사실
analyze: 분석하다
strength: 강점
weakness: 약점

📎 **확인문제**

● 다음 문장이 본문의 내용과 일치하면 T, 일치하지 않으면 F를 쓰시오.

1   Florists create something beautiful with flowers. ☐

2   Tom's high school taught him how to grow flowers. ☐

3   There's nothing florists can do except growing and caring for different types of

    flowers. ☐

4   Emma is fond of watching basketball. ☐

Director of a Musical Theater

Hi, I am Chris. As a director of a musical theater, I do a lot of things. I
자격을 나타내는 전치사(~로서)　　　　　　　　　　　　　　=many
audition the actors and I look for good, strong voices. After selecting
　　　　　　　　　　　　　　　　　　　전치사 after의 목적어로 쓰인 동명사
the cast, I teach them the songs for each scene.
　　　　　4형식 동사(+사람+사물)
Then, I put the cast and orchestra together for practice. During
　　　　　put A and B together: A와 B를 함께 모으다
the performance, I am in the orchestra area and conduct. It's my
　　　　　　　　　　　　　　　　　　　　　　　　가주어 it ~ 진주어 to V
responsibility to have each song played the same way every time. I
　　　　　　　사역동사+목적어+과거분사(목적어와 목적격보어의 관계가 수동일 때)　　　매번
direct the musicians and the singers to keep the show together.
　　　　　　　　　　　　　　　　　　to부정사의 부사적 용법 중 목적(~하기 위해서)
Conducting and directing is not just about waving my arms around!
　　　　　　　　　　　　　　　　　　　동명사(전치사의 목적어)

Ocean Scientist

My name is Yeji. I am an ocean scientist. Ocean science is a big field.
It includes studies of the oceans and the creatures living in them.
　　　　　　　　　　　　　　　　　　　the creatures를 수식하는 현재분사　=the oceans
Among other things, I have studied many kinds of fish living in the
seas near Korea. It is the growth ring in a fish that interests me. By
　　　　　　　　It is ~ that 강조 구문(the growth ring in a fish 강조)
looking at it, I can find out when and where the fish was born. All the
by Ving: V함으로써　　　　　　간접의문문(find out의 목적어)
information I get from fish is used to understand sea resources and
　　　앞에 관계대명사 that 생략　　　be used to V: V하는 데 사용되다
manage the oceans better. My job is important because it makes the
to understand와 병렬
best use of nature possible.

audition: 오디션을 보다
select: 선택하다, 선발하다
cast: (영화나 연극의) 출연자들
scene: 장면
orchestra: 오케스트라
performance: 공연, 연주
conduct: 지휘하다
ocean science: 해양 과학
field: 분야
interest: 흥미를 끌다
make the best use of: ~을 최대한 활용하다

확인문제

● 다음 문장이 본문의 내용과 일치하면 T, 일치하지 않으면 F를 쓰시오.

1 Chris directs a musical performance as a job. ☐

2 Chris became a director of a musical theater by audition. ☐

3 Chris do nothing during the performance. ☐

4 Yeji studies not only fish but also oceans. ☐

5 Yeji is interested in the growth ring in a fish. ☐

6 Yeji gets information from ocean to protect sea resources. ☐

● 우리말을 참고하여 빈칸에 알맞은 말을 쓰시오.

The World of Wonderful Jobs

Florist

1 Hi, I am Tom. A florist is someone _____ _____ beautiful things _____ flowers.

2 _____ _____ a florist, you _____ _____ _____ many things about flowers.

3 I _____ a high school _____ florists and gardeners.

4 It was _____ _____ _____ that I learned _____ _____ _____ and care _____ different types of flowers.

5 These days, florists can do _____ things.

6 I design _____ _____ sometimes and I _____ shops with flowers.

7 I am happy when I create _____ _____ with fresh flowers and _____.

8 If you like plants and the arts, I _____ _____ you become a florist.

Sport Data Analyst

9 I am Emma. I am a _____ _____ _____.

10 It sounds like a difficult job, _____ _____?

11 In fact, it is _____ _____ _____ _____. I work for a baseball team.

12 My job is _____ _____ _____ _____ and _____ a computer program _____ _____ data.

13 Then, I _____ the data _____ _____ my team's strengths and weaknesses.

14 If the team _____ their strengths and weaknesses, they can _____ _____ next time.

15 _____ I was young, I _____ _____ _____ a big fan of baseball.

플로리스트

1 안녕하세요. 저는 Tom입니다. 플로리스트란 꽃으로 아름다운 것들을 창조하는 사람입니다.

2 플로리스트가 되기 위해서 여러분은 꽃에 관해 많은 것을 알 필요가 있습니다.

3 나는 플로리스트와 정원사를 양성하는 고등학교에 다녔습니다.

4 제가 다양한 종류의 꽃을 기르고 다루는 방법을 배운 곳이 바로 이 학교에서였습니다.

5 오늘날, 플로리스트는 많은 다양한 일을 할 수 있습니다.

6 나는 때때로 영화 세트장을 디자인하고 꽃으로 상점을 꾸밉니다.

7 나는 싱싱한 꽃과 화초로 다채로운 무언가를 창조해 낼 때 행복합니다.

8 만약 당신이 식물과 예술을 좋아한다면, 나는 당신에게 플로리스트가 될 것을 강력히 추천합니다.

스포츠 데이터 분석가

9 나는 Emma입니다. 나는 스포츠 데이터 분석가입니다.

10 어려운 직업처럼 들리죠, 그렇지 않나요?

11 사실, 그것은 매우 재미있습니다. 나는 야구팀을 위해서 일합니다.

12 나의 일은 녹화된 경기를 보고 자료를 수집하기 위해 컴퓨터 프로그램을 실행하는 것입니다.

13 그리고 나서, 나는 내 팀의 강점과 약점을 보여 주기 위해서 그 자료들을 분석합니다.

14 만약 팀이 자신들의 강점과 약점을 이해하면, 그들은 다음번에 더 잘할 수 있습니다.

15 어렸을 때부터, 나는 야구의 열혈 팬이었습니다.

16 Now, in my work, I watch _____ _____ _____ _____
_____ _____.

17 This is a perfect job for me _____ _____ _____
_____ is my hobby!

Director of a Musical Theater

18 Hi, I am Chris. _____ a director of _____ _____
_____, I do a lot of things.

19 I _____ the actors and I _____ _____ good, strong
voices.

20 After _____ _____ _____ _____, I teach them the songs
_____ _____ _____.

21 Then, I _____ the cast and orchestra _____ for practice.

22 _____ the performance, I am in the orchestra area and
_____.

23 It's _____ _____ to have _____ song played the same
way every time.

24 I _____ the musicians and the singers _____ _____
the show _____.

25 _____ and _____ is not just about _____ my arms
around!

Ocean Scientist

26 My name is Yeji. I am an ocean scientist. Ocean science is
_____ _____ _____.

27 It _____ studies of the oceans and the creatures _____
_____ _____.

28 Among other things, I _____ _____ many kinds of fish
_____ in the seas near Korea.

29 It is _____ _____ _____ in a fish _____ interests
me.

30 _____ _____ at it, I can find out when and where the
fish was born.

31 All the information _____ _____ _____ fish _____
_____ _____ sea resources and _____ the
oceans better.

32 My job is important _____ it makes _____ _____
_____ of nature possible.

16 지금. 나는 일하는 중에 내내 야구를 봅니다.

17 야구 경기를 보는 것은 나의 취미이기 때문에 이것은 나에게 완벽한 직업입니다!

뮤지컬 극장 감독

18 안녕하세요. 나는 Chris입니다. 뮤지컬 극장 감독으로서 나는 많은 것들을 합니다.

19 나는 배우들을 대상으로 오디션을 실시하고, 훌륭하고 강한 목소리를 찾아냅니다.

20 배역에 맞는 배우를 고른 뒤에, 나는 그들에게 각 장면을 위한 노래를 가르칩니다.

21 그러고 나서, 나는 배우와 오케스트라를 함께 연습시킵니다.

22 공연 동안에, 나는 오케스트라석에 있고 지휘를 합니다.

23 각각의 노래가 매번 동일하게 연주되도록 만드는 것은 나의 책임입니다.

24 나는 공연을 제대로 진행하기 위해 연주자들과 가수들을 감독합니다.

25 지휘하고 감독하는 것은 단지 내 팔을 흔드는 것만이 아닙니다!

해양 과학자

26 나는 예지입니다. 나는 해양 과학자입니다. 해양 과학은 거대한 분야입니다.

27 그것은 바다와 그 안에 살고 있는 생물에 관한 연구를 포함합니다.

28 여러 가지 중에서 나는 한국 주변의 바다에 살고 있는 많은 종류의 물고기를 연구해 왔습니다.

29 나의 흥미를 끄는 것은 바로 물고기 안에 있는 나이테입니다.

30 나이테를 살펴봄으로써, 나는 언제 어디서 그 물고기가 태어났는지 알아낼 수 있습니다.

31 내가 물고기에서 얻은 모든 정보는 바다의 자원을 이해하고 바다를 더 잘 관리하기 위해 사용됩니다.

32 내 직업은 자연을 가장 잘 활용할 수 있게 한다는 점에서 중요합니다.

● 우리말을 참고하여 본문을 영작하시오.

The World of Wonderful Jobs
Florist

1 안녕하세요. 저는 Tom입니다. 플로리스트란 꽃으로 아름다운 것들을 창조하는 사람입니다.
➡ _____

2 플로리스트가 되기 위해서 여러분은 꽃에 관해 많은 것을 알 필요가 있습니다.
➡ _____

3 나는 플로리스트와 정원사를 양성하는 고등학교에 다녔습니다.
➡ _____

4 제가 다양한 종류의 꽃을 기르고 다루는 방법을 배운 곳이 바로 이 학교에서였습니다.
➡ _____

5 오늘날, 플로리스트는 많은 다양한 일을 할 수 있습니다.
➡ _____

6 나는 때때로 영화 세트장을 디자인하고 꽃으로 상점을 꾸밉니다.
➡ _____

7 나는 싱싱한 꽃과 화초로 다채로운 무언가를 창조해 낼 때 행복합니다.
➡ _____

8 만약 당신이 식물과 예술을 좋아한다면, 나는 당신에게 플로리스트가 될 것을 강력히 추천합니다.
➡ _____

Sport Data Analyst

9 나는 Emma입니다. 나는 스포츠 데이터 분석가입니다.
➡ _____

10 어려운 직업처럼 들리죠, 그렇지 않나요?
➡ _____

11 사실, 그것은 매우 재미있습니다. 나는 야구팀을 위해서 일합니다.
➡ _____

12 나의 일은 녹화된 경기를 보고 자료를 수집하기 위해 컴퓨터 프로그램을 실행하는 것입니다.
➡ _____

13 그러고 나서, 나는 내 팀의 강점과 약점을 보여 주기 위해서 그 자료들을 분석합니다.
➡ _____

14 만약 팀이 자신들의 강점과 약점을 이해하면, 그들은 다음번에 더 잘할 수 있습니다.
➡ _____

어렸을 때부터, 나는 야구의 열혈 팬이었습니다.
➡ _____

16 지금, 나는 일하는 중에 내내 야구를 봅니다.
➡ _____

17 야구 경기를 보는 것은 나의 취미이기 때문에 이것은 나에게 완벽한 직업입니다!
➡ _____

Director of a Musical Theater

18 안녕하세요. 나는 Chris입니다. 뮤지컬 극장 감독으로서 나는 많은 것들을 합니다.
➡ _____

19 나는 배우들을 대상으로 오디션을 실시하고, 훌륭하고 강한 목소리를 찾아냅니다.
➡ _____

20 배역에 맞는 배우를 고른 뒤에, 나는 그들에게 각 장면을 위한 노래를 가르칩니다.
➡ _____

21 그러고 나서, 나는 배우와 오케스트라를 함께 연습시킵니다.
➡ _____

22 공연 동안에, 나는 오케스트라 석에 있고 지휘를 합니다.
➡ _____

23 각각의 노래가 매번 동일하게 연주되도록 만드는 것은 나의 책임입니다.
➡ _____

24 나는 공연을 제대로 진행하기 위해 연주자들과 가수들을 감독합니다.
➡ _____

25 지휘하고 감독하는 것은 단지 내 팔을 흔드는 것만이 아닙니다!
➡ _____

Ocean Scientist

26 나는 예지입니다. 나는 해양 과학자입니다. 해양 과학은 거대한 분야입니다.
➡ _____

27 그것은 바다와 그 안에 살고 있는 생물에 관한 연구를 포함합니다.
➡ _____

28 여러 가지 중에서 나는 한국 주변의 바다에 살고 있는 많은 종류의 물고기를 연구해 왔습니다.
➡ _____

29 나의 흥미를 끄는 것은 바로 물고기 안에 있는 나이테입니다.
➡ _____

30 나이테를 살펴봄으로써, 나는 언제 어디서 그 물고기가 태어났는지 알아낼 수 있습니다.
➡ _____

31 내가 물고기에서 얻은 모든 정보는 바다의 자원을 이해하고 바다를 더 잘 관리하기 위해 사용됩니다.
➡ _____

32 내 직업은 자연을 가장 잘 활용할 수 있게 한다는 점에서 중요합니다.
➡ _____

[01~03] 다음 글을 읽고 물음에 답하시오.

Hi, I am Tom. A florist is someone who creates beautiful things with flowers. To become a florist, you need to know many things about flowers. I attended a high school for florists and gardeners. It was at this school that I learned how to grow and care for different types of flowers. (A)These days, florists can do a lot of different things. I design movie sets sometimes and I decorate shops with flowers. I am happy when I create something colorful with fresh flowers and greenery. If you like plants and the arts, I highly recommend you become a florist.

01 다음 중 밑줄 친 (A)를 대신하여 쓸 수 있는 것은?

① From time to time   ② Nowadays
③ Once in a while   ④ Hardly
⑤ Now and then

02 다음 중 위 글의 내용과 일치하는 것은?

① Tom didn't have to know many things about flowers to become a florist.
② Florists care for only flowers.
③ Tom is not satisfied with his job.
④ Tom doesn't recommend his job.
⑤ There is a school for students who want to be florists and gardeners.

서답형
03 According to the passage, who is a florist? Answer in English with a full sentence.

➡ _____

[04~06] 다음 글을 읽고 물음에 답하시오.

I am Emma. I am a sport data analyst. It sounds like a difficult job, doesn't it? In fact, it is a lot of fun. I work for a baseball team. My job is to watch recorded games and run a computer program to collect data. Then, I analyze the data to show my team's strengths and weaknesses. If the team understands their strengths and weaknesses, they can do better next time. Since I was young, I have been a big fan of baseball. Now, in my work, I watch baseball games all the time. This is a perfect job for me (A)_____ watching baseball games is my hobby!

04 다음 중 빈칸 (A)에 들어갈 말로 가장 적절한 것은?

① although   ② if   ③ because
④ when   ⑤ until

05 다음 중 위 글을 읽고 답할 수 있는 것은?

① When did Emma get the job?
② How many games does Emma watch a week?
③ What does Emma do after collecting data?
④ How old is Emma?
⑤ Is Emma good at baseball?

서답형
06 According to the passage, how can the team do better next time? Answer in English with a full sentence.

➡ _____

[07~10] 다음 글을 읽고 물음에 답하시오.

Hi, I am Chris. As a director of a musical theater, I do a lot of things. I audition the actors and I look for good, strong voices. After selecting the cast, I teach them the songs for each scene. Then, I put the cast and orchestra together for practice. During the performance, I am in the orchestra area and conduct. It's my responsibility to have each song (A)_____ the same way every time. I direct the musicians and the singers to keep the show together. Conducting and directing is not just about waving my arms around!

서답형

07 단어 play를 어법에 맞게 빈칸 (A)에 쓰시오.

➡ _____

중요

08 다음 중 뮤지컬 공연 감독이 하는 일이 <u>아닌</u> 것은?

① looking for good, strong voices
② teaching the cast the songs for each scene
③ conducting after the performance
④ directing the musicians and the singers
⑤ choosing actors for a musical performance

서답형

09 What does Chris do after he selects the cast? Answer in English.

➡ _____
_____

서답형

10 다음 빈칸에 들어갈 말을 위 글에서 찾아 쓰시오.

The _____ of a play or film is all the people who act in it.

[11~14] 다음 글을 읽고 물음에 답하시오.

My name is Yeji. I am an ocean scientist. Ocean science is a big field. ①It includes studies of the oceans and the creatures ② living in them. Among other things, I ③have studied many kinds of fish living in the seas near Korea. It is the growth ring in a fish ④ that interests me. (A)_____ looking at it, I can find out when and where the fish was born. All the information I get from fish is used to understand sea resources and ⑤manages the oceans better. My job is important because it makes the best use of nature possible.

11 밑줄 친 ①~⑤ 중 어법상 바르지 <u>않은</u> 것은?

①   ②   ③   ④   ⑤

12 다음 중 빈칸 (A)에 들어갈 말과 같은 말이 들어가는 것은? (대·소문자 무시)

① Can you pay attention _____ my speech?
② She is looking forward _____ seeing him.
③ It depends _____ you and your son.
④ Things will get better as time goes _____.
⑤ This medicine will take _____ your pain.

서답형

위 글의 내용에 맞게 빈칸에 알맞은 말을 쓰시오.

Ocean scientists study not only _____ _____ but also _____.

서답형

14 What can the growth ring in a fish tell Yeji? Answer in English with a full sentence.

➡ _____

[15~17] 다음 글을 읽고 물음에 답하시오.

Hi, I am Tom. A florist is someone (A)_____ creates beautiful things with flowers. To become a florist, you need to know many things about flowers. I attended a high school for florists and gardeners. It was at this school that I learned how to grow and care for different types of flowers. These days, florists can do a lot of different things. I design movie sets sometimes and I decorate shops with flowers. I am happy when I create something colorful with fresh flowers and greenery. If you like plants and the arts, I highly recommend you become a florist.

15 다음 중 빈칸 (A)에 들어갈 말로 적절한 것을 <u>모두</u> 고르시오.

① which   ② who   ③ that
④ what   ⑤ whose

16 다음 중 위 글의 내용과 일치하지 <u>않는</u> 것은?

① Tom is a florist.
② It is necessary to know many things about flowers to become a florist.
③ Florists always do the same things.
④ Tom creates something with flowers and greenery.
⑤ Tom feels happy when he does his job.

서답형
17 Where did Tom learn how to grow and care for different types of flowers? Answer in English with a full sentence.

➡ _____
   _____

[18~21] 다음 글을 읽고 물음에 답하시오.

I am Emma. I am a sport data analyst. It sounds like a difficult job, ⓐ_____?

[A] Then, I analyze the data to show my team's strengths and weaknesses. If the team understands their strengths and weaknesses, they can do better next time. Since I was young, I have been a big fan of baseball.

[B] In fact, it is a lot of fun. I work for a baseball team. My job is to watch recorded games and run a computer program to collect data.

[C] Now, in my work, I watch baseball games all the time. This is a perfect job for me because watching baseball games is my hobby!

서답형
18 빈칸 ⓐ에 알맞은 말을 쓰시오.

➡ _____

19 위 글의 흐름상 [A]~[C]를 바르게 배열한 것은?

① [A]–[C]–[B]   ② [B]–[A]–[C]
③ [B]–[C]–[A]   ④ [C]–[A]–[B]
⑤ [C]–[B]–[A]

20 According to Emma, what does she feel about her job?

① bored   ② tired   ③ annoyed
④ satisfied   ⑤ uninterested

서답형
21 Write the reason why Emma runs a computer program. Use the phrase 'in order to.'

➡ _____

[22~24] 다음 글을 읽고 물음에 답하시오.

Hi, I am Chris. As a director of a musical theater, I do a lot of things. I audition the actors and I look for good, strong voices. After selecting the cast, I teach them the songs for each scene. Then, I put the cast and orchestra together for practice. During the performance, I am in the orchestra area and conduct. It's my responsibility to have each song played the same way every time. I direct the musicians and the singers to keep the show together. Conducting and directing is not just about waving my arms around!

서답형

22 다음 빈칸에 들어갈 말을 위 글에서 찾아 어법에 맞게 쓰시오.

> If someone _____ an orchestra or choir, they stand in front of it and direct its performance.

중요

23 다음 중 위 글의 내용과 일치하는 것은?

① Chris acts on the stage of a musical theater.
② Chris has a good and strong voice for the musical.
③ The cast is selected and taught some songs by Chris.
④ Chris writes many songs for the musical and has them played.
⑤ The orchestra doesn't need a conductor.

서답형

24 According to the passage, what is Chris's responsibility? Answer in English with a full sentence.

➡ _____

_____

[25~27] 다음 글을 읽고 물음에 답하시오.

My name is Yeji. I am an ocean scientist. Ocean science is a big field. (①) It includes studies of the oceans and the creatures living in them. (②) Among other things, I have studied many kinds of fish living in the seas near Korea. (③) It is the growth ring in a fish that interests me. (④) All the information I get from fish is used to understand sea resources and manage the oceans better. (⑤) My job is important because it makes the best use of nature possible.

중요

25 ①~⑤ 중 주어진 문장이 들어가기에 가장 적절한 곳은?

> By looking at it, I can find out when and where the fish was born.

①   ②   ③   ④   ⑤

26 다음 중 위 글을 읽고 답할 수 있는 것은?

① What did Yeji want to be when she was young?
② How long has Yeji studied ocean science?
③ Why does Yeji study many kinds of fish living in the seas near Korea?
④ Why is Yeji's job important?
⑤ What college did Yeji graduate from?

27 다음 빈칸에 들어갈 말을 위 글에서 찾을 수 없는 것은?

① The price tag _____ tax.
② Damage to the environment affects all wild _____.
③ The country has a lot of energy _____.
④ You pay too much _____ to the news.
⑤ I want to _____ my life better.

[01~04] 다음 글을 읽고 물음에 답하시오.

Hi, I am Tom. A florist is someone who (A) create beautiful things with flowers. To become a florist, you need to know many things about flowers. I attended a high school for florists and gardeners. It was at this school that I learned how to grow and care for different types of flowers. These days, florists can do a lot of different things. I design movie sets sometimes and I decorate shops with flowers. I am happy when I create something colorful with fresh flowers and greenery. If you like plants and the arts, I highly recommend you become a florist.

01 밑줄 친 (A)를 어법에 맞게 고쳐 쓰시오.

➡ _____

02 What kind of high school did Tom attend? Answer in English.

➡ _____

03 What do we need to know in order to become a florist? Answer in English with a full sentence.

➡ _____

04 According to the passage, when does Tom feel happy? Answer in English.

➡ _____

[05~08] 다음 글을 읽고 물음에 답하시오.

I am Emma. I am a sport data analyst. It sounds like a difficult job, doesn't it? In fact, it is a lot of fun. I work for a baseball team. My job is to watch recorded games and run a computer program to collect data. Then, I analyze the data to show my team's strengths and weaknesses. If the team understands their (A)_____, they can do better next time. Since I was young, I have been a big fan of baseball. Now, in my work, I watch baseball games all the time. This is a perfect job for me because watching baseball games is my hobby!

05 빈칸 (A)에 들어갈 말을 위 글에서 찾아 세 단어로 쓰시오.

➡ _____

06 What does Emma do as a sport data analyst? Answer in English.

➡ _____

07 According to Emma, what is her hobby? Answer in English.

➡ _____

08 다음과 같이 풀이되는 말을 위 글에서 찾아 쓰시오.

a person whose job is to analyse a subject and give opinions about it

➡ _____

[09~12] 다음 글을 읽고 물음에 답하시오.

Hi, I am Chris. As a director of a musical theater, I do a lot of things. I audition the actors and I look for good, strong voices. After selecting the cast, I teach them the songs for each scene. Then, I put the cast and orchestra together for practice. During the performance, I am in the orchestra area and conduct. It's my responsibility to have each song played the same way every time. I direct the musicians and the singers to keep the show together. (A) Conducting and directing is not just about waving my arms around!

09 다음은 밑줄 친 (A)와 같은 의미이다. 빈칸에 알맞은 말을 쓰시오.

According to Chris, conducting and directing means much more than just _____ _____ _____.

10 Where is Chris during the performance?

➡ _____

11 What does Chris do to keep the show together? Answer in English with seven words.

➡ _____

12 It is ~ that 강조 구문을 활용하여 다음 대화에 알맞은 답을 쓰시오.

A: Chris, who do you audition?
B: _____

[13~16] 다음 글을 읽고 물음에 답하시오.

My name is Yeji. I am an ocean scientist. Ocean science is a big field. It includes studies of the oceans and the creatures living in them. Among other things, I have studied many kinds of fish living in the seas near Korea. It is the growth ring in a fish that interests me. By looking at it, I can find out when and where the fish was born. All the information I get from fish is used to understand sea resources and manage the oceans better. My job is important because it makes the best use of nature possible.

13 According to the passage, what interests Yeji? Answer in English with a full sentence.

➡ _____

14 Write the reason why Yeji says her job is important. Use the phrase 'It's because.'

➡ _____

15 What has Yeji studied as an ocean scientist? Answer in English with a full sentence.

➡ _____

16 According to the passage, what should we look at if we want to know when and where a fish was born?

➡ _____

Enjoy Writing C

My Dream Job

I like food from around the world and I am good at cooking.
전치사의 목적어

I can also make food look tasty and beautiful. For these reasons, it is a chef
사역동사+목적어+동사원형   look+형용사: ~하게 보이다   it is ~ that ... 강조구문: ~한 것은 바로 …다

that I want to be when I grow up. To achieve my dream, I will read magazines
~할 때   부사적 용법(목적)(= In order to[So as to] achieve)

about cooking. Also, I will go to France to learn various cooking skills. My

role model is my dad. He always thinks of new recipes and then cooks these

new dishes for us. I want to have my name remembered by people who enjoy
to us(×)   사역동사+목적어+과거분사(목적어의 수동 의미): 내 이름이 기억되도록 하다

my food.
주격 관계대명사절로 선행사 people을 수식

구문해설 · be good at: ~을 잘하다 · tasty: 맛있는 · reason: 이유 · chef: 요리사 · achieve: 이루다
· various: 다양한 · recipe: 요리법

내 꿈의 직업

나는 전 세계 음식을 좋아하고 요리를 잘한다. 나는 또한 음식을 맛있고 아름다워 보이게 만들 수 있다. 이러한 이유로 내가 자라서 되고 싶은 것은 요리사이다. 내 꿈을 이루기 위해, 나는 요리에 관한 잡지를 읽을 것이다. 또한 나는 프랑스에 가서 다양한 요리 기술을 익힐 것이다. 내 롤 모델은 나의 아빠이다. 그는 항상 새로운 요리법을 생각해 내시고 우리를 위해 이러한 요리를 만들어 주신다. 나는 내 이름이 내 음식을 좋아하는 사람들에게 기억되도록 하고 싶다.

Project

HELP WANTED!!
사람 구함

Do you like robots?

If your answer is yes, it is you that we are looking for.
'It is~ that' 강조 구문: you 강조

Please join us to train and fix robots.
to부정사의 부사적 용법(목적 또는 결과를 나타냄)

For more information, visit our website at www.robots.com.

구문해설 · wanted: ~을 구하는 · look for: ~을 찾다

사람 구합니다!

로봇을 좋아하시나요? 당신의 답이 예스라면, 당신이 바로 우리가 찾는 사람입니다. 우리와 함께 로봇을 훈련시키고, 고쳐 보세요. 더 자세한 사항은 우리 웹사이트 www.robots.com을 방문해 주세요.

Project Step 3

Are you good at training and fixing robots? If so, we're sure that you'll be a
동명사로 전치사 at의 목적어

good robot specialist. For more information, visit our websites.
셀 수 없는 명사

구문해설 · train: 훈련시키다 · fix: 고치다 · be sure that ~: ~을 확신하다 · specialist: 전문가

당신은 로봇을 훈련시키고 수리하는 것을 잘하나요? 만약 그렇다면, 우리는 당신이 좋은 로봇 전문가가 될 것이라고 확신합니다. 더 많은 정보를 위해서, 우리 웹사이트를 방문하세요.

영역별 핵심문제

Words & Expressions

01 다음 주어진 두 단어의 관계가 같도록 빈칸에 알맞은 단어를 쓰시오.

> highly : greatly = choose : _____

02 다음 글의 빈칸 (A)와 (B)에 들어갈 단어로 바르게 짝지어진 것은?

> I like food from around the world and I am good at cooking. I can also make food look tasty and beautiful. For these (A)_____, it is a chef that I want to be when I grow up. To (B)_____ my dream, I will read magazines about cooking. Also, I will go to France to learn various cooking skills.

① efforts – report ② efforts – achieve
③ reasons – conduct ④ reasons – fix
⑤ reasons – achieve

[03~04] 다음 영영 풀이에 해당하는 것을 고르시오.

03

> your job or duty to deal with something or someone

① resource   ② greenery
③ responsibility ④ historian
⑤ reporter

04

> to contain something as a part of something else, or to make something part of something else

① include   ② advise
③ lead   ④ collect
⑤ create

05 빈칸에 들어갈 말을 영어 설명을 읽고 주어진 철자로 시작하여 쓰시오. (복수형을 쓸 것)

> Ocean science includes studies of the oceans and the c_____ living in them. Among other things, I have studied many kinds of fish living in the seas near Korea.
> <영어설명> any large or small living thing that can move independently

06 다음 밑줄 친 부분의 뜻이 잘못된 것은?

① It is the growth ring in a fish that interests me. (나이테)
② Giving up smoking reduces the risk of heart disease. (줄이다)
③ I direct the musicians and the singers to keep the show together. (감독하다)
④ Since I was young, I have been a big fan of baseball. (~이기 때문에)
⑤ This is a perfect job for me because watching baseball games is my hobby! (완벽한)

Conversation

07 다음 대화의 빈칸에 들어갈 말로 적절한 것은?

> A: I want to be a radio program writer. What would help me become one?
> B: It _____ to me that writing your own stories would be helpful.

① leads   ② seems   ③ is
④ hopes   ⑤ happens

[08~10] 다음 대화를 읽고 물음에 답하시오.

Bora: What are you most interested in among the things on this list?

Jessie: I'm most interested in working outside and playing sports.

Bora: Well, (A)내 생각에 너는 현실적인 타입에 속하는 것 같아.

Jessie: What do you mean?

Bora: Most people belong to one of six personality types. Realistic is one of the types.

Jessie: Oh, that's interesting. What kind of jobs do they recommend for realistic types?

Bora: A farmer, a police officer, a soccer player, and so on.

Jessie: Oh, I have always wanted to be a soccer player.

Bora: That's good. I'm quite sure you could become a great soccer player.

08 밑줄 친 (A)의 우리말에 맞게 주어진 단어를 이용하여 영어로 쓰시오. (어형 변화 필수)

(seem / me / belong / the realistic type)

➡ _____

09 위 대화를 읽고 다음 물음에 영어로 답하시오.

Q: What is Jessie most interested in among the things on the list?

➡ _____

_____

10 위 대화의 내용과 일치하지 않는 것은?

① They are talking about personality types.
② Jessie belongs to the realistic type.
③ Bora recommends a soccer player for Jessie.
④ A farmer belongs to the realistic type.
⑤ Jessie wants to be a soccer player.

11 다음 대화의 빈칸에 들어갈 말을 주어진 단어를 알맞은 순서로 배열하여 완성하시오.

B: Do you cook often?

G: Yes, I try to cook every weekend. I want to be a chef someday.

B: What are you doing to make your dream come true?

G: I'm taking a cooking class. I try to think of new and creative dishes.

B: I'm _____.

(chef / good / quite / you / could / sure / be / a)

Grammar

[12~14] 다음 우리말에 맞게 영작한 것을 고르시오.

12

그의 아버지는 Tom에게 세차를 시켰다.

① Tom's father had him wash the car.
② Tom's father told him wash the car.
③ Tom's father had the car wash by him.
④ Tom's father let him washing the car.
⑤ Tom's father said him to wash the car.

13

내게 기운을 북돋아 주는 것은 내 아내이다.

① My wife who cheer me up counts.
② It is my wife that cheer me up.
③ My wife encourages me cheer up.
④ It cheers me up that my wife is.
⑤ It is my wife that cheers me up.

14

Marco는 펜스에 충돌하고 나서 다리가 부러졌다.

① Marco had his leg breaking the fence after hitting.

② Marco had him break his leg after hitting the fence.

③ Marco had got his leg breaking after being hit the fence.

④ Marco had his leg broken after hitting the fence.

⑤ Marco broke his leg after the fence hitting him.

15 다음 중 아래 그림의 내용을 설명하되, 어법상 성격이 <u>다른</u> 한 문장을 고르시오.

① It was a clown that was juggling with red balls.

② It was we that saw a clown juggling.

③ It was on the platform that a clown was performing.

④ It was exciting that my daddy and I were in the amusement park.

⑤ It was my daddy that was holding me up to watch the clown.

16 다음 중 어법상 올바른 문장은?

① David had the repairman fixed the fax machine.

② The police won't let the suspect leaving the country.

③ Her bright smile made Thompson feels so happy.

④ Mom finally allowed me to stay up all night with my friends.

⑤ Amy had her finger break while practicing kick boxing.

17 다음 중 우리말을 영작한 것이 <u>어색한</u> 것을 <u>고르면</u>?

① 어제 오후에 PC방에서 그를 만난 사람은 바로 나였다.

　→ It was I that met him at the Internet cafe yesterday afternoon.

② 아빠가 엄마를 처음 만난 것은 바로 아빠가 대학 신입생 때였다.

　→ It was when he was a freshman that my daddy first met my mom.

③ Bill이 MS를 만든 해는 1975년이었다.

　→ It was 1975 that Bill made MS.

④ 그 트럭을 고장낸 것은 Douglas였다.

　→ It was Douglas that broke the truck.

⑤ 오늘 아침에 그녀가 사장에게 받은 것은 바로 해고 통지서였다.

　→ It was a notice of dismissal that she received from the boss this morning.

18 다음 중 밑줄 친 부분의 쓰임이 〈보기〉와 같은 것은?

┌─ 보기 ─

John <u>had</u> the windows replaced an hour ago.

└─

① The food that I <u>had</u> was fantastic.

② The sports complex building <u>has</u> gas-fired central heating.

③ He <u>had</u> his head in his hands.

④ Sarah was <u>having</u> difficulty in staying awake.

⑤ We're <u>having</u> our car painted blue.

19 다음 중 밑줄 친 that의 쓰임이 나머지와 다른 하나는?

① It was on the snow that my dogs left their footprints.

② It is important that the actor should recover from despair.

③ It is this year that you will graduate from Balsan middle school.

④ It is the skill that makes me money.

⑤ It was those pancakes that my daddy sometimes made for me.

20 다음 중 어법상 어색한 문장은?

① The news made Christina cry a lot against her will.

② The designer had the dress to change from green color to orange.

③ Don't let the errors of the past destroy your present.

④ Yewon noticed a boy trying to get on the bus on her way to school.

⑤ Meditation helps you to escape from your grief.

21 다음 주어진 상황을 읽고, Peter가 여동생에게 할 말을 〈조건〉에 맞게 영작하시오.

- Peter's sister just broke her computer.
- Peter doesn't know how to fix the computer.
- He wants to make her relieved today.
  → Peter: I _____.

┌─ 조건 ┐
fix, have, today, 소유격, 미래시제 등을 활용할 것. 6단어로 빈칸을 채울 것.

Reading

[22~24] 다음 글을 읽고 물음에 답하시오.

Hi, I am Tom. A florist is someone who creates beautiful things with ①flowers. To become a florist, you need to know many things about flowers. I attended a high school for ②florists and gardeners. It was at this school that I learned how to grow and care for different types of flowers. These days, florists can do a lot of ③ different things. I design movie sets sometimes and I decorate shops with flowers. I am happy when I create something ④colorful with fresh flowers and greenery. If you like plants and the arts, I ⑤high recommend you become a florist.

22 위 글의 밑줄 친 ①~⑤ 중 글의 흐름상 어색한 것은?

①   ②   ③   ④   ⑤

23 위 글의 내용에 맞게 빈칸에 알맞은 말을 쓰시오.

The high school that Tom attended taught Tom _____.

24 다음 중 위 글을 읽고 답할 수 없는 것은?

① What does Tom do for a living?

② What do we need to know if we want to become a florist?

③ Where did Tom learn about growing and caring for different types of flowers?

④ Who recommended Tom to become a florist?

⑤ What does Tom do with flowers?

[25~27] 다음 글을 읽고 물음에 답하시오.

I like food from around the world and I am good at cooking. I can also make food look tasty and beautiful.

[A] He always thinks of new recipes and then cooks these new dishes for us. I want to have my name remembered by people who enjoy my food.

[B] Also, I will go to France to learn various cooking skills. My role model is my dad.

[C] For these reasons, it is a chef that I want to be when I grow up. To achieve my dream, I will read magazines about cooking.

25 자연스러운 글이 되도록 [A]~[C]를 바르게 배열한 것은?

① [A]–[C]–[B] ② [B]–[A]–[C]
③ [B]–[C]–[A] ④ [C]–[A]–[B]
⑤ [C]–[B]–[A]

26 위 글의 제목으로 가장 적절한 것은?

① France, the Dream Country
② My Dream Job, A Chef
③ My Mentor, My Father
④ Magazines That Will Help You
⑤ A World Famous Restaurant

27 위 글을 읽고 유추할 수 있는 것은?

① The writer wants to look beautiful.
② The writer is reading many books to become a writer.
③ The writer's father is a chef.
④ The writer travels all around the world.
⑤ The writer wants to remember people's name.

[28~30] 다음 글을 읽고 물음에 답하시오.

I am Emma. I am (A)_____. It sounds like a difficult job, doesn't it? In fact, it is a lot of fun. I work for a baseball team. My job is to watch recorded games and run a computer program to collect data. Then, I analyze the data to show my team's strengths and weaknesses. If the team understands their strengths and weaknesses, they can do better next time. Since I was young, I have been a big fan of baseball. Now, in my work, I watch baseball games all the time. This is a perfect job for me because watching baseball games is my hobby!

28 빈칸 (A)에 들어갈 말로 가장 적절한 것은?

① a cartoonist ② a sport data analyst
③ a florist ④ a director of musical
⑤ a baseball player

29 다음 중 위 글의 내용과 일치하는 것은?

① Emma thinks her job is very difficult.
② Emma doesn't want to know her team's weaknesses.
③ Emma didn't like baseball when she was young.
④ Emma likes baseball very much.
⑤ Emma always watches basketball games in her work.

30 According to the passage, what does Emma work for? Answer in English with a full sentence.

➡ _____

01 출제율 95%

다음 짝지어진 단어의 관계가 같도록 빈칸에 알맞은 말을 쓰시오.

> weakness : strength = follow : _____

02 출제율 90%

다음 영영 풀이에 해당하는 단어는?

> to give a short performance in order to show that you are suitable for a part in a film, play, show, etc.

① analyze　　② direct
③ audition　　④ display
⑤ exhibit

[03~04] 다음 대화를 읽고 물음에 답하시오.

Girl: I'm glad to meet you, Mr. Han. Could you please tell me what you do?

Mr. Han: Okay. I guide travelers to different places in China and give them information about where they should visit.

Girl: What else do you do?

Mr. Han: I tell them about popular culture and traditional food in China.

Girl: (A)In my opinion, knowing a lot about China is very important. Are you happy with your job?

Mr. Han: Yes. I really love my job.

03 출제율 90%

위 글의 밑줄 친 (A)와 같은 의미의 문장을 주어진 단어를 활용하여 쓰시오. (12 words)

> (seem / me)

➡ _____

04 출제율 100%

위 대화의 내용으로 보아 알 수 없는 것은?

① Mr. Han guides travelers to many places in China.
② The girl wants to know what Mr. Han does.
③ Mr. Han gives travelers information about where they should visit.
④ It seems to me that Mr. Han is a tour guide.
⑤ Mr. Han really loves popular culture and traditional food in China.

[05~06] 다음 대화를 읽고 물음에 답하시오.

Mr. Kang: What's wrong, Jisu?

Jisu: I want to be an animator, but my drawing skill is not (a)enough good.

Mr. Kang: Hmm... Being an animator is not just about (b)being a good artist.

Jisu: What should I do (c)to become an animator?

Mr. Kang: Read a lot of books to make good stories and (d)practice drawing every day.

Jisu: Okay, I'll do so.

Mr. Kang: I'm quite sure that you can be a good animator (e)if you try hard.

Jisu: Thank you very much.

05 출제율 90%

What does Mr. Kang advise Jisu to do? (대화에서 찾아 2가지를 쓰시오.)

➡ _____

06 출제율 96%

위 대화의 밑줄 (a)~(e) 중 어법상 어색한 것은?

① (a)　② (b)　③ (c)　④ (d)　⑤ (e)

[07~08] 다음 대화를 읽고 물음에 답하시오.

Bora: What are you most interested in among the things on this list?

Jessie: I'm most interested in working outside and playing sports.

Bora: Well, (A)_____.

Jessie: What do you mean?

Bora: Most people belong to one of six personality types. Realistic is one of the types.

Jessie: Oh, that's interesting. What kind of jobs do they recommend for realistic types?

Bora: A farmer, a police officer, a soccer player, and so on.

Jessie: Oh, I have always wanted to be a soccer player.

Bora: That's good. (B)_____.

07 위 글의 빈칸 (A)에 들어갈 말로 알맞은 것은? 출제율 95%

① it seems to me that you belong to the artistic type

② I'm quite sure you'll achieve your dream

③ I'm quite sure that people doing those jobs will be in need

④ it seems to me that you belong to the realistic type

⑤ I think that you belong to the soccer team

08 위 대화의 빈칸 (B)에 들어갈 말을 주어진 〈조건〉에 맞게 영어로 쓰시오. 출제율 90%

┌── 조건 ──┐
• 확실성 정도를 나타내는 표현을 쓸 것.
• 'quite sure', 'could become'을 사용할 것.
└──────┘

➡ _____

09 다음 대화의 밑줄 친 (A)를 do의 구체적인 의미가 나타나도록 바꾸어 쓰시오. 출제율 90%

B: Anne, I'm planning to visit the police station to see my uncle. He is a police officer.

G: Oh, I want to become a police officer someday.

B: (A)You do? Me, too. I have dreamed of becoming a police officer since I was ten.

G: Can I come with you, Matt? I want to meet your uncle and ask him something.

B: Sure. What are you going to ask?

G: I want to ask him what I need to do to become a police officer.

B: I see. I'm sure he would like to meet you.

➡ _____

10 다음 각 문장에 사용된 어법 사항을 〈보기〉에서 기호를 골라 괄호 안에 쓰시오. 출제율 95%

┌── 보기 ──┐
ⓐ It ~ that 강조 구문 문장
ⓑ It(가주어) ~ that(진주어) 구문 문장
└──────┘

(1) It is only through practice that you will achieve your goal. (   )

(2) It is wonderful that the whole family gets together on Chuseok. (   )

(3) It is when my kids smile at me that I feel the happiest. (   )

(4) It is Susan's idea that all the club members must gather here. (   )

(5) What was it that motivated Joe to learn engineering? (   )

11 다음 대화의 밑줄 친 우리말 해석과 같은 표현을 쓸 때 문장의 빈칸에 알맞은 말을 쓰시오. (출제율 90%)

> B: Did you finish the report about your role model?
> G: Yes, I did. I wrote about my role model, Ms. Shin. I want to be like her.
> B: What does she do?
> G: She teaches people how to stretch. She also helps them reduce stress and calm themselves.
> B: Good. 그녀가 그들의 몸과 마음을 둘 다 건강하게 유지하도록 돕는 것 같아.
> G: Yes, and I think it's great.

➡ _____ _____ that she helps to keep _____ their mind _____ body _____.

12 아래의 내용을 'It ~ that' 강조 구문으로 다시 설명한 문장 중 내용과 일치하지 <u>않는</u> 것을 고르시오. (출제율 95%)

> • One day, my uncle Steve accidentally spilled a glass of wine, so my computer broke down. He gave me his credit card and I had the computer repaired at the shop.

① It was Steve that broke my computer.
② It was by accident that my uncle spilled a glass of wine.
③ It was his credit card that my uncle gave to me.
④ It was my uncle Steve that fixed my computer at the shop.
⑤ It was at the shop that my computer was repaired.

13 다음 중 어법상 <u>어색한</u> 문장은? (출제율 95%)

① Laura had her umbrella stolen while she was texting her boyfriend.
② Wasn't it hard to have your son transferred?
③ As her husband was looking away, Gloria had her shoes shone.
④ The VIP customer ordered the clerk to have all her purchases packaged.
⑤ The robber forced her to have the money withdrawn from the ATM.

14 다음 중 어법상 옳은 것을 고르시오. (출제율 100%)

① The movie made me moving.
② The principal of my school had us to wait for the mayor to give a speech.
③ Her parents are so strict that they won't let Peggy going out tonight.
④ All the relatives at camping helped my daddy washed the dishes.
⑤ My wife had me stay still during the wedding.

15 다음 문장의 밑줄 친 ⓐ~ⓓ를 각각 순서대로 'It ~ that' 강조 구문으로 전환하시오. (출제율 90%)

> The newlyweds bought a table at the mall
> ⓐ   ⓑ   ⓒ
> 2 weeks ago.
> ⓓ

➡ (1) ⓐ _____
    _____

(2) ⓑ _____

(3) ⓒ _____

(4) ⓓ _____

[16~19] 다음 글을 읽고 물음에 답하시오.

Hi, I am Chris. (A)As a director of a musical theater, I do a lot of things. ① I audition the actors and I look for good, strong voices. ② Then, I put the cast and orchestra together for practice. ③ During the performance, I am in the orchestra area and conduct. ④ It's my responsibility to have each song played the same way every time. ⑤ I direct the musicians and the singers to keep the show together. Conducting and directing is not just about waving my arms around!

출제율 95%
16 다음 중 밑줄 친 (A)와 쓰임이 같은 것은?

① As you are here, you need to vote for us.
② This is as light as a feather.
③ He sat watching TV as she got ready.
④ He worked as a doctor for ten years.
⑤ As you were out, I left a message.

출제율 100%
17 ①~⑤ 중 다음 주어진 문장이 들어가기에 적절한 곳은?

> After selecting the cast, I teach them the songs for each scene.

①　　　②　　　③　　　④　　　⑤

출제율 90%
18 When Chris auditions the actors, what does he look for? Answer in English with a full sentence.

➡ _____

출제율 90%
19 Write the reason why Chris directs the musicians and the singers. Answer in English.

➡ _____
_____

[20~23] 다음 글을 읽고 물음에 답하시오.

My name is Yeji. I am an ocean scientist. Ocean science is a big field. It includes studies of the oceans and the creatures living in ⓐ them. Among other things, I have studied many kinds of fish (A)[living / live] in the seas near Korea. It is the growth ring in a fish that interests me. (B)[On / By] looking at it, I can find out when and where the fish was born. All the information I get from fish (C)[is / are] used to understand sea resources and manage the oceans better. My job is important because it makes the best use of nature possible.

출제율 95%
20 (A)~(C)에서 어법상 옳은 것끼리 바르게 짝지어진 것은?

① living – On – is　　② live – On – is
③ living – By – is　　④ live – By – are
⑤ living – By – are

출제율 100%
21 다음 중 위 글의 내용과 일치하는 것은?

① Yeji doesn't know anything about ocean science.
② What Yeji studies is a big field in Korea.
③ Fish that Yeji has studied live far from Korea.
④ What interests Yeji is the growth ring in a tree.
⑤ The information Yeji gathered about fish helps manage the oceans better.

출제율 90%
22 밑줄 친 ⓐ가 가리키는 것을 위 글에서 찾아 쓰시오.

➡ _____

출제율 90%
23 위 글의 내용과 일치하도록 빈칸에 알맞은 말을 쓰시오.

> Yeji gets _____ _____ _____ so that she can use it to understand sea resources.

01 다음 그림은 Bora가 관심을 가지고 있는 분야이다. 다음 〈조건〉에 따라 대화를 완성하시오.

technology

┤ 조건 ├
(A) 'interest'를 어형 변화하여 '기술에 관심이 있다'는 표현을 쓸 것.
(B) 확실성 정도를 나타내는 표현을 쓸 것. 'quite'를 사용할 것.

➡ A: _____. Which job would be right for me?
   B: _____ an app developer could be a good job for you.

02 다음 대화를 읽고 아래 요약문의 빈칸을 완성하시오.

B: Hello, what are you doing, Sumi?
G: I'm looking for a good recipe on the Internet. I need it for my family dinner today.
B: That is nice. Do you cook often?
G: Yes, I try to cook every weekend. I want to be a chef someday.
B: What are you doing to make your dream come true?
G: I'm taking a cooking class. I try to think of new and creative dishes.
B: I'm quite sure you could be a good chef.

➡ Sumi's _____ is to be a chef. _____ to me _____ class and _____ are important to _____ her dream.

03 다음 대화의 밑줄 친 (A)와 같은 의미가 되도록 주어진 단어를 이용하여 문장의 빈칸을 완성하시오.

M: What's wrong, Jisu?
G: I want to be an animator, but my drawing skill is not good enough.
M: Hmm... Being an animator is not just about being a good artist.
G: What should I do to become an animator?
M: Read a lot of books to make good stories and practice drawing every day.
G: Okay, I'll do so.
M: (A)I'm quite sure that you can be a good animator if you try hard.
G: Thank you very much.

➡ _____
_____ (doubt)

04 다음 그림을 보고, 주어진 어구를 알맞게 배열하여 문맥에 맞게 대화를 완성하시오. (단, 부사구를 강조하는 문장으로 쓰시오.)

Reporter: What is the biggest contribution to your winning this award today?
Winner: It _____
_____.

(award / that / because / received / was / of / my parents / I / this)

05 다음 우리말과 같은 뜻이 되도록 괄호 안에 있는 단어들을 활용하여, 글자 수에 맞게 영작하시오. (동사 형태 변화 가능)

(1) 그녀의 아버지는 Sally에게 Toto를 씻기라고 시켰다. (6 단어)

➡ _____

(2) 그녀의 아버지는 Toto가 Sally에 의해 씻겨지도록 시켰다. (7 단어)

(Sally, Toto, have, wash, father, by, her)

➡ _____

[06~08] 다음 글을 읽고 물음에 답하시오.

I like food from around the world and I am good at cooking. I can also make food look tasty and beautiful. For these reasons, it is a chef that I want to be when I grow up. To achieve my dream, I will read magazines about cooking. Also, I will go to France to learn various cooking skills. My role model is my dad. He always thinks of new recipes and then cooks these new dishes for us. I want to have my name remembered by people who enjoy my food.

06 What does the writer want to be when she grows up? Answer in English with a full sentence.

➡ _____

07 Write the two things that the writer will do in order to achieve her dream. Use the words 'first, second.'

➡ _____

_____

08 What does the writer's father always do?

➡ _____

_____

[09~11] 다음 글을 읽고 물음에 답하시오.

I am Emma. I am a sport data analyst. It sounds like a difficult job, doesn't it? In fact, it is a lot of fun. I work for a baseball team. My job is to watch (A)_____ games and run a computer program to collect data. Then, I analyze the data to show my team's strengths and weaknesses. If the team understands their strengths and weaknesses, they can do better next time. Since I was young, I have been a big fan of baseball. Now, in my work, I watch baseball games all the time. This is a perfect job for me because watching baseball games is my hobby!

09 주어진 단어를 빈칸 (A)에 어법에 맞게 쓰시오.

(record)

➡ _____

10 According to the passage, what is Emma's hobby? Answer in English with a full sentence.

➡ _____

11 What does Emma do all the time in her work? Answer in English with a full sentence.

➡ _____

01 다음 (A)는 관심 있는 분야이고 (B)는 장래 희망이다. 〈보기〉의 문장처럼 대화를 완성하시오.

(A)	(B)
• art	• a designer
• writing	• a poet
• sports	• a soccer player
• nature	• farmer

A: _____. Which job would be right for me?
B: _____ could be a good job for you.

02 다음 그림들을 보고, 괄호 안에 주어진 어휘를 모두 활용하여, 'have+목적어+과거분사'의 표현이 들어간 문장을 만드시오. (원하는 단어를 추가하되, 어법에 유의할 것.)

(phone / repair / yesterday) (Sophia / check / a mechanic / tomorrow)

(1) _____

(2) _____

03 다음 내용을 바탕으로 Jina의 장래 희망을 써 봅시다.

Q: What things do you like?
Jina: I like bags from around the world.
Q: What are you good at?
Jina: I am good at making things. I can also make what I made look beautiful.
Q: What do you want to be when you grow up?
Jina: It is a bag designer that I want to be when I grow up.
Q: What will you do to achieve your dream?
Jina: I will read fashion magazines. Also I will go to France to learn to design bags.

I like _____ the world and I am good at _____. I can also make _____. For these reasons, _____ I want to be when I grow up. To achieve my dream, I will _____. Also, I will _____.

단원별 모의고사

01 다음 단어에 대한 영어 설명이 <u>어색한</u> 것은?

① analyzsis: someone whose job is to analyze and examine something

② bank teller: a person whose job is to pay out and take in money in a bank

③ care for: to protect someone or something and provide the things they need, especially someone who is young, old or ill

④ developer: a person or company that creates new products, especially computer products such as software

⑤ make the best use of: to use something as much as you can

02 다음 중 짝지어진 대화가 <u>어색한</u> 것은?

① A: Did you finish the report about your role model?
  B: Yes, I did. I wrote about my role model, Mr. Kang.

② A: What does she do?
  B: She teaches people how to stretch.

③ A: What are you good at?
  B: I am good at writing stories.

④ A: What are you doing to make your dream come true?
  B: I'm taking a cooking class.

⑤ A: Are you happy with your job?
  B: In my opinion, going to fashion shows would be helpful.

03 다음 짝지어진 단어의 관계가 같도록 빈칸에 알맞은 말을 쓰시오.

> fix : repair = operate : _____

04 다음 영영풀이에 해당하는 단어를 고르시오.

> to bring a person or thing to a state or place

① handle　　② select
③ lead　　④ create
⑤ fetch

[05~06] 다음 대화를 읽고 물음에 답하시오.

A: I'm interested in animals. (A)_____
B: I think a pet hairdresser can be a good job for you.
A: What is a pet hairdresser?
B: (B)_____ He/She designs different hairstyles for pets.
A: That sounds nice. Why do you think it can be a good job for me?
B: You are interested in animals. And I know you are good at designing and making things.

05 위 대화의 빈칸 (A)에 들어갈 말로 알맞은 것은?

① Are you interested in animals?
② What do you do at a pet hair salon?
③ What is the best thing about a pet hairdresser?
④ Which job is right for me?
⑤ What do you think of a pet hairdresser?

06 위 대화의 A의 물음에 맞게, 주어진 어구를 알맞은 순서로 배열하여 빈칸 (B)를 완성하시오.

> (works / that's / a pet / who / at / hair salon / a person)

➡ _____

[07~08] 다음 대화를 읽고 물음에 답하시오.

Bora: What are you most interested in among the things on this list?

Jessie: I'm most interested in working outside and (a)playing sports.

Bora: Well, it (b)seems to me that you belong to the realistic type.

Jessie: What do you mean?

Bora: Most people (c)are belonged to one of six personality types. Realistic is one of the types.

Jessie: Oh, that's (d)interesting. What kind of jobs do they recommend for realistic types?

Bora: A farmer, a police officer, a soccer player, and so on.

Jessie: Oh, I have always (e)wanted to be a soccer player.

Bora: That's good. I'm quite sure you could become a great soccer player.

07 위 대화의 밑줄 친 (a)~(e) 중 어법상 어색한 것은?

① (a) ② (b) ③ (c) ④ (d) ⑤ (e)

08 What jobs do they recommend for the realistic type?

➡ They recommend _____

_____ .

[09~10] 다음 대화를 읽고 물음에 답하시오.

M: What's wrong, Jisu?

G: I want to be an animator, but my drawing skill is not good enough.

M: Hmm... Being an animator is not just about being a good artist.

G: _____

M: Read a lot of books to make good stories and practice drawing every day.

G: Okay, I'll do so.

M: (A)나는 네가 열심히 노력하면 훌륭한 만화 영화 제작자가 될 수 있다고 꽤 확신해.

G: Thank you very much.

09 위 대화의 빈칸에 들어갈 말로 알맞은 것은?

① How many books are you going to read?
② What should I do to become an animator?
③ I think that you can be a good novelist.
④ Can I get your advice on what to read?
⑤ What books do I have to read?

10 위 대화의 (A)의 우리말 해석에 맞게 주어진 어구를 알맞은 순서로 배열하시오.

(I'm / you / quite / if / that / can be / a good / you / animator / try hard / sure)

➡ _____

_____

11 다음을 읽고, 각 질문에 대한 답을 'It ~ that' 강조 구문으로 조건에 맞게 영작하시오.

> • Lucy started to read the novel last Sunday.
> • Austin wrote the novel two months ago.
> • Today's Tuesday and Lucy is still reading it.

(1) For how many days has Lucy been reading the novel? (for, 현재완료진행형을 쓸 것, 총 12단어)
➡ _____

(2) What is the name of the author of the novel that Lucy is reading? (who, novel, write를 이용할 것. 형태 변화 가능하며, 총 7단어)
➡ _____

12 다음 그림을 보고, 우리말에 맞게 주어진 어구를 배열하시오.

(1) 엄마는 나에게 쓰지 않는 물건들을 상자에 모으라고 시키셨다.

(me / the unused things / mom / in / had / put / the boxes).

➡ _____

(2) 나는 그 상자들을 자선단체에 기부하게 할 것이다.
(have / charity / will / donated / the boxes / I / to).

➡ _____

13 다음 각각의 그림을 보고, 우리말과 조건에 맞게 영작하시오. (어형 변화 가능)

(1) 엄마는 내가 혼자 힘으로 이를 닦도록 시켰다.
(me, have, brush, myself 활용, 총 8단어).

➡ _____

(2) 그렇게 많은 그릇을 닦고 있는 것은 바로 나의 개 Angel이다.
(dish, wash, so, 'It ~ that' 강조 구문을 활용할 것, 총 11단어)

➡ _____

14 다음 밑줄 친 부분과 어법상 쓰임이 같은 것은?

> The history teacher <u>had</u> all the students go on a field trip to Gyeongju.

① Elizabeth <u>had</u> every reason to get annoyed with that situation.
② Maya <u>had</u> an eye for both modern and ancient paintings.
③ We <u>had</u> him come here earlier.
④ Henry <u>had</u> coffee and cake for dessert.
⑤ Mike <u>had</u> a car accident two years ago.

[15~18] 다음 글을 읽고 물음에 답하시오.

Hi, I am Tom. A florist is someone who creates beautiful things with flowers. ① To become a florist, you need to know many things about flowers. ② It was at this school that I learned how to grow and care for different types of flowers. ③ These days, florists can do a lot of different things. ④ I design movie sets sometimes and I decorate shops with flowers. ⑤ I am happy when I create something colorful with fresh flowers and greenery. If you like (A)_____, I highly recommend you become a florist.

15 ①~⑤ 중 주어진 문장이 들어가기에 가장 적절한 곳은?

> I attended a high school for florists and gardeners.

①   ②   ③   ④   ⑤

16 빈칸 (A)에 들어갈 말로 가장 적절한 것은?

① drawing and writing
② thinking and doing
③ plants and the arts
④ the arts and the artist
⑤ planting and growing

17 다음 중 플로리스트의 일과 관련이 없는 것은?

① making beautiful things with flowers
② knowing many things about flowers
③ growing and caring for different types of flowers
④ decorating flowers with colored paper
⑤ designing movie sets

18 다음 중 위 글을 읽고 답할 수 없는 것은?

① What is a florist?
② What did Tom learn at his high school?
③ When does Tom feel happy?
④ Where does Tom work?
⑤ How does Tom decorate shops?

[19~21] 다음 글을 읽고 물음에 답하시오.

Hi, I am Chris. As a director of a musical theater, I do a lot of things. I audition the actors and I look for good, strong voices. After selecting the cast, I teach them the songs for each scene. Then, I put the cast and orchestra together for practice. During the performance, I am in the orchestra area and conduct. (A)각각의 노래가 매번 동일하게 연주되도록 만드는 것은 나의 책임입니다. I direct the musicians and the singers to keep the show together. Conducting and directing is not just about (B)waving my arms around!

19 According to the passage, when does Chris conduct? Answer in English with a full sentence.

➡ _____

20 다음 주어진 단어를 활용하여 밑줄 친 (A)를 영어로 쓸 때 빈칸에 알맞은 말을 쓰시오. 필요하다면 어형을 바꾸시오.

(responsibility / play / each / have / to / my / song)

➡ It's _____ the same way every time.

21 다음 중 밑줄 친 (B)와 쓰임이 같은 것은?

① Do you hear a baby crying in the room?
② The rising sun is very bright.
③ Making noises here is not helpful.
④ Jason is playing soccer outside.
⑤ We saw a boy dancing on the street.

22 다음 중 글의 흐름상 어색한 것은?

I like food from around the world and I am good at cooking. ①I can also make food look tasty and beautiful. ②For these reasons, it is a chef that I want to be when I grow up. ③To achieve my dream, I will read magazines about cooking. ④ Also, I will go to France to learn various cooking skills. ⑤My dad always thinks of new recipes and then cooks these new dishes for us. I want to have my name remembered by people who enjoy my food.

①   ②   ③   ④   ⑤

Lesson 4

Are You a Digital Citizen?

🎤 의사소통 기능

- 충고하기

  If I were you, I would change my password.

- 불허하기

  You're not supposed to use your personal information.

🎤 언어 형식

- to부정사의 의미상의 주어 'for+목적격'

  It is necessary **for you** to set some rules for using your smartphone.

- 가정법 과거: 'If+주어+동사의 과거형 ~, 주어+would/could+동사원형 …'

  If we had no smartphones, **our lives would be** difficult.

Words & Expressions

Key Words

- **addiction** [ədíkʃən] 명 중독
- **advantage** [ædvǽntidʒ] 명 장점, 유리함
- **alert** [əlɔ́ːrt] 명 알람소리, 경보
- **birth** [bəːrθ] 명 출생, 탄생
- **block** [blɑk] 동 차단하다, 막다
- **cause** [kɔːz] 동 야기하다, 원인이 되다
- **citizen** [sítəzən] 명 시민
- **comment** [kάment] 명 발언, 논평, 비평
- **contact** [kάntækt] 동 연락하다
- **conversation** [kὰnvərséiʃən] 명 대화
- **copyright** [kάpirait] 명 저작권
- **create** [kriéit] 동 창조하다, 만들다
- **creative** [kriéitiv] 형 창의적인
- **dangerous** [déindʒərəs] 형 위험한
- **detox** [diːtάks] 명 해독
- **device** [diváis] 명 기기, 장치
- **digital** [dídʒətl] 형 디지털의, 디지털 방식을 쓰는
- **disadvantage** [dìsədvǽntidʒ] 명 단점, 약점, 불리한 점
- **enjoyable** [indʒɔ́iəbl] 형 즐거운
- **focus** [fóukəs] 동 집중하다
- **form** [fɔːrm] 동 만들다, 형성시키다
- **guess** [ges] 동 추측하다
- **half** [hæf] 명 반, 절반
- **imagine** [imǽdʒin] 동 상상하다
- **instead** [instéd] 부 대신에
- **intend** [inténd] 동 ~할 작정이다
- **limit** [límit] 동 제한하다
- **message** [mésidʒ] 명 알림, 메시지
- **mistake** [mistéik] 명 실수
- **necessary** [nésəsèri] 형 필요한
- **noisy** [nɔ́izi] 형 시끄러운
- **outdoor** [áutdɔːr] 형 옥외의, 야외의
- **pain** [pein] 명 고통
- **password** [pǽswərd] 명 비밀번호
- **personal information** 개인 정보
- **post** [poust] 동 게시하다
- **posting** [póustiŋ] 명 인터넷이나 SNS에 올리는 글
- **reduce** [ridjúːs] 동 줄이다
- **refreshed** [rifréʃt] 형 상쾌한
- **respect** [rispékt] 동 존중하다, 존경하다
- **right** [rait] 명 권리 부 바로
- **score** [skɔːr] 명 점수
- **share** [ʃɛər] 동 공유하다
- **spend** [spend] 동 (시간을) 보내다
- **suggest** [səgdʒést] 동 제안하다
- **symbol** [símbəl] 명 상징
- **tired** [taiərd] 형 피곤한, 지친
- **uncomfortable** [ənkámfərtəbəl] 형 불편한
- **until** [əntíl] 전 ~까지
- **wise** [waiz] 형 현명한

Key Expressions

- **be addicted to** ~에 중독되다
- **be good for** ~에 좋다
- **be supposed to+동사원형** ~해야 한다
- **can't help it** 어쩔 수 없다
- **figure out** 알아내다, 계산하다
- **for a while** 잠시 동안
- **for free** 무료로
- **in fact** 사실
- **It seems that+주어+동사** ~인 것 같다
- **on the other hand** 반면에
- **put aside** 치우다
- **right away** 당장
- **set up** 설정하다
- **share A with B** A를 B와 공유하다
- **stay away from** ~에서 떨어져 있다, ~을 멀리하다
- **such as** ~와 같은
- **take A into B** A를 B로 가져가다

Word Power

※ 서로 비슷한 뜻을 가진 어휘
- ☐ **limit** : **restrict** (제한하다)
- ☐ **focus** : **concentrate** (집중하다)
- ☐ **conversation** : **dialogue** (대화)

- ☐ **uncomfortable** : **uneasy** (불편한)
- ☐ **enjoyable** : **pleasurable** (즐거운)
- ☐ **suggest** : **propose** (제안하다)

※ 서로 반대되는 뜻을 가진 어휘
- ☐ **advantage** (장점) ↔ **disadvantage** (단점)
- ☐ **reduce** (줄이다) ↔ **increase** (늘리다, 증가하다)
- ☐ **dangerous** (위험한) ↔ **safe** (안전한)

- ☐ **birth** (출생) ↔ **death** (죽음)
- ☐ **create** (창조하다) ↔ **destroy** (파괴하다)
- ☐ **respect** (존중하다) ↔ **disregard** (무시하다)

English Dictionary

- ☐ **addiction** 중독
  → an inability to stop doing or using something, especially something harmful
  무언가, 특히 해로운 것을 하는 것이나 사용하는 것을 중단하지 못하는 것

- ☐ **advantage** 장점
  → something that may help one to gain favorable result
  유리한 결과를 얻는 데 도움이 될 만한 것

- ☐ **alert** 경고, 알림
  → a warning to people to be prepared to deal with something dangerous.
  위험한 것을 처리할 대비가 되도록 사람들에게 하는 경고

- ☐ **be addicted to** ~에 중독되다
  → to be physically and mentally dependent on an particular substance
  특정한 물질에 신체적으로, 정신적으로 의존하다

- ☐ **birth** 출생
  → an act of being born
  태어나는 행위

- ☐ **comment** 논평, 해설, 비평
  → something that you say about someone or something
  누군가나 무엇에 관해 당신이 말하는 것

- ☐ **contact** 연락하다
  → to communicate with someone by calling or sending them a letter, email, etc.
  전화를 걸거나 편지나 이메일 등을 보냄으로써 누군가와 연락하다

- ☐ **conversation** 대화
  → talk between two or more people in which thoughts, feelings, and ideas are expressed, or questions are asked and answered
  생각, 감정, 아이디어가 표현되거나, 질문과 답변이 되는 두 명 또는 그 이상의 사람들 사이의 이야기

- ☐ **copyright** 저작권
  → a right to sell a book, music, film, etc.
  책, 음악, 영화 등을 판매하는 권리

- ☐ **device** 기기, 장치
  → a mechanical object that is made for a particular purpose
  특정한 목적을 위해 만들어진 기계적인 물체

- ☐ **digital** 디지털 방식을 쓰는
  → storing pictures, sound, etc. in a number of small signals or showing them in numbers
  다수의 작은 신호로 사진, 소리 등을 저장하거나 그것을 숫자로 보여주는

- ☐ **figure out** 알아내다, 이해하다
  → to understand or solve something
  무언가를 이해하거나 해결하다

- ☐ **half** 반, 절반
  → one of two equal parts of something
  어떤 것의 두 개의 동일한 부분 중 하나

- ☐ **intend** ~할 작정이다
  → to plan to do something; to have an action planned in your mind
  어떤 일을 할 계획을 세우다; 마음 속에 계획된 행동을 가지다

- ☐ **message** 메시지
  → a spoken or written piece of information that you send to someone
  당신이 누군가에게 보내는 말이나 서면 정보

- ☐ **mistake** 실수
  → an action, decision, or judgment that produces an unwanted or unintentional result
  원하지 않거나 의도하지 않은 결과를 생성하는 행동, 결정 또는 판단

- ☐ **symbol** 상징
  → a thing that is regarded as representing for another
  또 다른 것을 대표하는 것으로 여겨지는 것

01 다음 문장의 빈칸에 공통으로 들어갈 말로 가장 알맞은 것은?

- The number of students is _____ this year.
- My weight was _____ when I stopped eating sugar.

① increased   ② developed
③ created   ④ reduced
⑤ selected

02 다음 문장의 빈칸에 주어진 철자로 시작하는 단어를 쓰시오.

Be careful that your playing video games doesn't lead to a_____.

03 다음 우리말에 맞게 빈칸에 세 단어를 쓰시오.

나는 고칼로리 음식을 멀리하려고 노력한다.

➡ I try to _____ _____ _____ high-calorie foods.

[04~05] 다음 설명에 해당하는 단어를 고르시오.

04

to communicate with someone by calling or sending them a letter, email, etc.

① reduce   ② contact
③ conversation   ④ guess
⑤ post

05

a thing that is regarded as representing for another

① gift   ② score
③ citizen   ④ pain
⑤ symbol

06 다음 문장의 빈칸에 들어갈 말이 바르게 짝지어진 것은?

(A) I sat on a bench and read a book _____.
(B) I have to _____ the number of guests because my house is too small.

	(A)	(B)
①	instead	guess
②	instead	increase
③	for a while	limit
④	right away	create
⑤	for a while	guess

07 다음 짝지어진 단어의 관계가 같도록 빈칸에 알맞은 말을 쓰시오.

advantage – disadvantage : _____ – birth

08 다음 빈칸에 공통으로 들어갈 말은?

- To fight the addiction, China's Internet _____ Camps are growing rapidly.
- _____ diets have increasingly become popular as fast and easy ways to get rid of toxins in your body and to lose weight.

① Game   ② Drug
③ Vegetable   ④ Detox
⑤ Digital

01 다음 빈칸에 들어갈 말을 〈보기〉에서 찾아 쓰시오.

┌─ 보기 ─┐
necessary   such as   form   refreshed
└─────┘

(1) Please rearrange the letters to _____ a new word.

(2) I love Korean foods _____ Bibimbap or Bulgogi.

(3) After a sound sleep, I felt _____.

(4) It is _____ for us to drink lots of water every day.

02 다음 문장은 '스마트폰 중독 증상'에 관한 내용이다. 빈칸에 들어갈 단어를 주어진 〈영영풀이〉를 보고 쓰시오.

I would feel _____ without constant access to information through my smartphone.

＜영영풀이＞
not feeling comfortable and pleasant, or not making you feel comfortable and pleasant

03 다음 우리말과 같은 표현이 되도록 문장의 빈칸을 채우시오.

(1) Frank는 게임에 중독되어 있다.
➡ Frank is _____ to games.

(2) 너는 여기에 6시에 오기로 되어 있었다.
➡ You were _____ to be here at six o'clock.

(3) 나의 부모님은 선생님의 논평을 읽었다.
➡ My parents read the teacher's _____.

(4) 내 친구는 내가 방문했을 때 나에게 집 비밀번호를 알려 주었다.
➡ My friend told me the _____ to her house when I visited there.

04 영영풀이에 해당하는 단어를 〈보기〉에서 찾아 첫 번째 빈칸에 쓰고, 두 번째 빈칸에는 우리말 뜻을 쓰시오.

┌─ 보기 ─┐
detox   digital   conversation   mistake
└─────┘

(1) _____: storing pictures, sound, etc. in a number of small signals or showing them in numbers: _____

(2) _____: an action, decision, or judgment that produces an unwanted or unintentional result: _____

(3) _____: a period when you stop taking unhealthy or harmful foods, drinks, or drugs into your body for a period: _____

(4) _____: talk between two or more people in which thoughts, feelings, and ideas are expressed, or questions are asked and answered: _____

05 빈칸에 공통으로 들어갈 단어를 쓰시오.

• Various Korean food recipes will be _____ed on the Seoul tourism website.

• I took many pictures and _____ed them on Instagram.

Conversation

교과서

1 충고하기

• **If I were you, I would change my password.**
만약 내가 너라면, 비밀번호를 바꿀 것이다.

■ 'If I were you, I would ~.'는 충고할 때 사용하는 표현으로 '내가 너라면 ~할 것이다[~할 텐데].'로 해석한다.

A: I want to exercise every day, but I don't have enough time. 매일 운동하고 싶은데, 시간이 별로 없어.

B: If I were you, I'd ride a bicycle to school. 내가 너라면 자전거를 타고 등교하겠어.

■ 충고할 때 사용하는 다양한 표현
• 'You'd better ~.'는 주로 부모님이나 선생님처럼 더 권위가 있는 사람이 긴급한 상황이나 충고가 필요한 상황에서 쓴다. 친구 사이에 충고를 하는 경우에는 'You should ~.'를 더 많이 쓴다. 충고하는 말 앞에 I think나 Maybe를 써서 좀 더 부드럽게 말할 수 있다.

A: I have a cold. 저는 감기에 걸렸어요.

B: You'd better go home and get some rest. 너는 집에 가서 좀 쉬는 게 낫겠구나.

■ 충고에 답할 때
상대방의 충고에는 'I see. / Okay, thanks. / All right. / That's a good idea.' 등으로 답하며, 'I'll keep that in mind.'와 같은 다짐을 함께 말할 수도 있다.

핵심 Check

1. 다음 대화의 빈칸에 들어갈 말로 알맞지 <u>않은</u> 것은?

A: I have a cold.

B: _____ go home and get some rest.

① You should

② You had better

③ Maybe you should

④ I'm quite sure that I

⑤ I think you should

② 불허하기

> • You're not supposed to use your personal information.
> 너는 너의 개인 정보를 사용하면 안 된다.

■ 'You're not supposed to ~.'는 '~해서는 안 된다.'라는 의미로 불허를 나타내는 표현이다. 이때 'be not supposed to+동사원형'은 'must not', 'should not', 'cannot' 또는 'had better not' 등으로 바꾸어 사용할 수 있다. 또는 부정명령문 'Don't+동사원형 ~.'을 사용하여 '~하지 마!'라는 불허(금지)의 의미를 나타낼 수 있다. 불허하는 또 다른 표현으로 'be not allowed to+동사원형'을 사용하여 '~하도록 허가되지 않다'는 의미를 나타낼 수 있다.

- **A**: Excuse me. You shouldn't use your cell phone here.
  실례합니다. 당신은 여기서 휴대전화를 사용하시면 안 됩니다.
  B: Oh, I'm sorry. 오, 미안합니다.

- You can't play with Dad's shoe. 아빠 신발을 가지고 놀면 안 돼.

- **A**: Is it okay if I take a picture? 내가 사진을 찍어도 괜찮을까요?
  B: No, you're not allowed to do that. 아니요, 사진을 찍으면 안 됩니다.

불허하기 여러 가지 표현

- You are not supposed to ~. 너는 ~해서는 안 된다.

- You are not allowed to ~. 너는 ~해서는 안 된다.

- You should not ~. 너는 ~하지 말아야 한다.

- You must not ~. 너는 ~하지 말아야 한다.

핵심 Check

2. 다음 대화의 빈칸에 들어갈 말로 성격이 **다른** 하나는?

   A: Do you talk to strangers online?
   B: Yes.
   A: You _____ talk to strangers online.

   ① should not
   ② must not
   ③ are not supposed to
   ④ had better not
   ⑤ are allowed to

Listen & Speak 1 A-1

G: You ❶look tired, Peter.

B: I played computer games until late, so last night I slept for less than four hours.

G: ❷Playing computer games too much is not good for your health.

B: I know, Jenny, but I can't stop it. I think ❸I'm addicted to it.

G: ❹If I were you, I would set a daily plan to limit game time.

B: ❺That's a good idea. Thanks.

G: 너 피곤해 보인다, Peter.

B: 나 늦게까지 게임을 해서, 어젯밤에 4시간도 못 잤어.

G: 컴퓨터 게임을 너무 많이 하는 건 네 건강에 좋지 않아.

B: 나도 알아, Jenny, 그런데 멈출 수가 없어. 난 그것에 중독된 것 같아.

G: 만약 내가 너라면, 게임 시간을 제한하기 위해 일일 계획을 짤 거야.

B: 그거 좋은 생각이네. 고마워.

❶ 'look+형용사'로 '~처럼 보이다'라는 뜻이다.
❷ 동명사(Playing) 주어로 동사는 단수 취급한다.
❸ 'be addicted to ~'는 '~에 중독되다'는 의미다.
❹ 가정법과거형(If+주어+과거동사[were] ~, 주어+would[could/should/might]+동사원형)으로 충고할 때 사용하는 표현이다. '내가 너라면 ~할 것이다[~할 텐데]'로 해석한다.
❺ 상대방이 해 준 충고에 대한 답으로 I see. / Okay, thanks. / All right. 등으로 바꾸어 말할 수 있다.

Check(√) True or False

(1) Peter is addicted to the computer games.　　　　　T ☐ F ☐

(2) Jenny sets a daily plan to limit game time.　　　　T ☐ F ☐

Listen & Speak 2 A-1

G: James, what are you doing?

B: I'm posting some of the pictures ❶that I took with Sarah today.

G: Did you ask Sarah ❷if you could post them online?

B: No, but I think it's okay because she looks good in the pictures.

G: ❸You're not supposed to post someone's pictures without asking.

B: Oh, maybe you're right. I'll call Sarah and ask her right away.

G: James, 뭐 하고 있니?

B: 나 오늘 Sarah와 함께 찍은 사진들 중 몇 장을 올리고 있어.

G: 네가 그걸 온라인에 올려도 될지 Sarah에게 물어봤어?

B: 아니, 그렇지만 그녀가 잘 나왔으니까 괜찮을 것 같아.

G: 너는 다른 사람들의 사진을 물어보지 않고 올리면 안 돼.

B: 오, 네 말이 맞을지 몰라. 내가 지금 당장 Sarah에게 전화해서 물어볼게.

❶ 목적격 관계대명사절로 선행사 the pictures를 수식하는 역할을 한다.
❷ ask의 직접목적어로 '~인지 아닌지'로 해석한다.
❸ '~해서는 안 된다'라는 의미로 불허를 나타내는 표현이다. 이때 'be not supposed to+동사원형'은 'must not', 'should not' 등으로 바꾸어 쓸 수 있다.

Check(√) True or False

(3) James is posting some pictures without asking Sarah.　　T ☐ F ☐

(4) Sarah looks good in the pictures.　　　　　　　　　　T ☐ F ☐

Listen & Speak 1 A-2

W: Tony, you ❶spend too much time on your smartphone.

B: My friends get together on SNS almost every day, so ❷I can't help it, Mom.

W: ❸If I were you, I would suggest doing outdoor activities to your friends.

B: Outdoor activities?

W: Yes. You can do a lot of great activities such as soccer or skating.

B: All right. I will suggest them today.

❶ spend+시간+on+명사: ～에 시간을 보내다
❷ 'can't[cannot] help it'에서 'help'는 '피하다, 그만두다'라는 의미를 가진다.
❸ 가정법과거형으로 be동사는 were를 사용하고, 주절에는 조동사 과거형을 사용한다. suggest는 목적어로 동명사(doing)를 취한다.

Listen & Speak 2 A-2

G: David, let's watch this new movie on the computer.

B: On the computer?

G: Yes. ❶I have a website we can download it from for free.

B: You're not supposed to download movies from that website, Catherine. It's against the law.

G: Really? I didn't know ❷that.

B: ❸Why don't we go to the movie theater, instead?

G: Okay. Let's go.

❶ I have a website (which/that) we can download it from for free. 전치사 from의 목적어 대신 사용된 목적격 관계대명사가 생략되어 있다. 'for free'는 '무료로'의 뜻이다.
❷ 'that'은 앞 문장의 'It's against the law'를 가리키는 인칭대명사이다.
❸ 'Why don't we+동사원형 ～?'은 '～하는 게 어때?'라고 제안할 때 사용하는 표현이다.

Real Life Talk

Bora: Seho, look! Somebody posted strange things on your SNS. I don't think you posted ❶them.

Seho: Really? Who did this?

Bora: I think someone figured out your password.

Seho: What should I do?

Bora: If I were you, I would change my password.

Seho: I think ❷I should.

Bora: Is your password easy to guess?

Seho: I used my birth date.

Bora: That is not good. In fact, it is a big mistake. ❸You're not supposed to use your personal information when you make a password.

Seho: Okay, I see. I will change it to a stronger ❹one.

❶ 'them'은 'strange things'를 가리키는 인칭대명사다.
❷ I should change my password.를 줄여 사용한 표현이다.
❸ '～해서는 안 된다'는 의미로 불허를 나타내는 말이다.
❹ 'one'은 'password'를 가리키는 부정대명사다.

Wrap Up

B: What are you doing, Sohee?

G: I'm writing a posting about the restaurant I visited today.

B: Those are great pictures. Did you take all of them?

G: No. I took the pictures from someone's blog.

B: Then ❶you're not supposed to post them on your blog.

G: Why not?

B: Because only the blog owner has the right ❷to use them.

G: Oh, I see.

❶ 불허를 표현하는 말로, 'be not supposed to'는 'should not'이나 'must not'으로 바꾸어 쓸 수 있다.
❷ 명사 the right를 수식하는 형용사적 용법이다.

● 다음 우리말과 일치하도록 빈칸에 알맞은 말을 쓰시오.

Listen & Speak 1 A

1. G: You look _____, Peter.

   B: I played computer games _____ late, so last night I slept for _____ _____ four hours.

   G: _____ computer games too much is not _____ _____ your health.

   B: I know, Jenny, but I _____ _____ it. I think I'm _____ to it.

   G: If I _____ you, I _____ _____ a daily plan to _____ game time.

   B: That's a good idea. Thanks.

2. W: Tony, you _____ too much time _____ your smartphone.

   B: My friends get together on SNS _____ every day, so I _____ _____ _____, Mom.

   W: _____ _____ _____ _____, I would _____ _____ outdoor activities to your friends.

   B: _____ activities?

   W: Yes. You can do _____ _____ _____ great activities _____ _____ soccer or skating.

   B: All right. I will _____ them today.

Listen & Speak 2 A

1. G: James, what are you doing?

   B: I'm _____ some of the pictures _____ I _____ with Sarah today.

   G: Did you ask Sarah _____ you could _____ them online?

   B: No, but I think it's okay because she _____ _____ in the pictures.

   G: You're _____ _____ _____ post someone's pictures _____ _____.

   B: Oh, maybe you're right. I'll call Sarah and ask her _____ _____.

해석

1. G: 너 피곤해 보인다, Peter.
   B: 나 늦게까지 게임을 해서, 어젯밤에 4시간도 못 잤어.
   G: 컴퓨터 게임을 너무 많이 하는 건 네 건강에 좋지 않아.
   B: 나도 알아, Jenny, 그런데 멈출 수가 없어. 난 그것에 중독된 것 같아.
   G: 만약 내가 너라면, 게임 시간을 제한하기 위해 일일 계획을 짤 거야.
   B: 그거 좋은 생각이네. 고마워.

2. W: Tony, 너 스마트 폰에 너무 많은 시간을 보내는구나.
   B: 제 친구들은 거의 매일 SNS에서 만나기 때문에, 저도 어쩔 수 없어요, 엄마.
   W: 만약 내가 너라면, 친구들에게 야외 활동을 하자고 제안할 거야.
   B: 야외 활동이요?
   W: 응. 너는 축구나 스케이트 타기 등과 같은 많은 멋진 활동을 할 수 있어.
   B: 알겠어요. 오늘 제안해 볼게요.

1. G: James, 뭐 하고 있니?
   B: 나 오늘 Sarah와 함께 찍은 사진들 중 몇 장을 올리고 있어.
   G: 네가 그걸 온라인에 올려도 될지 Sarah에게 물어봤니?
   B: 아니, 그렇지만 그녀가 사진들 속에서 멋져 보이기 때문에 괜찮을 것 같아.
   G: 너는 다른 사람들의 사진을 물어보지 않고 올리면 안 돼.
   B: 오, 네 말이 맞을지 몰라. 내가 지금 당장 Sarah에게 전화해서 물어볼게.

2. **G:** David, _____ watch this new movie on the computer.

   B: _____ the computer?

   G: Yes. I have a website we can _____ it from _____ _____.

   B: You're not _____ _____ _____ movies from that website, Catherine. It's _____ the law.

   G: Really? I didn't know that.

   B: _____ _____ _____ go to the movie theater, _____?

   G: Okay. Let's go.

Real Life Talk

Bora: Seho, look! Somebody _____ strange things _____ your SNS. I don't think you _____ them.

Seho: Really? Who did this?

Bora: I think someone _____ _____ your _____.

Seho: _____ _____ I do?

Bora: If I _____ you, I would _____ my password.

Seho: I think I _____.

Bora: Is your password _____ _____ _____?

Seho: I used my _____ _____.

Bora: That is not good. _____ _____, it is a big mistake. You'_____ _____ _____ _____ _____ _____ your _____ _____ when you make a password.

Seho: Okay, I see. I will _____ it to a _____ _____.

Wrap Up

B: What are you doing, Sohee?

G: I'm writing a _____ about the restaurant I visited today.

B: Those are great pictures. Did you _____ all of them?

G: No. I _____ the pictures from someone's _____.

B: Then you'_____ _____ _____ _____ _____ them on your blog.

G: _____ _____?

B: Because only the blog _____ has the _____ to use them.

G: Oh, I see.

해석

2. **G:** David, 컴퓨터로 이 신작 영화 보자.
   B: 컴퓨터로?
   G: 응. 우리가 그것을 무료로 내려 받을 수 있는 웹 사이트가 있어.
   B: 너는 그런 웹 사이트에서 영화를 내려 받으면 안 돼, Catherine. 그건 법에 어긋나.
   G: 정말? 그런지 몰랐어.
   B: 대신, 우리 영화관에 가는 건 어떨까?
   G: 좋아. 가자.

보라: 세호야, 봐! 누군가 네 SNS에 이상한 것을 올렸어. 나는 네가 그것들을 올렸다고 생각하지 않아.
세호: 정말? 누가 그랬지?
보라: 내 생각에 누군가 네 비밀번호를 알아낸 것 같아.
세호: 어떻게 해야 하지?
보라: 내가 너라면 비밀번호를 바꾸겠어.
세호: 내 생각에도 그래야 할 것 같아.
보라: 네 비밀번호는 추측하기 쉽니?
세호: 내 생일 날짜를 사용했어.
보라: 그것은 좋지 않아. 사실 그건 큰 실수야. 비밀번호를 만들 때 개인 정보를 사용하지 말아야 해.
세호: 그래, 알았어. 그걸 더 강한 것으로 바꿀 거야.

B: 뭐 하고 있니, 소희야?
G: 나는 오늘 방문했던 식당에 관한 게시 글을 쓰고 있어.
B: 멋진 사진들이네. 그것들을 네가 다 찍었니?
G: 아니. 누군가의 블로그에서 사진들을 가져왔어.
B: 그럼 너는 그것들을 네 블로그에 게시하면 안 돼.
G: 왜 안 돼?
B: 왜냐하면 그 블로그 주인만이 그것들을 사용할 권리가 있거든.
G: 오, 알겠어.

01 우리말 해석에 맞도록 문장의 빈칸에 알맞은 말을 쓰시오.

만약 내가 너라면, 화면 잠금을 설정할 거야.

➡ _____ _____ _____ _____, I would set up screen lock.

02 다음 대화의 빈칸에 들어갈 말로 알맞은 것은?

A: Do you use the same password for a long time?
B: Yes.
A: _____ the same password for a long time.

① I question whether you should not use
② You have to use
③ I'm not quite sure that you're not supposed to use
④ You're not supposed to use
⑤ You should use

03 다음 대화의 빈칸에 들어갈 말로 적절하지 <u>않은</u> 것은?

A: It seems that someone checks my smartphone. What should I do?
B: _____

① If I were you, I would set up screen lock.
② You'd better set up screen lock.
③ You're not supposed to set up screen lock.
④ You have to set up screen lock.
⑤ You should set up screen lock.

04 다음 대화의 밑줄 친 말의 의도로 알맞은 것은?

A: Have you posted bad comments online?
B: Yes.
A: <u>You're not supposed to post bad comments online.</u>

① 용서하기   ② 확실성 정도 표현하기
③ 관심 표현하기   ④ 화남 표현하기
⑤ 불허하기

01 다음 대화의 (A)~(D)를 알맞은 순서로 배열한 것은?

> W: Tony, you spend too much time on your smartphone.
> (A) Outdoor activities?
> (B) If I were you, I would suggest doing outdoor activities to your friends.
> (C) Yes. You can do a lot of great activities such as soccer or skating.
> (D) My friends get together on SNS almost every day, so I can't help it, Mom.
> B: All right. I will suggest them today.

① (A)–(C)–(B)–(D)
② (B)–(A)–(C)–(D)
③ (C)–(B)–(A)–(D)
④ (D)–(B)–(A)–(C)
⑤ (D)–(C)–(A)–(B)

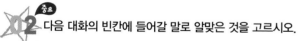

02 다음 대화의 빈칸에 들어갈 말로 알맞은 것을 고르시오.

> A: A stranger keeps texting me. What should I do?
> B: _____

① If I were you, I would play outside more often.
② If I were you, I would change my password.
③ If I were you, I would block the number.
④ If I were you, I would not eat sweet things.
⑤ If I were you, I would not use my smartphone.

서답형

03 다음 대화의 밑줄 친 우리말에 맞게 주어진 단어를 이용하여 영어로 쓰시오. (단어 하나를 추가하시오.)

> G: David, let's watch this new movie on the computer.
> B: On the computer?
> G: Yes. I have a website we can download it from for free.
> B: You're not supposed to download movies from that website, Catherine. 그건 법에 어긋나.

> it's / the / law

➡ _____

04 다음 중 짝지어진 대화가 어색한 것은?

① A: How often do you change your password?
   B: I change it every month.
② A: It seems that I spend too much time on the Internet. What should I do?
   B: If I were you, I would play outside more often.
③ A: It seems that someone checks my smartphone. What should I do?
   B: If I were you, I would set up screen lock.
④ A: What are you doing, Sohee?
   B: I'm writing a posting about the restaurant I visited today.
⑤ A: Somebody posted strange things on your SNS.
   B: What should you do?

Conversation **71**

서답형

05 다음 대화의 밑줄 친 문장과 같은 의미가 되도록 바꿔 쓸 때, 주어진 단어를 이용하여 빈칸을 채우시오.

> A: Do you use the same password for a long time?
> B: Yes.
> A: You should not use the same password for a long time.

➡ You _____ use the same password for a long time. (suppose)

[06~08] 다음 대화를 읽고 물음에 답하시오.

> G: You ⓐlook tired, Peter.
> B: I played computer games ⓑuntil late, so last night I slept for less than four hours.
> G: Playing computer games too much ⓒis not good for your health.
> B: I know, Jenny, but I ⓓcan't stop it. I think I'm ⓔaddict to it.
> G: (A)If I were you, I would set a daily plan to limit game time.
> B: That's a good idea. Thanks.

06 위 대화의 밑줄 친 (A)의 의도로 알맞은 것은?

① 조언 구하기　　　② 충고하기
③ 확신 표현하기　　④ 궁금증 표현하기
⑤ 가능성 묻기

07 위 대화를 읽고 답할 수 없는 것은?

① Why is Peter tired?
② What problem does Peter have and what is Jenny's advice?
③ What kind of game does Jenny suggest to Peter?
④ Does Peter know playing computer games too much is not good for his health?
⑤ What is Peter planning to do?

08 위 대화의 밑줄 친 ⓐ~ⓔ 중 어법상 어색한 것은?

① ⓐ　② ⓑ　③ ⓒ　④ ⓓ　⑤ ⓔ

[09~10] 다음 대화를 읽고 물음에 답하시오.

> B: What are you doing, Sohee?
> G: I'm writing a ⓐposting about the restaurant I visited today.
> B: Those are great pictures. Did you ⓑtake all of them?
> G: No. I took the pictures from ⓒsomeone's blog.
> B: Then you're ⓓsupposed to post them on your blog.
> G: Why not?
> B: Because only the blog owner has ⓔthe right to use them.
> G: Oh, I see.

09 위 대화의 흐름상 밑줄 친 ⓐ~ⓔ 중, 어휘의 쓰임이 어색한 것은?

① ⓐ　② ⓑ　③ ⓒ　④ ⓓ　⑤ ⓔ

중요
10 위 대화의 내용과 일치하지 않는 것은?

① Sohee visited the restaurant that had great pictures.
② Sohee didn't take the pictures of the restaurant.
③ Sohee took the pictures from someone's blog.
④ Sohee didn't know the reason why she shouldn't post the pictures that she took from someone's blog.
⑤ Sohee's friend is talking about the copyright.

[01~02] 다음 대화를 읽고 물음에 답하시오.

Bora: Seho, look! Somebody posted strange things on your SNS. I don't think you posted them.

Seho: Really? Who did this?

Bora: I think someone figured out your password.

Seho: What should I do?

Bora: (A)_____

Seho: I think I should.

Bora: Is your password easy to guess?

Seho: I used my birth date.

Bora: That is not good. In fact, it is a big mistake. You're not supposed to use your personal information when you make a password.

Seho: Okay, I see. I will change it to a stronger one.

01 위 대화의 빈칸 (A)에 들어갈 말을 〈조건〉에 맞게 쓰시오.

┤ 조건 ├
- If와 조동사 would를 사용할 것.
- 비밀번호를 바꾸라는 충고의 표현을 사용할 것.

➡ _____

02 위 대화를 읽고 다음 물음에 영어로 답하시오. (다섯 단어로 답할 것.)

Q: What did Seho use when he made his password?

➡ _____

03 다음 대화의 빈칸에 들어갈 말로 자연스러운 것을 〈보기〉에서 찾아 쓰시오.

G: James, what are you doing?

B: I'm posting some of the pictures that I took with Sarah today.

G: (A)_____

B: No, but I think it's okay because she looks good in the pictures.

G: (B)_____
_____

B: Oh, maybe you're right. (C)_____

┤ 보기 ├
- Did you ask Sarah if you could post them online?
- I'll call Sarah and ask her right away.
- You're not supposed to post someone's pictures without asking.

04 대화의 내용상 빈칸에 알맞은 말을 주어진 〈조건〉에 맞게 영어로 쓰시오.

┤ 조건 ├
- 'supposed'를 사용하여 불허의 표현을 쓸 것.
- 'download', 'that website'를 사용할 것.

G: David, let's watch this new movie on the computer.

B: On the computer?

G: Yes. I have a website we can download it from for free.

B: (A)_____
_____, Catherine. It's against the law.

G: Really? I didn't know that.

B: Why don't we go to the movie theater, instead?

G: Okay. Let's go.

Grammar

교과서

1 to부정사의 의미상의 주어: 'for+목적격'

> • It is necessary **for you** to keep it secret. 당신이 그것을 비밀로 유지하는 것이 필요하다.
> • It will be impossible **for Billy** to get an A. Billy가 A를 받는 것은 불가능할 것이다.

■ 동작의 행위자(agent): 동사가 행하는 동작을 '누가' 하는지 나타내는 말을 동작의 행위자라고 한다. 주어가 대부분 행위자이지만 그렇지 않은 경우, '의미상의 주어'라고 한다.

• I want to buy the car. 나는 그 차를 사기를 원한다.
: 문장의 주어 I가, 동사 want와 to부정사 to buy의 행위자

→ I want Sam to buy the car. 나는 Sam이 그 차를 사기를 원한다.
: Sam이 to buy의 행위자 = 의미상의 주어

■ 'It' 가주어, 'to' 진주어 문장에서 to부정사의 '의미상의 주어'는 'for+목적격' 형태로 표현한다.

• It is important **for me** to learn another language. 내가 다른 언어를 배우는 것은 중요하다.
• It was easy **for her** to solve the math problem. 그녀가 그 수학 문제를 푸는 것은 쉬웠다.
• It is necessary **for Brian** to tell the truth to his friends. Brian이 그의 친구들에게 진실을 말하는 것이 필요하다.

■ to부정사의 의미상의 주어가 일반 사람을 가리킬 때는 생략할 수 있다.

• It is necessary (**for us**) to drink enough water. (우리가) 충분한 물을 마시는 것이 필요하다.
• It is not difficult (**for people**) to follow the rules. 규칙을 지키는 것은 어렵지 않다.
• It is easy to make spaghetti. 스파게티를 만드는 것은 쉽다. (일반 사람)

→ It is easy **for me** to make spaghetti. 내가 스파게티를 만드는 것은 쉽다. (특정인)

■ 사람의 성격, 태도 등을 나타내는 형용사는 'of+목적격' 형태로 의미상의 주어를 표현한다.

• It was kind **of you** to help the kids. 그 아이들을 당신이 도운 것은 친절했다.
• It was foolish **of him** to stay up all night playing cards. 그가 카드 게임을 하느라 밤을 새운 것은 어리석은 짓이었다.

핵심 Check

1. 다음 괄호 안에서 알맞은 단어를 고르시오.

(1) It is wise (for / of) Jane to save money for her future.

(2) It was hard (for / of) me to believe her promise.

② 가정법 과거: 'If+주어+동사 과거형 ~, 주어+would/could+동사원형 …'

> • **If** I **had** more money, I **could buy** a new computer. 내가 돈이 더 많다면, 새 컴퓨터를 살 수 있을 텐데.
> • **If** Sally **lived** in Tokyo, she **would have** sushi every morning. Sally가 Tokyo에 산다면, 그녀는 매일 아침 초밥을 먹을 텐데.

- 가정법 과거: '만약 ~라면 …할 텐데'의 뜻으로, 현재 사실을 반대로 가정하거나 실현 가능성이 없는 일에 대해서 가정할 때 쓰며, 'If+주어+동사 과거형 ~, 주어+would/could+동사원형 …'의 형태로 나타낸다.

  - **If** he **knows** Lisa's phone number, **he will call** her. 그가 Lisa의 전화번호를 안다면, 그녀에게 전화할 것이다.
    (조건문, 알고 있을지도 모름)
  - **If** he **knew** Lisa's phone number, **he would call** her. 그가 Lisa의 전화번호를 안다면, 그녀에게 전화할 텐데.
    (가정법 과거, 현재 사실의 반대 가정)
    = **As** he **doesn't know** Lisa's phone number, **he won't call** her. 그가 Lisa의 전화번호를 모르기 때문에, 그는 그녀에게 전화하지 않을 것이다.
  - **If** I **were** Amy, **I would not meet** him. 내가 Amy라면, 나는 그를 만나지 않을 텐데.

- 'be' 동사는 주어의 인칭 및 수와 관계 없이 'were'를 쓴다. 단, 현대 영어에서는 주어가 1, 3인칭 단수일 때 'was'를 쓰기도 한다.

  - **If** he **were not[wasn't]** blind, **he could see** them. 그가 눈이 보인다면, 그들을 볼 수 있을 텐데.

- 가정법 과거완료는 이미 일어난 과거 사실을 반대로 가정하는 데 사용하며, 'If+주어+had+과거분사 ~, 주어+would/could+have+과거분사 …'의 형태로 나타낸다.

  - If Irene **had seen** that, she **would have helped** us. Irene이 그것을 보았다면, 그녀는 우리를 도와주었을 텐데.

- 가정법의 다양한 표현들로 직설법의 의미를 나타낼 수 있다.

  - **As** she **is** poor, she **cannot** buy the necklace. 그녀가 가난하기 때문에, 목걸이를 살 수 없다. (직설법)
    → **If** she **were not** poor, she **could buy** the necklace. 그녀가 가난하지 않으면, 목걸이를 살 수 있을 텐데. (가정법)
    → **Were** she not poor, she **could buy** the necklace. (If 생략 가능, 도치문으로 가정)

- without이나 but for는 '~이 없다면'의 뜻으로 가정법 구문에 쓰인다. without이나 but for는 If it were not(=Were it not for)로 바꿔 쓸 수 있다.

  → **Without** music, the world **would** be a dull place. 음악이 없다면 세계는 따분한 곳이 될 텐데.
  → **If it were not for** music, the world **would** be a dull place.
  → **Were it not for** music, the world **would** be a dull place. (If 생략 후 도치)

핵심 Check

2. 다음 우리말에 맞게 괄호 안의 어구를 바르게 배열하시오.

Paul이 그것을 알면, 비밀번호를 바꿀 텐데. (Paul, the password, knew, he, change, would, it, if)

➡ _____

01 다음 각 가정법 문장에서 어법상 <u>어색한</u> 단어를 한 개씩만 찾아 고치시오.

(1) If we have no smartphones, our lives would be difficult.

_____ ➡ _____

(2) If he had a flying car, he will go to Paris.

_____ ➡ _____

(3) If she has a million dollars, she would travel around the world.

_____ ➡ _____

(4) I will set a daily plan to limit game time if I were you.

_____ ➡ _____

02 다음 중 어법상 바르지 <u>않은</u> 것은?

① Is your password easy to guess?
② It is interesting for David to draw beautiful mountains.
③ It was not easy of him to swim at the beach.
④ It's necessary for you to respect others.
⑤ It will be possible for me to learn yoga next month.

03 다음 빈칸에 들어갈 말로 알맞은 것은?

| If there _____ no televisions, it would not be easy to watch dramas. |

① had   ② are   ③ have been
④ were   ⑤ is

04 다음 문장을 가주어 It과 to부정사를 이용하여 다시 쓰시오.

| Living without a smartphone is not easy for you. |

➡ _____

01 다음 문장의 밑줄 친 ①~⑤ 중 어법상 어색한 것은?

> It was <u>very</u> honest <u>for</u> you to tell the truth,
>   ①   ②
>
> <u>though</u> it was <u>not easy</u> to do <u>that</u>.
>   ③   ④   ⑤

02 다음 중 빈칸에 들어갈 말이 나머지와 <u>다른</u> 것은?

① It's not safe _____ the babies to play on the swings.
② It is necessary _____ Minju to gain weight.
③ It seems hard _____ the team to win the game.
④ It was rude _____ Charles to ask his teacher such questions.
⑤ Is it okay _____ me to get in?

03 다음 중 어법상 <u>어색한</u> 문장은?

① If I were in Sydney, I couldn't attend my friend's wedding.
② If Andy knew the solution, he could tell me right now.
③ If Paul pushed him hard, Jay could be hurt.
④ If he had an island, he won't build any houses on it.
⑤ If it were not for the help by the mechanic, we would not able to drive.

04 다음 중 같은 뜻을 가진 문장끼리 짝지어진 것은?

① I didn't have a car, so I couldn't drive.
　= If I had a car, I couldn't drive.
② Minsu doesn't have a computer, so he wants to have one.
　= Minsu wants if he had a computer.
③ I don't study hard, so I can't succeed.
　= If I studied hard, I could succeed.
④ She can't write a letter to Sam, so she knows his address.
　= She could write a letter to Sam, if she knew his address.
⑤ It is raining, so Sarah stays home.
　= If it rains, Sarah would stay home.

05 다음 중 빈칸 ⓐ~ⓕ에 같은 단어가 들어가는 것끼리 바르게 짝지어진 것은?

> • It was kind ⓐ_____ her to look after the babies in the orphanage.
> • It wasn't hard ⓑ_____ the students to understand the professor's lecture.
> • It is impossible ⓒ_____ me to exercise for an hour at 6 every morning.
> • It was stupid ⓓ_____ the young lady to reject the offer.
> • It is dangerous ⓔ_____ her to cut the rope with that plastic knife.
> • It is careless ⓕ_____ him to tell her my secret plans.

① ⓐ, ⓒ　　　② ⓑ, ⓓ, ⓔ
③ ⓒ, ⓔ, ⓕ　　④ ⓐ, ⓓ, ⓕ
⑤ ⓑ, ⓓ, ⓔ

[06~08] 다음 우리말과 일치하도록 괄호 안에 주어진 어구를 바르게 배열하시오.

06

> 내가 너라면, 나는 너의 친구들에게 야외 활동을 하자고 제안할 텐데.
> (suggest, outdoor activities, were, to, you, I, I, if, doing, your friends, would)

➡ _____

_____

07

> Smith가 자전거를 타는 것은 쉽다.
> (a bike, for, easy, is, to, Smith, ride, it)

➡ _____

08

> 텔레비전이 없다면, 우리가 뉴스를 시청하는 것이 쉽지 않을 텐데.
> (there, to, it, not, be, the news, easy, if, for, no, us, watch, would, were, televisions)

➡ _____

_____

09 다음 중 밑줄 친 부분의 쓰임이 나머지 넷과 <u>다른</u> 것은?

① <u>It</u> will be fun for us to learn how to play basketball.

② <u>It</u>'s good for her to walk for half an hour every day.

③ Isn't <u>it</u> easy to understand the rules of the game?

④ <u>It</u> is too dark to play outside.

⑤ I think that <u>it</u> is necessary for you to finish the homework.

10 다음 문장의 빈칸 (A)~(C)에 들어갈 말로 가장 적절한 것은?

> • If my school (A)_____ early, I would go see a movie.
> • Were it not for the water, the living things in earth (B)_____ be dead.
> • If I (C)_____ a car, I could go on a picnic more often.

	(A)	(B)	(C)
①	finishes	will	have
②	finishes	could	have
③	will finish	could	had had
④	finished	would	had
⑤	finished	will	had

11 다음 중 어법상 옳은 문장은?

① It is difficult of us to move those heavy chairs into the classroom.

② It is very nice for Angela to invite me to her wedding party.

③ It is not hard of me to speak French as well as English.

④ Is it okay for my to leave work a little earlier than usual today?

⑤ It was very cruel of you to mention his poor childhood experience.

12 다음 우리말을 조건에 맞게 영작하시오.

> Laura가 충분한 시간이 있으면, 서울에 더 오래 머무를 수 있을 텐데.
> (stay, long, can, enough 활용. If로 시작, 총 11 단어로 할 것, 단어 변형 가능)

➡ _____

_____

서답형

13 다음 대화가 자연스럽게 이뤄지도록 주어진 단어를 모두 활용하여 문장을 완성하시오. (1 단어는 어법에 맞게 바꿀 것.)

> Grandma: On this cold day, who opened the window? Somebody left the window open and all the plants froze to death.
> Suho: My younger sister Sujin did.
> Grandma: _____
>
> _____
>
> (open, for, it, the window, to, her, was, careless, leave)

중요

14 다음 중 어법상 <u>어색한</u> 것은?

① If you told this to him, he would be mad at me.
② If Abe got up early, he wouldn't be late for school.
③ If Sally had worn the jacket, she wouldn't have got a cold.
④ If Chris hadn't missed the subway, he would not be late for school.
⑤ If I were the President, my family would be proud of me.

15 다음 우리말을 영작할 때, 옳지 <u>않은</u> 문장을 고르시오.

> 공기가 없다면, 우리는 살 수 없을 텐데.

① If there were no air, we couldn't live.
② If it were not for air, we couldn't live.
③ If there is no air, we couldn't live.
④ Were it not for air, we couldn't live.
⑤ Without air, we couldn't live.

중요

16 다음 중 어법상 올바른 문장의 개수는?

> ⓐ It is clever of him using the tools.
> ⓑ It is very stupid for Mark to do such a thing in public.
> ⓒ It was impossible for Janet to arrive at the party on time.
> ⓓ It's important of their mothers to watch the kids play together happily.
> ⓔ It is generous of Susan to help the old lady to find the way to the city hall.
> ⓕ It was quite importantly for the teachers to make the subject easy to understand.
> ⓖ It is not easy for the girls to pass by their favorite snack bar.
> ⓗ It was wise of Dahyun not to spend her money on such a thing.

① 1개 ② 2개 ③ 3개 ④ 4개 ⑤ 5개

17 다음 중 밑줄 친 부분의 쓰임이 나머지 넷과 <u>다른</u> 것은?

① <u>It</u> is fun for her to speak in Chinese.
② <u>It</u> will soon be the lunch time.
③ <u>It</u> is not hard to search for much information on the Internet.
④ <u>It</u> was natural for you to bring the books here.
⑤ <u>It</u> was my pleasure to meet the beautiful person like you.

서답형

18 다음 문장에서 어법상 <u>어색한</u> 부분을 한 단어만 찾아서 고치시오. (고친 단어는 2개 이상이어도 상관없다.)

> If you took the subway instead of the taxi, you would have saved much time.

➡ _____

01 다음 우리말과 일치하도록 괄호 안에 주어진 단어들을 바르게 배열하여 문장을 완성하시오.

(1) 우리가 스마트폰을 갖고 있지 않으면, 우리는 더 자주 밖에서 놀 텐데.

➡ If we _____

_____ often. (play, smartphones, outside, didn't, we, more, would, have)

(2) 텔레비전이 없다면, 우리가 뉴스를 확인하는 것이 더 어려워질 텐데.

➡ If there were no televisions, _____

_____ the news.

(for, it, to, difficult, would, check, us, more, be)

(3) 당신이 디지털 발자국(디지털 정보 기록)을 관리하는 것이 정말로 필요하다.

➡ It's really _____

_____. (footprint, to, for, your, manage, you, necessary, digital

(4) 우리가 디지털 장비를 효과적으로 사용하는 것은 매우 지혜로운 것이다.

➡ It is _____

_____. (wise, efficiently, to, of, use, digital, us, very, devices)

02 다음 〈보기〉의 문장과 같은 뜻이 되도록 괄호 안에 주어진 조건에 맞게 빈칸을 채우시오.

┌─ 보기 ├─────────────

Without money, we could not trade things easily.

└─────────────────

(1) _____ money, we could not trade things easily. (it, be동사 활용, 5단어)

(2) _____ money, we could not trade things easily. (there, no 활용, 4 단어)

(3) _____ money, we could not trade things easily. (it, be동사 활용, 4 단어)

(4) _____ money, we can trade things easily. (직설법, 접속사 as 활용, 3 단어)

03 다음 그림을 보고, 우리말에 맞게 괄호 안의 단어를 배열하여 빈칸을 채우시오.

┌─────────────────────┐
│ 비가 오지 않으면, 나의 개와 산책을 할 수 있을 │
│ 텐데. │
│ → If _____. │
│ (dog, walk, I, with, it, do, a, rain, for, │
│ can, my, go) 총 12 단어, 어형 변화 가능) │
└─────────────────────┘

04 다음 주어진 문장과 뜻이 같도록 빈칸을 알맞게 채우시오.

┌─────────────────────┐
│ Since David doesn't exercise regularly, │
│ he can't be in good shape. │
│ ➡ If David _____ │
│ in good shape. │
└─────────────────────┘

05 다음 우리말을 괄호 안에 주어진 어구를 사용하여 영작하시오. (필요시 단어를 추가하거나 변형할 것)

(1) 어른들조차 바다에서 수영하는 것은 매우 위험하다.

➡ It is _____

_____.

(dangerous, very, even, in the sea)

(2) 당신이 그 계곡을 건너려고 노력하는 것은 어리석은 일이다.

➡ It is _____

(try, the valley, foolish, cross)

(3) 민서가 어제 가족들과 카드 게임을 한 것은 재미있었다.

➡ It was _____

_____.

(Minseo, yesterday, play cards, fun)

06 다음 각 가정법 문장에서 어법상 어색한 부분을 모두 찾아 바르게 고치시오.

(1) If I have a girlfriend, I would see the movie with her.
(2) Sandra couldn't be late for the meeting yesterday if she had caught the bus.
(3) If you was the girl, you would understand her situation.
(4) If I am the superhero, I could save the world and defeat the monsters.
(5) If it not for your help, she could not survive the disease.

(1) _____
(2) _____
(3) _____
(4) _____
(5) _____

07 다음 각 문장에서 어법상 어색한 단어를 한 개씩만 찾아 모두 고치시오.

(1) It was fun for Amy and her family to sitting around the campfire.
(2) It is good for your to make a smile all the time.
(3) It was interesting of Grace to meet the young boy who could play chess well.
(4) It was cruel for the host of the show to make the singer sing that song again.
(5) It is necessary for customs officers checked all the baggage at the airport.

(1) _____ (2) _____
(3) _____ (4) _____
(5) _____

08 다음 〈보기〉와 같이 직설법 문장을 가정법으로 고치시오.

┌ 보기 ┐

As I am not a bird, I won't fly to her.

→ If I were a bird, I would fly to her.

(1) As there isn't another me, I can't make him share my work.

➡ _____

_____

(2) As I am not you, I won't reduce my time on smartphone by half.

➡ _____

_____

(3) As we have televisions, it is easy for us to watch the music shows.

➡ _____

(4) As Sally isn't in Hawaii, she isn't happy.

➡ _____

Time for Digital Detox

Hi, students! When you wake up in the morning, what is the first thing
시간을 나타내는 접속사 (~할 때)
you do? Do you read SNS postings on your smartphone? Imagine your
Social Networking Service의 앞 글자를 딴 약자   Imagine (that): ~을 상상해 보아라
smartphone is not near you. How do you feel?

Students, please check items on the list that are true for you.
주격 관계대명사(선행사: items)

Are you addicted to your smartphone?

□ Without my smartphone, I feel uncomfortable.
2형식 동사(+형용사 보어)

□ I take my smartphone into the bathroom.
take A into B: A를 B로 가져가다

□ It is more enjoyable to spend time on my smartphone than with
가주어 it ~ 진주어 to부정사
  friends.

□ I often check SNS postings while studying.
= while I am studying

□ I try to reduce the time I spend on my smartphone, but I fail.

□ I check my smartphone right after I hear the sound of an alert.
~한 후에 바로

□ I have my smartphone next to me while I'm eating.
~ 옆에   = while eating

What is your score? Did you check more than half?

If so, you may have a problem with smartphone addiction.
= If you checked more than half
Smartphone addiction causes you to spend too much time on your
cause A to ~ : A가 ~하게 하다
smartphone. Also, you cannot focus on your studies and may have
추측의 조동사
a pain in your neck. Then now is the time for you to start digital
to부정사의 의미상 주어(for+목적격)
detox. Digital detox means staying away from digital devices, such as
동명사(means의 목적어)   = like(~와 같은)
smartphones and computers, for a while.

digital: 디지털의
posting: 인터넷이나 SNS에 올리는 글
be addicted to: ~에 중독되다
enjoyable: 즐거운
alert: 경보, 알림 소리
half: 절반
addiction: 중독
detox: (인체 유해물질의) 해독
stay away from: ~에서 떨어져 있다
device: 장치
such as: ~와 같은

📎 **확인문제**

● 다음 문장이 본문의 내용과 일치하면 T, 일치하지 않으면 F를 쓰시오.

1 Students must check items on the list that are not true for them. ☐

2 The items are about whether or not you are addicted to your computer. ☐

3 Smartphone addiction can make your neck painful. ☐

Digital detox will help you a lot. You can enjoy freedom from the noisy digital world. You can focus more on your work.

Sometimes you can feel refreshed and <u>have new</u>, creative ideas.
(you can) have new, creative ideas

Digital detox will also <u>help you spend</u> more time with <u>others</u>.
help+목적어+(to) V   = other people

<u>Living without a smartphone</u>, however, <u>is</u> not easy. So, <u>it is</u>
동명사 주어(스마트폰 없이 사는 것)   동명사 주어 (단수 취급)   가주어 it

necessary <u>for you</u> to set some rules for <u>using</u> your smartphone.
to부정사의 의미상 주어(for+목적격)   동명사(전치사의 목적어)

You then need to follow the rules. Now, please form groups and, in

your group, <u>create</u> rules for using your smartphones.
form and create 병렬 연결

By Yerim, Yongmin, and Hojin

We will turn off our smartphones <u>while studying</u>.
= while we are studying

We will not take our smartphones into the bathroom.

We will keep our smartphones out of the bedroom and <u>not use</u> <u>them</u> at
(we will) not use   = smartphones

night.

By Jina, Hosung, and Minsu

• More Time for Outside Activities – We will <u>spend</u> more time
spend+시간+Ving: V하느라 시간을 보내다

<u>playing</u> outside without our smartphones.

• Fewer SNS Messages – We will post <u>fewer</u> SNS messages on our
셀 수 있는 명사 수식

smartphones.

By Jiho, Sohee, and Yumin

If I were you, I would reduce my time on my smartphone by half.
If+주어+동사의 과거형 ~, 주어+would/could+동사원형 …: 만약 ~라면 …할 텐데 (가정법 과거)

If I were you, I would turn off all alerts.

You did a good job, students! <u>If we had no smartphones</u>, our lives
'스마트폰이 없다면'이라고 현재 사실을 반대로 가정하는 가정법 과거

would be more difficult, but too much use of a smartphone is

dangerous. With digital detox, you can become a wise smartphone user.

---

freedom: 자유
noisy: 시끄러운, 소란한
refreshed: 상쾌한
necessary: 필요한
form: 만들다, 형성하다
create: 창조하다, 만들다
message: 알림, 메시지
dangerous: 위험한
wise: 현명한

확인문제

• 다음 문장이 본문의 내용과 일치하면 T, 일치하지 <u>않으면</u> F를 쓰시오.

1 Digital detox is recommended to someone who is addicted to his or her smartphone.

☐

2 It is easy to live without smartphones. ☐

3 Our lives are easier because there are smartphones. ☐

● 우리말을 참고하여 빈칸에 알맞은 말을 쓰시오.

Time for Digital Detox

1 Hi, students! _____ you wake up _____ _____ _____, _____ is the first thing you do?

2 Do you _____ SNS postings _____ your smartphone?

3 _____ your smartphone _____ not _____ you. _____ do you feel?

4 Students, please _____ _____ on the list _____ true for you.

5 _____ you _____ to your smartphone?

6 _____ my smartphone, I _____ _____.

7 I _____ my smartphone _____ the bathroom.

8 It is more _____ _____ spend time on my smartphone than with friends.

9 I often check SNS postings _____ _____.

10 I try to _____ the time _____ _____ _____ on my smartphone, but I fail.

11 I check my smartphone _____ _____ I hear the sound of _____ _____.

12 I have my smartphone _____ _____ me _____ I'm eating.

13 _____ is your _____ ? Did you _____ more than _____ ?

14 If so, you may _____ a problem _____ smartphone addiction.

15 Smartphone addiction _____ _____ _____ _____ _____ too much time _____ your smartphone.

16 Also, you cannot _____ _____ your studies and may _____ _____ _____ in your neck.

17 Then now is the time _____ _____ _____ _____ digital detox.

1 안녕하세요, 학생 여러분! 여러분은 아침에 일어났을 때, 가장 먼저 하는 일이 무엇인가요?

2 스마트폰으로 SNS 게시물을 읽나요?

3 스마트폰이 여러분 근처에 있지 않다고 상상해 보세요. 기분이 어떤가요?

4 학생 여러분, 이 목록에서 여러분에게 맞는 항목들을 표시해 보세요.

5 너는 스마트폰에 중독되었는가?

6 나는 스마트폰이 없으면, 불편함을 느낀다.

7 나는 스마트폰을 화장실에 가져간다.

8 나는 친구들과 함께 시간을 보내는 것보다 스마트폰을 하면서 보내는 시간이 더 즐겁다.

9 나는 공부하면서 SNS 게시물을 종종 확인한다.

10 나는 스마트폰을 사용하는 시간을 줄이려고 노력하지만, 실패한다.

11 나는 알림음을 듣자마자 스마트폰을 확인한다.

12 나는 식사 중에 스마트폰을 옆에 둔다.

13 여러분의 점수는 어떤가요? 절반보다 더 많이 표시했나요?

14 만약 그렇다면, 여러분은 스마트폰 중독의 문제를 가지고 있을지도 모릅니다.

15 스마트폰 중독은 여러분이 스마트폰에 너무 많은 시간을 보내게 만듭니다.

16 또한 여러분은 학업에 집중할 수 없고 목에 통증이 있을지도 모릅니다.

17 그렇다면 지금 여러분은 디지털 디톡스를 시작할 시간입니다.

18 Digital detox _____ _____ _____ _____ digital devices, such as smartphones and computers, _____ a while.

19 Digital detox will _____ you a lot. You can enjoy _____ _____ the _____ digital world.

20 You can _____ more _____ your work. Sometimes you can _____ _____ and have new, _____ _____.

21 Digital detox will also _____ you _____ more time with others.

22 _____ without a smartphone, _____ _____ not easy.

23 So, it is _____ _____ _____ to set some rules _____ using your smartphone.

24 You then _____ _____ _____ the rules.

25 Now, please _____ groups and, in your group, _____ _____ for _____ your smartphone.

<By Yerim, Yongmin, and Hojin>

26 We will _____ _____ our smartphones _____ studying.

27 We will not _____ our smartphones _____ the bathroom.

28 We will _____ our smartphones _____ _____ _____ and not use _____ at night.

<By Jina, Hosung, and Minsu>

29 _____ _____ _____ Outside Activities – We will _____ _____ _____ outside without our smartphones.

30 _____ SNS Messages – We will post _____ SNS messages _____ our smartphones.

<By Jiho, Sohee, and Yumin>

31 If _____ _____ you, I _____ reduce my time on my smartphone _____ _____.

32 If _____ _____ you, I _____ turn _____ all alerts.

33 You did a good job, students! If we _____ no smartphones, our lives _____ _____ more difficult, but _____ _____ use of a smartphone is dangerous.

34 _____ digital detox, you can become a _____ smartphone user.

18 디지털 디톡스는 스마트폰과 컴퓨터 같은 디지털 기기들로부터 잠시 동안 떨어져 있는 것을 의미합니다.

19 디지털 디톡스는 여러분을 많이 도와줄 것입니다. 여러분은 시끄러운 디지털 세계로부터 자유를 즐길 수 있습니다.

20 여러분은 하는 일에 더욱 집중할 수 있습니다. 종종 여러분은 상쾌함을 느끼고 새롭고 창의적인 아이디어를 얻을 수 있습니다.

21 디지털 디톡스는 또한 여러분이 다른 사람들과 더 많은 시간을 보내도록 도와줄 것입니다.

22 하지만 스마트폰 없이 사는 것은 쉽지 않습니다.

23 그러므로 여러분은 스마트폰을 사용하기 위한 몇 가지 규칙을 정할 필요가 있습니다.

24 그리고 나서 여러분은 그 규칙들을 따라야 합니다.

25 자, 조를 형성하고, 여러분의 조에서, 스마트폰을 사용하기 위한 규칙을 만들어 보세요.

〈예림, 용민, 호진으로부터〉

26 우리는 공부하는 동안 스마트폰을 끌 것이다.

27 우리는 화장실에 스마트폰을 가져가지 않을 것이다.

28 우리는 밤에 스마트폰을 침실 밖에 두고 사용하지 않을 것이다.

〈지나, 호성, 민수로부터〉

29 야외 활동을 위한 더 많은 시간 – 우리는 스마트폰 없이 밖에서 노는 데 더 많은 시간을 보낼 것이다.

30 SNS는 더 적게 – 우리는 스마트폰에 SNS 메시지를 더 적게 올릴 것이다.

〈지호, 소희, 유민〉

31 만약 내가 너라면, 나는 스마트폰에 쓰는 시간을 절반으로 줄일 것이다.

32 만약 내가 너라면, 모든 알림을 끌 것이다.

33 잘했어요, 학생 여러분! 만약 스마트폰이 없다면 우리의 삶이 더 힘들겠지만, 스마트폰을 너무 많이 사용하는 것은 위험합니다.

34 디지털 디톡스와 함께, 여러분은 현명한 스마트폰 사용자가 될 수 있습니다.

● 우리말을 참고하여 본문을 영작하시오.

1 ▶ 안녕하세요, 학생 여러분! 여러분은 아침에 일어났을 때, 가장 먼저 하는 일이 무엇인가요?
➡ _____

2 ▶ 스마트폰으로 SNS 게시물을 읽나요?
➡ _____

3 ▶ 스마트폰이 여러분 근처에 있지 않다고 상상해 보세요. 기분이 어떤가요?
➡ _____

4 ▶ 학생 여러분, 이 목록에서 여러분에게 맞는 항목들을 표시해 보세요.
➡ _____

5 ▶ 너는 스마트폰에 중독되었는가?
➡ _____

6 ▶ 나는 스마트폰이 없으면, 불편함을 느낀다.
➡ _____

7 ▶ 나는 스마트폰을 화장실에 가져간다.
➡ _____

8 ▶ 나는 친구들과 함께 시간을 보내는 것보다 스마트폰을 하면서 보내는 시간이 더 즐겁다.
➡ _____

9 ▶ 나는 공부하면서 SNS 게시물을 종종 확인한다.
➡ _____

10 ▶ 나는 스마트폰을 사용하는 시간을 줄이려고 노력하지만, 실패한다.
➡ _____

11 ▶ 나는 알림음을 듣자마자 스마트폰을 확인한다.
➡ _____

12 ▶ 나는 식사 중에 스마트폰을 옆에 둔다.
➡ _____

13 ▶ 여러분의 점수는 어떤가요? 절반보다 더 많이 표시했나요?
➡ _____

14 ▶ 만약 그렇다면, 여러분은 스마트폰 중독의 문제를 가지고 있을지도 모릅니다.
➡ _____

15 ▶ 스마트폰 중독은 여러분이 스마트폰에 너무 많은 시간을 보내게 만듭니다.
➡ _____

16 ▶ 또한 여러분은 학업에 집중할 수 없고 목에 통증이 있을지도 모릅니다.
➡ _____

17 ▶ 그렇다면 지금 여러분은 디지털 디톡스를 시작할 시간입니다.
➡ _____

18 ▶ 디지털 디톡스는 스마트폰과 컴퓨터 같은 디지털 기기들로부터 잠시 동안 떨어져 있는 것을 의미합니다.
➡ _____

19 디지털 디톡스는 여러분을 많이 도와줄 것입니다. 여러분은 시끄러운 디지털 세계로부터 자유를 즐길 수 있습니다.
➡ _____

20 여러분은 하는 일에 더욱 집중할 수 있습니다. 종종 여러분은 상쾌함을 느끼고 새롭고 창의적인 아이디어를 얻을 수 있습니다.
➡ _____

21 디지털 디톡스는 또한 여러분이 다른 사람들과 더 많은 시간을 보내도록 도와줄 것입니다.
➡ _____

22 하지만 스마트폰 없이 사는 것은 쉽지 않습니다.
➡ _____

23 그러므로 여러분은 스마트폰을 사용하기 위한 몇 가지 규칙을 정할 필요가 있습니다.
➡ _____

24 그리고 나서 여러분은 그 규칙들을 따라야 합니다.
➡ _____

25 자, 조를 형성하고, 여러분의 조에서, 스마트폰을 사용하기 위한 규칙을 만들어 보세요.
➡ _____

By Yerim, Yongmin, and Hojin

26 우리는 공부하는 동안 스마트폰을 끌 것이다.
➡ _____

27 우리는 화장실에 스마트폰을 가져가지 않을 것이다.
➡ _____

28 우리는 밤에 스마트폰을 침실 밖에 두고 사용하지 않을 것이다.
➡ _____

By Jina, Hosung, and Minsu

29 야외 활동을 위한 더 많은 시간 – 우리는 스마트폰 없이 밖에서 노는 데 더 많은 시간을 보낼 것이다.
➡ _____

30 SNS는 더 적게 – 우리는 스마트폰에 SNS 메시지를 더 적게 올릴 것이다.
➡ _____

By Jiho, Sohee, and Yumin

31 만약 내가 너라면, 나는 스마트폰에 쓰는 시간을 절반으로 줄일 것이다.
➡ _____

32 만약 내가 너라면, 모든 알림을 끌 것이다.
➡ _____

33 잘했어요, 학생 여러분! 만약 스마트폰이 없다면 우리의 삶이 더 힘들겠지만, 스마트폰을 너무 많이 사용하는 것은 위험합니다.
➡ _____
_____

34 디지털 디톡스와 함께, 여러분은 현명한 스마트폰 사용자가 될 수 있습니다.
➡ _____

[01~03] 다음 글을 읽고 물음에 답하시오.

Hi, students! When you wake up in the morning, what is the first thing you do? Do you read SNS postings on your smartphone? Imagine your smartphone is not near you. How do you feel?

Students, please check items on the list that are true for you.

Are you addicted to your smartphone?
☐ Without my smartphone, I feel uncomfortable.
☐ I take my smartphone into the bathroom.
☐ It is more enjoyable to spend time on my smartphone than with friends.
☐ I often check SNS postings (A)_____ studying.
☐ I try to reduce the time I spend on my smartphone, but I fail.
☐ I check my smartphone right after I hear the sound of an alert.
☐ I have my smartphone next to me (B)_____ I'm eating.

01 빈칸 (A)와 (B)에 공통으로 들어갈 말로 가장 적절한 것은?

① for   ② though   ③ since
④ while   ⑤ during

서답형

02 주어진 어구를 바르게 배열하여 다음 물음의 대답을 완성하시오.

Q: According to the passage, what is the list about?

A: It is _____

_____ .

(your smartphone / about / addicted / whether or not / are / to / you)

03 다음 중 위 글에서 유의어를 찾을 수 있는 것을 모두 고르시오.

① cut down   ② comfortable   ③ false
④ beside   ⑤ save

[04~06] 다음 글을 읽고 물음에 답하시오.

What is your score? Did you check more than half?

If so, you may have a problem with smartphone addiction. Smartphone addiction causes you (A)_____ too much time on your smartphone. Also, you cannot focus on your studies and may have a pain in your neck. Then now is the time for you to start digital detox. Digital detox means staying away from digital devices, such as smartphones and computers, for a while.

서답형

04 빈칸 (A)에 동사 'spend'를 어법에 맞게 쓰시오.

➡ _____

05 Which is TRUE according to the passage?

① Smartphone addiction is related to too little use of digital devices.
② Smartphone addiction helps people to focus on their studies.
③ Too much use of smartphone causes you to have a pain on your wrist.
④ People who are addicted to smartphone need to start to use their smartphones more often.
⑤ There is a solution for people who are addicted to their smartphones.

서답형

06 다음과 같이 풀이되는 말을 위 글에서 찾아 쓰시오.

> treatment given to people who are addicted to something in order to stop them from being addicted

➡ _____

[07~09] 다음 글을 읽고 물음에 답하시오.

Digital detox will help you a lot. You can enjoy freedom from the noisy digital world. You can focus more on your work. Sometimes you can feel refreshed and have new, creative ideas. Digital detox will also help you spend more time with others. Living without a smartphone, (A)_____, is not easy. So, it is necessary (B)_____ you to set some rules for using your smartphone. You then need to follow the rules.

07 다음 중 빈칸 (A)에 들어갈 말로 가장 적절한 것은?

① for example ② therefore
③ that's why ④ in other words
⑤ however

08 다음 중 빈칸 (B)에 들어갈 말로 가장 적절한 것은?

① at ② in ③ on ④ for ⑤ of

중요

09 Which one is the benefit of digital detox?

① to enjoy the noisy digital world
② to focus on your smartphone
③ to have creative ideas
④ to spend more time with your smartphone
⑤ to make your life easy

[10~12] 다음 글을 읽고 물음에 답하시오.

Now, please form groups and, in your group, create rules for using your smartphone.

By Yerim, Yongmin, and Hojin
We will ①turn off our smartphones while studying.
We will not take our smartphones into the bathroom.
We will keep our smartphones ②out of the bedroom and not use them at night.

By Jina, Hosung, and Minsu
• More Time for Outside Activities – We will spend more time ③playing outside ④with our smartphones.
• Fewer SNS Messages – We will post fewer SNS messages on our smartphones.

By Jiho, Sohee, and Yumin
If I were you, I would ⑤reduce my time on my smartphone by half.
If I were you, I would turn off all alerts.

서답형

10 다음은 위 글의 제목이다. 빈칸에 들어갈 말을 위 글에서 찾아 쓰시오.

> _____ _____ _____ Our Smartphones

중요

11 ①~⑤ 중 글의 흐름상 어색한 것은?

① ② ③ ④ ⑤

서답형

12 According to Yerim, Yongmin, and Hojin, where will they not take their smartphones? Answer in English with a full sentence.

➡ _____
_____

[13~16] 다음 글을 읽고 물음에 답하시오.

Hi, students! When you wake up in the morning, ⓐ처음으로 하는 게 무엇인가요? Do you read SNS postings on your smartphone? Imagine your smartphone is not near you. How do you feel?

Students, please check items on the list that are true for you.

Are you addicted to your smartphone?

□ Without my smartphone, I feel uncomfortable.

□ I take my smartphone into the bathroom.

□ It is more enjoyable to spend time on my smartphone than with friends.

□ I often check SNS postings while studying.

□ I try to reduce the time I spend (A)_____ my smartphone, but I fail.

□ I check my smartphone right after I hear the sound of an alert.

□ I have my smartphone next to me while I'm eating.

What is your score? Did you check more than half? If so, you may have a problem with smartphone addiction.

13 다음 중 빈칸 (A)에 들어갈 말과 같은 말이 들어가는 것은?

① Are you interested _____ the subject?

② She will get _____ the station on time.

③ Can you stay _____ me?

④ He used to take pictures _____ us.

⑤ It depends _____ your ability.

서답형

14 주어진 단어를 바르게 배열하여 밑줄 친 우리말 ⓐ를 영어로 쓰시오.

(do / is / thing / what / first / the / you)

➡ _____

15 다음 중 위 글의 내용과 일치하는 것은?

① The passage is about how to use smartphones wisely.

② There are eight items on the list.

③ The writer recommends that we should never use our smartphone.

④ You may have a problem with smartphone addiction if you checked more than half.

⑤ You should check the items that aren't true to you.

16 다음 중 스마트폰 중독 사항에 해당하지 <u>않는</u> 사람은?

① Amie: I don't feel comfortable when my smartphone is not near me.

② Bryan: I want my smartphone to be with me when I eat my meal.

③ Chris: As soon as I hear the sound of an alert, I check my smartphone.

④ David: I prefer playing with my friends to spending time on my smartphone.

⑤ Eden: I always check SNS postings with my smartphone.

[17~20] 다음 글을 읽고 물음에 답하시오.

Smartphone addiction causes you to spend too much time on your smartphone.

[A] Digital detox will help you a lot. You can enjoy freedom from the noisy digital world. You can focus more on your work. Sometimes you can feel refreshed and have new, creative ideas. Digital detox will also help you spend more time with others.

[B] Also, you cannot focus on your studies and may have a pain in your neck. Then now is the time for you to start digital detox. Digital detox means staying away from digital devices, such as smartphones and computers, for a while.

[C] Living without a smartphone, however, is not easy. ⓐ_____, it is necessary for you to set some rules for using your smartphone. You then need to follow the rules.

17 다음 중 빈칸 ⓐ에 들어갈 말로 가장 적절한 것은?

① On the contrary   ② That is
③ So   ④ Otherwise
⑤ Unless

18 자연스러운 글이 되도록 [A]~[C]를 바르게 배열하시오.

① [A]–[C]–[B]   ② [B]–[A]–[C]
③ [B]–[C]–[A]   ④ [C]–[A]–[B]
⑤ [C]–[B]–[A]

19 다음 중 위 글을 읽고 답할 수 있는 것은?

① Who invented smartphones?
② How much time is needed to do digital detox?
③ What does digital detox mean?
④ Who did digital detox for the first time?
⑤ How many rules do we have to follow?

20 What does smartphone addiction cause you to do? Answer in English with a full sentence.

➡ _____

_____

[21~23] 다음 글을 읽고 물음에 답하시오.

Now, please form groups and, in your group, create rules for using your smartphone.

By Yerim, Yongmin, and Hojin

We will turn off our smartphones while studying.

We will not take our smartphones into the bathroom.

We will keep our smartphones out of the bedroom and not use them at night.

By Jina, Hosung, and Minsu

• More Time for Outside Activities – We will spend more time playing outside without our smartphones.

• Fewer SNS Messages – We will post fewer SNS messages on our smartphones.

By Jiho, Sohee, and Yumin

If I were you, I would reduce my time on my smartphone by half.

If I were you, I would turn off all alerts.

You did a good job, students! If we (A)_____ no smartphones, our lives would be more difficult, but too much use of a smartphone is dangerous. With digital detox, you can become a wise smartphone user.

21 동사 'have'를 어법에 맞게 빈칸 (A)에 쓰시오.

➡ _____

22 학생들의 규칙에 해당하지 않는 것은?

① to turn off smartphones while studying
② to reduce their time on smartphone by half
③ not to use their smartphones at night
④ to do digital detox every day
⑤ to post fewer SNS messages on their smartphones

23 What do Jiho, Sohee, and Yumin want to turn off?

➡ _____

[01~04] 다음 글을 읽고 물음에 답하시오.

Students, please check items on the list that are true for you.

Are you addicted to your smartphone?

□ Without my smartphone, I feel uncomfortable.

□ I take my smartphone into the bathroom.

□ It is more enjoyable to spend time on my smartphone than with friends.

□ I often check SNS postings while studying.

□ (A)I try to reduce the time I spend on my smartphone, but I succeed.

□ I check my smartphone right after I hear the sound of an alert.

□ I have my smartphone next to me while I'm eating.

What is your score? Did you check more than half? (B)If so, you may have a problem with smartphone addiction.

01 중요 밑줄 친 (A)를 문맥에 맞게 고쳐 쓰시오.

➡ _____

_____

02 다음 중 위 글의 내용과 일치하지 <u>않는</u> 것을 두 군데 찾아 바르게 고쳐 쓰시오.

Hi, my name is Norman. Recently, I have noticed that I am addicted to my smartphone. I take my smartphone into the bathroom and I feel comfortable without my smartphone. Besides, I have my smartphone far from me while eating. And I am busy checking SNS postings while studying.

➡ _____

03 밑줄 친 (B)가 의미하는 것을 구체적으로 쓰시오.

➡ _____

04 중요 위 글의 내용에 맞게 빈칸에 알맞은 말을 쓰시오.

When I hear the sound of an alert, _____ _____ _____ immediately.

[05~09] 다음 글을 읽고 물음에 답하시오.

Smartphone addiction causes you to spend too much time on your smartphone. Also, you cannot focus on your studies and may have a pain in your neck. Then now is the time for you to start digital detox. Digital detox means staying away from digital devices, such as smartphones and computers, for a while.

Digital detox will help you a lot. You can enjoy freedom from the noisy digital world. You can focus more on your work. Sometimes you can feel refreshed and have new, creative ideas. Digital detox will also help you spend more time with others.

Living without a smartphone, however, is not easy. So, it is necessary for you to set some rules for using your smartphone. You then need to follow the rules. Now, please form groups and, in your group, create rules for using your smartphone.

05 In addition to spending too much time on smartphones, what are the problems of smartphone addiction? Answer in English with a full sentence.

➡ _____

_____

06 According to the passage, what do we need to do to spend more time with others?

➡ _____

07 With digital detox, what can we enjoy from the noisy digital world? Answer in English with a full sentence.

➡ _____

08 What do we need to do after setting some rules for using smartphones? Answer in English with six words.

➡ _____

09 According to the passage, what is necessary for us to do for using our smartphone?

➡ _____
  _____

[10~14] 다음 글을 읽고 물음에 답하시오.

By Yerim, Yongmin, and Hojin
We will turn off our smartphones while studying.
We will not take our smartphones into the bathroom.
We will keep our smartphones out of the bedroom and not use (A)them at night.
By Jina, Hosung, and Minsu
• More Time for Outside Activities – We will spend more time playing outside without our smartphones.
• Fewer SNS Messages – We will post fewer SNS messages on our smartphones.
By Jiho, Sohee, and Yumin
If I were you, I would reduce my time on my smartphone by half.

If I were you, I would turn off all alerts.
You did a good job, students! If we had no smartphones, our lives would be more difficult, but too much use of a smartphone is dangerous. With digital detox, you can become a wise smartphone user.

10 밑줄 친 (A)가 가리키는 것을 위 글에서 찾아 쓰시오.

➡ _____

11 According to Yerim, Yongmin, and Hojin, what will they do while studying?

➡ _____
  _____

12 위 글의 내용에 맞게 빈칸에 알맞은 말을 쓰시오.

Jina will _____ _____ _____ _____ _____ instead of playing with her smartphone.

13 How does the writer think about too much use of a smartphone? Answer in English with a full sentence.

➡ _____

14 다음 호진이의 일기의 빈칸에 알맞은 말을 쓰시오.

When I was addicted to my smartphone, I used to _____ _____ _____ _____ the bathroom, but I don't do it anymore after I started to digital detox.

Reading **93**

해석

Enjoy Writing C

If There Were No Smartphones

There would be some advantages and some disadvantages if there were no
가정법 과거형으로 주절에는 '조동사 과거형+동사원형'을 사용한다.   'If+주어+과거동사'로 be동사는 were를 사용한다.

smartphones. First, let's talk about some advantages.

If we didn't have smartphones, we would play outside more often. Plus,
가정법 과거형으로 'If+주어+과거동사 ~   주어+would+동사원형'을 사용한다.   게다가(첨가의 의미)

we would be safe from neck pain. On the other hand, there would be some
반면에

disadvantages. If there were no smartphones, it would not be easy for us to
→직설법: As there are smartphones. it is easy for us to contact people.   가주어   의미상 주어 진주어

contact people. Also, it would take so long for us to find information.
it takes+시간+for+목적격+to부정사: ~가 ~하는 데 시간이 걸리다

구문해설 ·advantage 장점 ·disadvantage 단점 ·plus 게다가 ·pain 고통 ·contact 연락하다
·information 정보

만약 스마트폰이 없다면
만약 스마트폰이 없다면 몇몇 장점과 단점이 있을 것이다. 첫째로 몇 가지 장점을 이야기해 보자. 만약 우리가 스마트폰을 가지고 있지 않다면, 우리는 밖에서 더 자주 놀 것이다. 게다가, 우리는 목통증의 위험이 없을 것이다. 반면에 몇 가지 단점도 있을 것이다. 만약 스마트폰이 없다면, 우리는 사람들에게 연락하는 것이 쉽지 않을 것이다. 또한 우리가 정보를 찾는 데 시간이 많이 걸릴 것이다.

Project 2

It is necessary for us to be digital citizens!
가주어   의미상의 주어 진주어

If there were no Internet or SNS, our lives would be more difficult. So, it is
가정법 과거   조동사 과거+원형   가주어

very important for us to use digital devices wisely as a digital citizen.
의미상의 주어 진주어   전치사(~로서)

I respect myself and others on SNS.
재귀대명사(주어 = 목적어)

I never share my password with anyone.
부정문에서 사용된 anyone

I use kind words.

I never use bad words.

I don't spend too much time online.

구문해설 ·device: 기기 ·citizen: 시민 ·password: 비밀번호

우리는 디지털 시민이 될 필요가 있다!
만약 인터넷이나 SNS가 없다면, 우리의 삶은 더 힘들 것이다. 그래서 우리는 디지털 시민으로서 디지털 기기들을 현명하게 사용하는 것이 중요하다.
나는 SNS에서 내 자신과 다른 사람들을 존중한다.
나는 절대 내 비밀번호를 누구와도 공유하지 않는다.
나는 친절한 말을 쓴다.
나는 나쁜 말을 절대 쓰지 않는다.
나는 온라인에서 너무 많은 시간을 보내지 않는다.

Project 3

It's very important for everyone to become a digital citizen. Our group will
to부정사의 의미상 주어   진주어

show you what digital citizens do. Please enjoy.
4형식 동사   간접의문문(의문사+주어+동사)

구문해설 ·important: 중요한 ·citizen: 시민

모두가 디지털 시민이 되는 것은 매우 중요해. 우리 모둠이 디지털 시민이 무엇을 하는지 보여줄게. 재미있게 봐.

01 다음 주어진 두 단어의 관계가 같도록 빈칸에 알맞은 단어를 쓰시오.

> limit : restrict = dialogue : _____

02 다음 문장의 빈칸 (A)와 (B)에 들어갈 단어가 바르게 짝지어진 것은?

> • The President wants to (A)_____ more jobs for young people.
> • He spent an (B)_____ afternoon at the park with his lovely daughter.

① imagine – easy
② reduce – uncomfortable
③ post – enjoyable
④ create – unhappy
⑤ create – enjoyable

[03~04] 다음 영영풀이에 해당하는 것을 고르시오.

03

> an inability to stop doing or using something, especially something harmful

① advantage   ② danger
③ addiction   ④ posting
⑤ alert

04

> something that may help someone to gain a favorable result

① advantage   ② detox
③ comfort   ④ alert
⑤ disadvantage

05 다음 문장의 빈칸에 들어갈 말을 쓰시오.

> A _____ is the right a creator has over his or her literary and artistic works.

06 다음 대화의 밑줄 친 부분을 같은 말로 바꾸어 쓸 때 문장의 빈칸을 채우시오.

> A: Have you posted bad comments online?
> B: Yes.
> A: You're not supposed to post bad comments online.

➡ If I _____ you, I _____ _____ _____ bad comments online.

07 아래 그림의 여학생의 문제점을 읽고, 남학생이 해 줄 충고의 말을 〈조건〉에 맞게 완성하시오.

I can't focus on my studies.

┌─ 조건 ─┐
• If를 사용할 것.
• 'put aside', 'the smartphone'을 사용할 것.

➡ Boy: _____

_____

08 대화의 빈칸에 들어갈 말을 주어진 어구를 알맞은 순서로 배열하여 완성하시오.

> B: What are you doing, Sohee?
> G: I'm writing a posting about the restaurant I visited today.
> B: Those are great pictures. Did you take all of them?
> G: No. I took the pictures from someone's blog.
> B: Then you're not supposed to post them on your blog.
> G: Why not?
> B: _____
> _____ (the right / only / because / to use / the blog owner / has / them)
> G: Oh, I see.

[09~11] 다음 대화를 읽고 물음에 답하시오.

> Bora: Seho, look! Somebody posted strange things on your SNS. I don't think you posted them.
> Seho: Really? Who did this?
> Bora: I think someone figured out your password.
> Seho: What should I do?
> Bora: (A)_____
> Seho: I think I should.
> Bora: Is your password easy to guess?
> Seho: I used my birth date.
> Bora: That is not good. In fact, it is a big mistake. You're not supposed to use your personal information when you make a password.
> Seho: Okay, I see. I will change it to a stronger one.

09 What is Seho not supposed to use when he makes a password? Answer in English.

➡ _____
_____

10 빈칸 (A)에 들어갈 말로 알맞은 것은?

① If I were you, I would not use my cellphone.
② If I were you, I would set up screen lock.
③ If I were you, I would sell my smartphone and buy a cellphone which I couldn't play games on.
④ If I were you, I would set a daily plan to limit game time.
⑤ If I were you, I would change my password.

11 위 대화의 내용과 일치하지 <u>않는</u> 것은?

① Somebody posted strange things on Seho's SNS.
② Seho used his birth date when he made a password.
③ Bora suggested to Seho that his password should be easy to guess.
④ Seho is not supposed to use his personal information when he makes a password.
⑤ Seho will change his password to a stronger one.

Grammar

[12~14] 다음 우리말에 맞게 영작한 것은?

12
> Peter가 그의 아버지를 돕다니 착하다.

① It is nice of Peter to help his father.
② It will be nice for Peter to help his father.
③ It is nice for Peter to help his father.
④ Peter is nice of to help to his father.
⑤ Peter is nice for to help to his father.

13

> 만일 눈이 충분히 온다면 우리가 눈사람을 만들 수 있을 텐데.

① If we have enough snow, we could make a snowman.

② Had we snow enough, we can make a snowman.

③ If it didn't snow much, we wouldn't make a snowman.

④ If it snows enough, we would make a snowman.

⑤ If it snowed enough, we could make a snowman.

14

> 당신이 긍정적인 마음으로 사는 것이 훨씬 더 건강에 좋을 것이다.

① It is quite healthier for yours to live with a positive mind.

② It will be much healthier of you to live with a positive mind.

③ To live with a positive mind will be very healthier for you.

④ It will be much healthier for you to live with a positive mind.

⑤ It would be quite healthier for you to live with a positive mind.

15 다음 주어진 문장을 가정법으로 바르게 고친 것은?

> As John didn't return the car to his girlfriend, she hated him.

① If John returns the car to his girlfriend, she won't hate John.

② If John returned the car to his girlfriend, she would hate John.

③ If John didn't return the car to his girlfriend, she wouldn't hate John.

④ If John had returned the car to his girlfriend, she wouldn't have hated John.

⑤ If John hadn't returned the car to his girlfriend, she would have hated John.

16 다음 중 어법상 올바른 문장의 개수는 <u>모두</u> 몇 개인가?

> ⓐ It is difficult for the young kids to diligent all the time.
>
> ⓑ It is possibly for Tom to paint the fences.
>
> ⓒ It won't be easy of the researchers to find out the solution to the problem.
>
> ⓓ Is it interesting for they to watch the pingpong games?
>
> ⓔ It was necessary for me to going abroad to make my dreams come true.
>
> ⓕ It is very polite of her to say hello to every adult she meets.
>
> ⓖ It's important for the students not be late for school.

① 1개 ② 2개 ③ 3개 ④ 4개 ⑤ 5개

17 다음 중 밑줄 친 부분의 쓰임이 〈보기〉와 같은 것은?

> ┤ 보기 ├
>
> Did you ask Sarah <u>if</u> you could post them online?

① James could call Seohyun <u>if</u> he knew her phone number.

② I would build a beautiful house on the beach <u>if</u> I had an island.

③ Our lives would be difficult <u>if</u> there were no computers.

④ Sarah would wonder <u>if</u> she could succeed in the future when young.

⑤ It would be hard to take pictures <u>if</u> we didn't have smartphones.

18 다음 〈보기〉에 주어진 어구를 활용하여, 우리말과 일치하도록 그림을 참고하여 어법상 알맞은 형태로 바꿔 배열하시오. (사용하지 않는 단어는 없어야 한다.)

┤ 보기 ├
the house, the race, play, win, work hard on it, now, at that time, stand strong, be lazy, be hungry

• 그 때 놀지 않았더라면, 지금 배고프지 않을 텐데.
• 내가 열심히 만들었다면, 그 집이 튼튼하게 서 있었을 텐데.
• 내가 게으르지 않았더라면, 경주를 이길 수 있었을 텐데.

(A)   (B)   (C)

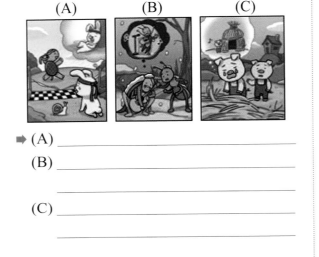

➡ (A) _____
　(B) _____
　　　_____
　(C) _____
　　　_____

19 다음 중 밑줄 친 It[it]의 쓰임이 나머지와 다른 하나는?

① It was difficult for the students in the hall to answer the professor's question.
② It is a ten minutes' walk from here to the museum.
③ Is it so important for us to learn the grammar in foreign languages?
④ It isn't easy for the politician to solve the problem of the city.
⑤ It is good for the old people to take a walk for half an hour every day.

[20~23] 다음 글을 읽고 물음에 답하시오.

　Smartphone addiction causes you to spend too much time on your smartphone. ① Also, you cannot focus on your studies and may have a pain in your neck. ② Then now is the time for you to start digital detox. Digital detox means staying away from digital devices, such as smartphones and computers, for a while. ③ You can enjoy freedom from the noisy digital world. ④ You can focus more on your work. ⑤ Sometimes you can feel refreshed and have new, creative ideas. Digital detox will also help you spend more time with others.

20 ①~⑤ 중 주어진 문장이 들어가기에 가장 적절한 곳은?

Digital detox will help you a lot.

①　　②　　③　　④　　⑤

21 다음 중 스마트폰 중독에 해당하는 증상으로 적절한 것은?

① hardly spending time on your smartphone
② doing your homework
③ focusing on your studies
④ having a pain in your neck
⑤ having new, creative ideas

22 다음 빈칸에 알맞은 말을 위 글의 내용에 맞게 쓰시오.

A: Somi, you look really good.
B: Thanks. Actually I feel refreshed.
A: How come?
B: I started _____ _____ in order to enjoy freedom from the noisy digital world.
A: That sounds great.

23 What does digital detox mean? Answer in English with a full sentence.

➡ _____

_____

_____

26 위 글의 내용에 맞게 빈칸에 알맞은 말을 쓰시오.

According to Yerim's group, they won't take their smartphones into the bedroom and won't _____ _____

_____.

[24~26] 다음 글을 읽고 물음에 답하시오.

Living without a smartphone, however, is not ①easy. So, it is necessary for you (A)to set some rules for using your smartphone. You then need to ②follow the rules. Now, please form groups and, in your group, create rules for using your smartphone.

By Yerim, Yongmin, and Hojin

We will turn off our smartphones while ③studying.

We will not take our smartphones into the bathroom.

We will keep our smartphones out of the bedroom and not use them at night.

By Jina, Hosung, and Minsu

• More Time for Outside Activities – We will spend ④less time playing outside without our smartphones.

• ⑤Fewer SNS Messages – We will post fewer SNS messages on our smartphones.

[27~29] 다음 글을 읽고 물음에 답하시오.

①There would be some advantages and some disadvantages if there were no smartphones. First, let's talk about some (A)_____ . ②If we didn't have smartphones, we would play outside more often. ③Plus, we would be safe from neck pain. ④And it is convenient for us to find the place we don't know how to get to. On the other hand, there would be some (B)_____ . If there were no smartphones, it would not be easy for us to contact people. ⑤Also, it would take so long for us to find information.

27 빈칸 (A)와 (B)에 알맞은 말을 위 글에서 찾아 쓰시오.

➡ (A) _____ (B) _____

28 다음 중 위 글을 읽고 답할 수 있는 것은?

① For what was a smartphone invented?

② How can we use smartphones wisely?

③ What makes it easy for us to contact people?

④ How long does it take for people to find information with smartphones?

⑤ Why do people like to play outside?

24 다음 중 밑줄 친 (A)와 쓰임이 같은 것은?

① You should do your best to be a winner.

② The insect is climbing to get to the top.

③ You need something to read.

④ It is essential to listen to your parents.

⑤ The game is dangerous to watch.

25 ①~⑤ 중 글의 흐름상 어색한 것은?

① ② ③ ④ ⑤

29 ①~⑤ 중 글의 흐름상 어색한 문장은?

① ② ③ ④ ⑤

출제율 95%

01 다음 짝지어진 단어의 관계가 같도록 빈칸에 알맞은 말을 쓰시오. (주어진 철자로 시작할 것)

> reduce – increase : destroy – c_____

출제율 90%

02 다음 영영풀이에 해당하는 단어는?

> a warning to people to be prepared to deal with something dangerous

① device
② half
③ alert
④ pain
⑤ message

[03~04] 다음 대화를 읽고 물음에 답하시오.

G: David, let's watch this new movie on the computer.
B: On the computer?
G: Yes. (A)우리가 그것을 무료로 내려 받을 수 있는 웹 사이트가 있어. (I / free / we / have / it / can / a / website / from / for / download)
B: You're not supposed to download movies from that website, Catherine. It's against the law.
G: Really? I didn't know that.
B: Why don't we go to the movie theater, instead?
G: Okay. Let's go.

출제율 90%

03 위 대화의 밑줄 친 (A)의 우리말에 맞게 주어진 단어를 알맞은 순서로 배열하시오.

➡ _____

출제율 100%

04 위 대화의 내용과 일치하지 <u>않는</u> 것은?

① Catherine suggested that they should watch the new movie at the theater.

② David advised Catherine not to download the new movie.
③ Downloading movies from that website for free is against the law.
④ Catherine didn't know downloading movies from that website for free is against the law.
⑤ Catherine will go to the movie theater with David.

[05~06] 다음 대화를 읽고 물음에 답하시오.

G: You look tired, Peter.
B: (a)I played computer games until late, so last night I slept for more than four hours.
G: Playing computer games too much is not good for your health.
B: I know, Jenny, but I can't stop it. I think I'm addicted to it.
G: (A)_____
B: That's a good idea. Thanks.

출제율 100%

05 위 대화의 빈칸 (A)에 들어갈 말로 알맞은 것은?

① You're not supposed to use the same password for a long time.
② If I were you, I would set a daily plan to limit game time.
③ You're not supposed to talk to strangers online.
④ If I were you, I would not post bad comments online.
⑤ If I were you, I would respect copyright.

출제율 90%

06 위 대화의 밑줄 친 (a)에서 의미상 어색한 부분을 찾아 바르게 고치시오.

➡ _____

Bora: Seho, look! Somebody (a)posted strange things on your SNS. I don't think you posted them.

Seho: Really? Who did this?

Bora: I think someone (b)figured out your password.

Seho: What should I do?

Bora: If I were you, I would (c)change my password.

Seho: I think I should.

Bora: Is your password (d)difficult to guess?

Seho: I used my birth date.

Bora: That is not good. In fact, it is a big mistake. You're not supposed to use your (A)_____ when you make a password.

Seho: Okay, I see. I will change it to a (e)stronger one.

출제율 95%

07 위 대화의 빈칸 (A)에 들어갈 말로 알맞은 것은?

① copyright
② bank account
③ complicated number
④ past
⑤ personal information

출제율 100%

08 위 글의 흐름상 밑줄 (a)~(e) 중 어휘의 쓰임이 어색한 것은?

① (a) ② (b) ③ (c) ④ (d) ⑤ (e)

출제율 90%

09 대화의 밑줄 친 우리말에 맞게 주어진 단어를 활용하여 영어로 쓰시오.

W: Tony, you spend too much time on your smartphone.

B: My friends get together on SNS almost every day, so I can't help it, Mom.

W: 만약 내가 너라면, 친구들에게 야외 활동을 하자고 제안할 거야. (if / be / you / suggest / do / outdoor activities / to your friends)

B: Outdoor activities?

W: Yes. You can do a lot of great activities such as soccer or skating.

B: All right. I will suggest them today.

➡ _____
_____

G: James, what are you doing?

B: I'm posting some of the pictures that I took with Sarah today.

G: Did you ask Sarah (a)if you could post them online?

B: No, but I think it's okay because she looks good in the pictures.

G: You're not supposed to post someone's pictures (A)_____ (ask).

B: Oh, maybe you're right. I'll call Sarah and ask her right away.

출제율 90%

10 위 대화의 흐름상 빈칸 (A)에 들어갈 말을 주어진 단어를 활용하여 쓰시오. (two words)

➡ _____

출제율 100%

11 밑줄 친 (a)와 같은 의미로 사용된 것은?

① If you see him, give him this note.
② He's a good driver, if he is a little over-confident.
③ Do you know if he's married?
④ I am sorry if I disturbed you.
⑤ If you sit down for a few moments, I'll tell the manager you're here.

12 다음 각 문장에 밑줄 친 It[it]이 어떤 용법으로 쓰였는지 〈보기〉에서 기호를 골라 괄호 안에 쓰시오.

┌─── 보기 ───
ⓐ 가주어-진주어 구문의 It[it]
ⓑ It ~ that 강조 구문의 It[it]
ⓒ 비인칭 주어 It
└────────────

(1) It is 20 kilometers from here to the hotel. (　)

(2) It was her birthday present that her father bought at the mall. (　)

(3) It is clever of the students to recycle the waste material. (　)

(4) It is for my family that I have worked so hard day and night. (　)

(5) It is not true that we will hold a graduation party. (　)

13 다음 중 어법상 올바른 문장은?

① Her father would feel happy if she makes it to the finals.

② There were no smartphone, if they would be hard to communicate.

③ What would Kelly do if it rained on her wedding day?

④ If she were not so hungry, she will share her meal with me.

⑤ Paul will be really sad if you left him.

14 다음 중 어법상 올바른 문장은?

① It was kind for Nelly to show him the way to the station.

② It is difficult for Yuna to skating on the ice.

③ It is necessary for those people inside the cave to get some fresh air.

④ It was dangerous of Cindy to jump out of a moving train.

⑤ It is impossible for he to mastering the Latin grammar in a week.

15 괄호 안의 조건과 가정법을 이용하여 다음 대화의 빈칸을 알맞게 채우시오.

(1) A: Does Sophie know my phone number?
   B: No, but if she ＿＿＿＿＿＿＿, she ＿＿＿＿＿ you. (know, will, call 활용)

(2) A: Is William a police officer?
   B: No, but if he ＿＿＿＿＿＿＿, he ＿＿＿＿＿ the evidence. (be, will, find out 활용)

(3) A: Did Lucy see the accident?
   B: No, but if she ＿＿＿＿＿＿＿, she ＿＿＿＿＿ frightened. (see, will, be 활용)

(4) A: Didn't Alfredo join your club?
   B: Yes, but if he ＿＿＿＿＿＿＿, he ＿＿＿＿＿＿. (not, join, can, succeed 활용)

[16~18] 다음 글을 읽고 물음에 답하시오.

Hi, students! When you wake up in the morning, what is the first thing you do? Do you read SNS postings on your smartphone? Imagine your smartphone is not near you. How do you feel?

Students, please check items on the list that are true for you.

(A)＿＿＿＿＿＿＿＿＿＿＿＿＿＿

□ Without my smartphone, I feel uncomfortable.

□ I take my smartphone into the bathroom.

- It is more enjoyable to spend time on my smartphone than with friends.
- I often check SNS postings while studying.
- I try to reduce the time I spend on my smartphone, but I fail.
- I check my smartphone right after I hear the sound of an alert.
- I have my smartphone next to me while I'm eating.

What is your (B)score? Did you check more than half? If so, you may have a problem with smartphone addiction.

출제율 95%

16 주어진 단어를 바르게 나열하여 빈칸 (A)에 들어갈 말을 쓰시오. 필요하다면 어형을 바꾸시오.

> (smartphone / are / your / addict / to / you)?

➡ _____

출제율 100%

17 다음 중 위 항목에 해당하는 사항이 <u>아닌</u> 것은?

① to feel uncomfortable without smartphones

② to spend more time with smartphones rather than with friends

③ to bring one's smartphone anywhere he or she goes

④ to fail to decrease the time to be spent on smartphones

⑤ to turn off all the alerts in order to focus on his or her study

출제율 90%

18 다음 중 밑줄 친 (B)와 쓰임이 같은 것을 <u>모두</u> 고르시오.

① This is an orchestral score.

② You have to score the test.

③ I got a perfect score on the test.

④ She thought the film score was beautiful.

⑤ The player wanted to score a goal.

[19~21] 다음 글을 읽고 물음에 답하시오.

Smartphone addiction causes you to spend too much time on your smartphone. ① Also, you cannot focus on your studies and may have a pain in your neck. ② Digital detox means staying away from digital devices, such as smartphones and computers, for a while. ③ Digital detox will help you a lot. You can enjoy freedom from the noisy digital world. ④ You can focus more on your work. Sometimes you can feel refreshed and have new, creative ideas. Digital detox will also help you spend more time with others. ⑤

출제율 100%

19 ①~⑤ 중 다음 문장이 들어가기에 가장 적절한 곳은?

> Then now is the time for you to start digital detox.

①   ②   ③   ④   ⑤

출제율 100%

20 Which is TRUE about digital detox?

① It doesn't make students focus on their studies.

② It makes students feel comfortable with their necks.

③ It results in smartphone addiction.

④ It makes students be familiar with their smartphones.

⑤ It makes students free from the digital world.

출제율 90%

21 According to the passage, what makes you have a pain in your neck? Answer in English with a full sentence.

➡ _____

_____

01 다음 대화를 읽고 질문에 대한 대답을 완성하시오.

> G: David, let's watch this new movie on the computer.
>
> B: On the computer?
>
> G: Yes. I have a website we can download it from for free.
>
> B: You're not supposed to download movies from that website, Catherine. It's against the law.
>
> G: Really? I didn't know that.
>
> B: Why don't we go to the movie theater, instead?
>
> G: Okay. Let's go.

Q: Why shouldn't Catherine download movies from the website for free?

➡ Because _____.

02 다음 대화를 읽고 아래 요약문의 빈칸을 완성하시오.

> W: Tony, you spend too much time on your smartphone.
>
> B: My friends get together on SNS almost every day, so I can't help it, Mom.
>
> W: If I were you, I would suggest doing outdoor activities to your friends.
>
> B: Outdoor activities?
>
> W: Yes. You can do a lot of great activities such as soccer or skating.
>
> B: All right. I will suggest them today.

➡ My son, Tony, _____ too much time on his _____. He and his friends _____ _____ on _____ almost every day. I told him _____ _____ doing _____ _____ with his friends.

03 다음 대화의 밑줄 친 (A)와 같은 의미가 되도록 주어진 단어를 사용하여 영작하시오.

> G: James, what are you doing?
>
> B: I'm posting some of the pictures that I took with Sarah today.
>
> G: Did you ask Sarah if you could post them online?
>
> B: No, but I think it's okay because she looks good in the pictures.
>
> G: (A)You must not post someone's pictures without asking.
>
> B: Oh, maybe you're right. I'll call Sarah and ask her right away.

➡ _____
_____ (supposed)

04 다음 사진을 보고, 주어진 어구를 알맞게 배열하여 대화를 완성하시오.

> Liz: Olly, have you had a good trip to Busan?
>
> Olly: I'm sorry to tell you that I wasn't able to go there.
>
> Liz: Why? You wanted to see the fireworks festival there, right?
>
> Olly: Yeah. If _____
> _____.
>
> (in Busan, I, seen, have, been, I, the fireworks festival, had, could)

05 다음 우리말과 같은 뜻이 되도록 주어진 단어들을 활용하여, 글자 수에 맞게 영작하시오. (필요한 단어 보충 및 동사 형태 변화 가능)

(Sally, you, really, too, for, of, boring, careless, stay home, reach out, on, to, a big dog, a sunny day)

(1) Sally는 맑은 날 집안에만 있는 것이 너무 지루했다. (과거시제, 13 단어)

➡ _____

(2) 당신이 커다란 개에게 손을 내미는 것은 정말 부주의하다. (현재시제, 13 단어)

➡ _____

[06~10] 다음 글을 읽고 물음에 답하시오.

(A)_____ without a smartphone, however, is not easy. So, it is necessary for you (B)_____ some rules for using your smartphone. You then need (C)_____ the rules. Now, please form groups and, in your group, create rules for using your smartphone.

By Yerim, Yongmin, and Hojin

We will turn off our smartphones while studying.

We will not take our smartphones into the bathroom.

(D)We will keep our smartphones out of the bedroom and use them at night.

By Jina, Hosung, and Minsu

• More Time for Outside Activities – We will spend more time playing outside without our smartphones.

• Fewer SNS Messages – We will post fewer SNS messages on our smartphones.

By Jiho, Sohee, and Yumin

If I were you, I would reduce my time on my smartphone by half.

(E)내가 너라면, 나는 모든 알림을 끌 거야.

You did a good job, students! If we had no smartphones, our lives would be more difficult, but too much use of a smartphone is dangerous. With digital detox, you can become a wise smartphone user.

06 주어진 단어를 내용과 어법에 맞게 빈칸 (A)~(C)에 쓰시오.

(follow / set / live)

➡ (A)_____ (B)_____ (C)_____

07 글의 흐름에 맞게 밑줄 친 (D)를 올바른 문장으로 고쳐 쓰시오.

➡ _____

_____

08 주어진 어구를 활용하여 밑줄 친 우리말 (E)를 영어로 쓰시오.

(be / turn / all alerts / if)

➡ _____

09 According to the passage, what is dangerous? Answer in English with a full sentence.

➡ _____

10 What are Jina, Hosung, and Minsu going to do? Use the phrase 'be going to.'

➡ _____

_____

창의사고력 서술형 문제

01 온라인에서 해서는 안 되는 일에 대해, 〈보기〉의 문장처럼 불허를 표현하는 대화를 만드시오.

- post bad comments online
- talk to strangers online
- use the same password for a long time

보기

A: Do you talk to strangers online?
B: Yes.
A: You're not supposed to talk to strangers online.

(1) A: _____
  B: _____
  A: _____

(2) A: _____
  B: _____
  A: _____

02 텔레비전이 없을 때의 장점과 단점을 참고하여 다음 글의 빈칸에 알맞은 말을 쓰시오.

<advantages>
1. We will spend more time with our family.
2. We will be healthier because we will have more time to exercise.
<disadvantages>
1. It will not be easy for us to watch movies.
2. It will be more difficult for us to check the news.

If There Were No _____
There would be some advantages and some disadvantages if there were no _____.
First, let's talk about some advantages. If we didn't have televisions, _____
_____. Plus, _____ because we would have more time to
exercise. On the other hand, there would be some disadvantages. If there were no
televisions, _____. Also, _____
_____.

단원별 모의고사

01 다음 단어에 대한 영어 설명이 <u>어색한</u> 것은?

① copyright: a right to sell a book, music, film, etc.

② comment: something that you say about someone or something

③ half: one of two equal parts of something

④ create: to plan to do something or to have an action planned in your mind

⑤ be addicted to: to be physically and mentally dependent on an particular substance

02 다음 짝지어진 단어의 관계가 같도록 빈칸에 알맞은 말을 쓰시오.

safe – dangerous : advantage – _____

03 다음 영영풀이에 해당하는 단어를 고르시오.

a mechanical object that is made for a particular purpose

① password   ② detox
③ device   ④ addiction
⑤ material

04 다음 중 짝지어진 대화가 <u>어색한</u> 것은?

① A: What should I do to be a digital citizen?
   B: You should protect your private information.

② A: I was wondering if we could get a pet.
   B: You'd better talk to your dad about it.

③ A: I talked to strangers online yesterday.
   B: I think you must not talk to strangers online.

④ A: Can I bring my dog here with me?
   B: You're not supposed to bring your dog here.

⑤ A: Do you use the same password for a long time?
   B: You should not use your personal information.

[05~06] 다음 대화를 읽고 물음에 답하시오.

G: James, what are you doing?
B: I'm posting some of the pictures that I took with Sarah today.
G: (A)_____
B: No, but I think it's okay because she looks good in the pictures.
G: (B)<u>You're not supposed to post someone's pictures without asking.</u>
B: Oh, maybe you're right. I'll call Sarah and ask her right away.

05 위 대화의 빈칸 (A)에 들어갈 말로 알맞은 것은?

① Are you interested in taking pictures?

② Did Sarah like your pictures?

③ Have you ever received text messages from strangers?

④ Did you ask Sarah if you could post them online?

⑤ Did you change your password every month?

06 위 대화의 밑줄 친 (B)와 같은 의미가 되도록 'If I were you'를 이용하여 충고의 표현을 쓰시오.

➡ If I were you, _____

_____.

[07~08] 다음 대화를 읽고 물음에 답하시오.

Bora: Seho, look! Somebody posted strange things on your SNS. I don't think you posted (a)them. (①)

Seho: Really? Who did this?

Bora: I think someone figured out your password. (②)

Seho: What should I do?

Bora: If I (b)am you, I would change my password.

Seho: I think I should. (③)

Bora: Is your password (c)easy to guess?

Seho: I used my birth date.

Bora: That is not good. (④) You're not supposed (d)to use your personal information when you make a password.

Seho: Okay, I see. (⑤) I will change it to a stronger (e)one.

07 위 대화의 밑줄 친 (a)~(e) 중 어법상 어색한 것은?

① (a)　② (b)　③ (c)　④ (d)　⑤ (e)

08 위 대화의 (①)~(⑤) 중 주어진 문장이 들어갈 위치로 알맞은 것은?

| In fact, it is a big mistake. |

①　②　③　④　⑤

09 다음 대화의 빈칸 (A)에 들어갈 말로 알맞은 것은?

G: David, let's watch this new movie on the computer.

B: On the computer?

G: Yes. I have a website we can download it from for free.

B: You're not supposed to download movies from that website, Catherine. It's against the law.

G: Really? I didn't know that.

B: Why don't we go to the movie theater, (A)_____?

G: Okay. Let's go.

① instead　　　② however

③ though　　　④ therefore

⑤ moreover

10 다음 대화의 빈칸에 들어갈 알맞은 단어를 쓰시오.

G: You look tired, Peter.

B: I played computer games until late, so last night I slept for less than four hours.

G: Playing computer games too much is not good for your health.

B: I know, Jenny, but I can't stop it. I think I'm _____ to it.

G: If I were you, I would set a daily plan to limit game time.

B: That's a good idea. Thanks.

[11~12] 다음 대화를 읽고 물음에 답하시오.

B: What are you doing, Sohee?

G: I'm writing a posting about the restaurant I visited today.

B: Those are great pictures. Did you (a)take all of them?

G: No. I (b)took the pictures from someone's blog.

B: Then (A)너는 그것들을 네 블로그에 게시하면 안 돼 (post / you're / your / not / them / to / supposed / on / blog)

G: Why not?

B: Because only the blog owner has the right to use them.

G: Oh, I see.

11 위 대화의 (A)의 우리말에 맞게 주어진 단어를 알맞은 순서로 배열하시오.

➡ _____

12 위 대화의 밑줄 친 (a)와 (b)의 뜻을 각각 쓰시오.

➡ (a)_____ (b) _____

13 다음 중 밑줄 친 부분의 쓰임이 <u>다른</u> 것은?

① I'd go out to see the movie <u>if</u> it stopped raining.

② I had no idea <u>if</u> the rumor would turn out true.

③ <u>If</u> Angella studied harder, she would get a scholarship.

④ <u>If</u> he were a flim director, he could get me in one of his movies.

⑤ She could call her supervisor anytime <u>if</u> she needed help in doing research.

14 다음 문장을 <보기>와 같이 바꿔 쓰시오.

┌─ 보기 ├─
To find the living things on Mars is impossible. (we)

➡ It is impossible for us to find the living things on Mars.
└─────────────

(1) To build the castle in a month was not possible. (the villagers)

➡ _____

_____

(2) Not to show respect for the old man is rude. (Thomas)

➡ _____

(3) Taking drugs on an airplane is impossible. (the Chinese girl)

➡ _____

_____

15 다음 표를 보고 we를 의미상의 주어로 하여, 찬반의 빈칸에 알맞게 쓰시오.

OK	Not OK
easy to spend more time with our family	not easy to watch shows and dramas
healthier to have more time to exercise	difficult to check the news

(1) It's OK.

If there were no televisions,

it _____

_____.

it _____

_____.

(2) It's not OK.

If there were no televisions,

it _____

_____.

it _____

_____.

16 다음 중 〈보기〉 문장의 밑줄 친 would와 쓰임이 같은 것은?

> ┤ 보기 ├
> Brian would attend the meeting if his professor recommended him to.

① I would like to be a superhero.

② I would not choose that car if I were you.

③ Samantha's family would go on a picnic to the lake park when she was young.

④ Ariel said that she would visit the land of human beings beyond the sea.

⑤ Would you do me a favor?

17 다음 주어진 〈보기〉의 문장과 같은 뜻이 되도록 빈칸에 알맞은 말을 쓰시오.

> ┤ 보기 ├
> If Susie were not poor, she could go abroad to study arts.

➡ As Susie _____ poor, she _____ go abroad to study arts.

[18~22] 다음 글을 읽고 물음에 답하시오.

Smartphone addiction causes you to spend too much time on your smartphone. Also, you cannot focus on your studies and may have a pain in your neck. ⓐ그렇다면 지금 여러분은 디지털 디톡스를 시작할 시간입니다. ① Digital detox means staying away from digital devices, such as smartphones and computers, for a while. ② Digital detox will help you a lot. You can enjoy freedom from the noisy digital world. You can focus more on your work. Sometimes you can feel refreshed and have new, creative ideas. ③ Digital detox will also help you spend more time with others.

Living without a smartphone, however, is not easy. ④ So, it is necessary (A)_____ you to set some rules for using your smartphone. ⑤ Now, please form groups and, in your group, create rules for using your smartphone.

18 다음 중 빈칸 (A)에 들어갈 말과 다른 말이 들어가는 것은?

① It is important _____ her to get the message.

② It is dangerous _____ him to cross the road alone.

③ It is hard _____ you to do the job all by yourself.

④ It is possible _____ them to read the book out loud.

⑤ It is polite _____ her to say such nice words.

19 ①~⑤ 중 다음 문장이 들어가기에 가장 적절한 곳은?

> You then need to follow the rules.

①   ②   ③   ④   ⑤

20 주어진 단어를 활용하여 밑줄 친 우리말 ⓐ를 영어로 쓰시오.

> (then / now / the time / you / start)

➡ _____

21 다음 중 디지털 디톡스의 효과에 해당하지 <u>않는</u> 것은?

① to enjoy freedom from noisy digital world
② to feel refreshed
③ to come up with creative ideas
④ to spend more time all alone
⑤ to focus more on your work

22 다음 중 위 글을 읽고 답할 수 있는 것은?

① How painful is the neck pain?
② How long does it take to do digital detox successfully?
③ How noisy is the digital world?
④ How many rules are there for using smartphones?
⑤ What problems does smarthpone addiction cause?

23 자연스러운 글이 되도록 (A)~(C)를 바르게 나열하시오.

There would be some advantages and some disadvantages if there were no smartphones. First, let's talk about some advantages.
(A) If there were no smartphones, it would not be easy for us to contact people. Also, it would take so long for us to find information.
(B) Plus, we would be safe from neck pain. On the other hand, there would be some disadvantages.
(C) If we didn't have smartphones, we would play outside more often.

➡ _____

[24~25] 다음 글을 읽고 물음에 답하시오.

By Yerim, Yongmin, and Hojin
We will turn off our smartphones while studying.
We will not take our smartphones into the bathroom.
We will keep our smartphones out of the bedroom and not use them at night.
By Jina, Hosung, and Minsu
• More Time for Outside Activities – We will spend more time playing outside without our smartphones.
• Fewer SNS Messages – We will post fewer SNS messages on our smartphones.
By Jiho, Sohee, and Yumin
If I were you, I would reduce my time on my smartphone by half.
If I were you, I would turn off all alerts.

24 주어진 어구를 바르게 나열하여 위 글의 제목을 쓰시오.

(digital detox / the rules / can / what / be / of)

➡ _____

25 다음 중 글의 내용과 일치하지 <u>않는</u> 것은?

① Yongmin won't take his smartphone into the bathroom.
② Jina will have more time for outside activities.
③ Jiho will reduce her time on her smartphone by half.
④ Yumin will post fewer SNS messages on her smartphone.
⑤ Hojin will not use his smartphone at night.

MEMO

Lesson 5

Love for My Country

🎤 의사소통 기능

- 알고 있는지 묻기
  You know about Yun Dongju, don't you?
- 희망 · 기대 표현하기
  I'm looking forward to the visit.

🎤 언어 형식

- '과거완료' had + 과거분사
  I was hungry because I **had not eaten** breakfast.
- '목적'을 나타내는 so that 구문
  I waved at my sister **so that** she could find me.

Words & Expressions
교과서

Key Words

- **amusement park** 놀이동산
- **burial** [bériəl] 명 매장, 장례식
- **bury** [béri] 동 묻다, 매장하다
- **circle** [sə́:rkl] 명 원
- **clearly** [klíərli] 부 분명하게
- **complete** [kəmplí:t] 동 끝내다 형 완전한
- **corner** [kɔ́:rnər] 명 구석, 모퉁이
- **crown** [kraun] 명 왕관
- **deep** [di:p] 형 깊은
- **desire** [dizáiər] 명 바람, 갈망
- **direct** [dirékt] 동 감독하다. 지휘[총괄]하다
- **during** [djúəriŋ] 전 ~ 동안
- **educate** [édʒukèit] 동 교육시키다
- **entrance** [éntrəns] 명 입구
- **exhibition** [èksəbíʃən] 명 전시회
- **feed** [fi:d] 동 먹이를 주다, 먹이다
- **flag** [flæg] 명 깃발
- **foggy** [fɔ́:gi] 형 안개 낀
- **general** [dʒénərəl] 명 장군 형 일반적인
- **god** [gɑd] 명 신
- **government** [gʌ́vərmmənt] 명 정부
- **hall** [hɔ:l] 명 홀, 현관
- **Hallyu** 명 한류, 한국 문화 열풍
- **harmony** [hɑ́:rməni] 명 조화
- **independence** [ìndipéndəns] 명 독립
- **Japanese** [dʒæpəní:z] 명 일본인, 일본어 형 일본의
- **kill** [kil] 동 죽이다
- **leader** [lí:dər] 명 지도자, 리더
- **main** [mein] 형 주된, 주요한
- **mean** [mi:n] 동 의미하다

- **member** [mémbər] 명 구성원, 회원
- **mission** [míʃən] 명 임무
- **model** [mɑ́dl] 명 모형
- **movement** [mú:vmənt] 명 (정치적, 사회적) 운동
- **museum** [mju:zí:əm] 명 박물관
- **organization** [ɔ̀rgənizéiʃən] 명 조직, 기구
- **palace** [pǽlis] 명 궁전
- **patriotic** [pèitriɑ́tik] 형 애국적인
- **peace** [pi:s] 명 평화
- **poem** [póuəm] 명 시
- **president** [prézədənt] 명 대통령, 의장, 회장
- **process** [prɑ́ses] 명 과정
- **protect** [prətékt] 동 보호하다
- **republic** [ripʌ́blik] 명 공화국
- **respect** [rispékt] 명 존경, 경의
- **rule** [ru:l] 명 통치, 지배
- **sacrifice** [sǽkrəfàis] 명 희생 동 희생하다
- **secret** [sí:krit] 명 비밀 형 비밀의
- **specialist** [spéʃəlist] 명 전문가
- **spread** [spred] 동 퍼지다, 퍼뜨리다
- **statue** [stǽtʃu:] 명 조각상
- **teen** [ti:n] 명 십대
- **throughout** [θru:áut] 전 ~의 도처에, ~ 내내
- **tomb** [tu:m] 명 묘, 무덤
- **treasure** [tréʒər] 명 보물
- **volunteer work** 자원봉사 활동
- **water** [wɔ́:tər] 동 (화초 등에) 물을 주다
- **war** [wɔ:r] 명 전쟁, 싸움
- **wish** [wiʃ] 명 소원, 바람
- **zip code** 우편 번호

Key Expressions

- **be in need** ~가 필요하다
- **belong to** ~에 속하다
- **carry out** ~을 수행하다
- **hear of** ~에 관해 듣다
- **look forward to**+명사/동명사 ~을 기대하다
- **look like**+명사 ~처럼 보이다
- **put on** ~을 입다
- **so that**+주어+동사 ~하기 위해서

Word Power

※ 서로 비슷한 뜻을 가진 어휘
□ **desire** : **wish** (바람, 소원)
□ **bury** : **inter** (매장하다, 묻다)
□ **protect** : **defend** (보호하다)
□ **statue** : **figure** (조각상)

□ **harmony** : **accord** (조화)
□ **rule** : **reign** (통치)
□ **specialist** : **expert** (전문가)
□ **educate** : **teach** (교육하다, 가르치다)

※ 서로 반대되는 뜻을 가진 어휘
□ **dependence** (의존) ↔ **independence** (독립)
□ **complete** (완전한) ↔ **incomplete** (불완전한)

□ **entrance** (입구) ↔ **exit** (출구)
□ **deep** (깊은) ↔ **shallow** (얕은)

English Dictionary

□ **amusement park** 놀이공원
→ a large outdoor area with fairground rides, shows, and other entertainments
박람회장 놀이기구, 쇼, 그리고 다른 오락거리가 있는 넓은 야외 공간

□ **burial** 매장, 장례식
→ the act of putting a dead body into the ground, or the ceremony connected with this
사체를 땅에 묻는 행위, 또는 이와 관련된 의식

□ **bury** 묻다
→ to place a dead body in the ground, or to put something in the ground and cover it
사체를 땅에 묻거나 어떤 것을 땅에 묻고 그것을 덮다

□ **carry out** 수행하다
→ to do or complete something, especially that you have said you would do or that you have been told
특히 당신이 하겠다고 말해 왔거나 들어 온 일을 하거나 끝내다

□ **crown** 왕관
→ a circular ornament made of gold and decorated head with jewels that is worn by a king or queen on their head
왕이나 여왕이 머리에 쓰는 금으로 만들어지고 보석으로 장식된 원형 장식물

□ **exhibition** 전시회
→ a public display of art works, pictures or other interesting things
예술 작품, 그림 또는 기타 흥미로운 것들의 공개 전시

□ **flag** 깃발
→ a piece of cloth that is usually attached at the end of a pole and represents a country or association
보통 기둥 끝에 붙어 있고 국가나 협회를 대표하는 천 조각

□ **look forward to** 기대하다
→ to feel pleased and excited about something that is going to happen
앞으로 일어날 일에 대해 기쁘고 흥분하다

□ **mission** 임무
→ any work that someone believes it is their duty to do
누군가가 자신이 할 의무라고 믿는 일

□ **organization** 조직
→ a group of people working together for a purpose of being organized
조직화될 목적으로 함께 일하는 사람들의 집단

□ **palace** 궁전
→ a large house that is the official home of a king and queen
왕과 왕비의 공식적인 주택인 큰 집

□ **poem** 시
→ a piece of writing that uses beautiful words that imply deep meanings and sounds rhythmical when you read
깊은 의미를 암시하고 읽을 때 리드미컬하게 들리는 아름다운 단어를 사용하는 한 편의 글

□ **process** 과정
→ a series of things that happen one after another for a particular result
특정한 결과를 위해 차례로 일어나는 일련의 일들

□ **republic** 공화국
→ a country governed by elected representatives
선출직 대표들에 의해 통치되는 나라

□ **sacrifice** 희생
→ giving up of something valuable for a specific purpose
특정한 목적을 위해 귀중한 어떤 것을 포기하는 것

□ **statue** 조각상
→ a sculptured figure of a person, animal, etc. in bronze, stone, wood, etc.
청동, 돌, 나무 등에 조각된 사람이나 동물 등의 형상

□ **tomb** 무덤
→ a large stone structure or underground room where someone, especially an important person, is buried
누군가, 특히 중요한 사람이 묻혀 있는 큰 돌 구조물이나 지하 공간

□ **treasure** 보물
→ what is highly valued
매우 귀중한 것

01 중요 다음 문장의 빈칸에 들어갈 말로 가장 알맞은 것은?

> Churchill's _____ stands outside the parliament building.

① exhibition
② entrance
③ statue
④ poem
⑤ specialist

02 서답형 빈칸에 주어진 〈영영풀이〉에 해당하는 단어를 쓰시오.

> Nigeria gained _____ from Britain in 1960.

┌─영영풀이─
freedom from being governed or ruled by another country
└

03 서답형 다음 우리말에 맞게 빈칸에 세 단어를 쓰시오.

> 너한테 멋진 생일 선물 받기를 기대하고 있을게!

➡ I will _____ _____ _____ receiving a nice birthday present from you!

[04~05] 다음 설명에 해당하는 단어를 고르시오.

04

> a public display of art works, pictures or other interesting things

① flag
② exhibition
③ comment
④ mission
⑤ treasure

05

> a large stone structure or underground room where someone, especially an important person, is buried

① palace
② statue
③ burial
④ crown
⑤ tomb

06 중요 다음 빈칸에 들어갈 말로 가장 알맞은 것끼리 짝지어진 것은?

> (A) Fire quickly _____ throughout the building.
> (B) Voting is part of your _____ duty.

	(A)	(B)
①	sacrifice	patriotic
②	water	general
③	spread	patriotic
④	feed	creative
⑤	spread	secret

07 서답형 다음 짝지어진 단어의 관계가 같도록 빈칸에 알맞은 말을 쓰시오.

> desire – wish : expert – _____

08 중요 다음 문장의 빈칸에 들어갈 말은?

> I want to let many people know that Dokdo _____ Korea.

① puts on
② carries on
③ consists of
④ belongs to
⑤ turns down

116   Lesson 5. Love for My Country

01 다음 빈칸에 들어갈 말을 〈보기〉에서 찾아 쓰시오.

┌─ 보기 ─┐
kill   movement   harmony   poem
└────────┘

(1) Many religious leaders work hard to bring peace and _____ to the world.

(2) She was a renowned scientist and pioneer of the global environmental _____.

(3) Lack of rain could _____ the crops.

(4) Her _____s tell us to be strong and live bravely.

02 다음 글은 빈칸에 들어갈 단어에 대한 설명이다. 알맞은 단어를 쓰시오.

A _____ is a country where power is held by the people or the representatives that they elect.

03 다음 우리말과 같은 표현이 되도록 문장의 빈칸을 채우시오.

(1) 그녀는 병원 정문 근처에 주차 공간을 발견했다.
➡ She found a parking space close to the hospital's main _____.

(2) 만델라는 대통령이 되었을 때 이미 70대였다.
➡ Mandela was already in his seventies when he became _____.

(3) 영국 정부는 원조를 보내겠다고 제안했다.
➡ The UK _____ has offered to send aid.

(4) 나는 여행 갔을 때 많은 일본 음식을 먹었다.
➡ I ate a lot of _____ food when I went on my trip.

04 영영풀이에 해당하는 단어를 〈보기〉에서 찾아 첫 번째 빈칸에 쓰고, 두 번째 빈칸에는 우리말 뜻을 쓰시오.

┌─ 보기 ─┐
poem   organization   sacrifice   amusement park
└────────┘

(1) _____ : a large outdoor area with fairground rides, shows, and other entertainments: _____

(2) _____ : a group of people working together for a purpose of being organized: _____

(3) _____ : a piece of writing that uses beautiful words that imply deep meanings and sounds rhythmical when you read: _____

(4) _____ : giving up of something valuable for a specific purpose: _____

05 다음 빈칸에 공통으로 들어갈 단어를 쓰시오.

• Some people think physical education and art classes are a _____ waste of time.
• Sometimes he spends 20 hours to _____ just one piece of artwork.

Conversation

1 알고 있는지 묻기

You know about Yun Dongju, don't you?

너는 윤동주에 대해 알고 있지, 그렇지 않니?

■ 'You know ~, don't you?'는 알고 있는지 물어보는 표현이다.
또한 'Do you know about ~? / Did you know that ~? / Are you aware of ~? / Are you aware that ~?' 등을 이용하여 알고 있는지 물을 수 있다.

무언가에 대해 들어서 알고 있는지 물을 때는 'Did you hear about ~?'(너는 ~에 대해 들었니?)라고 말한다. 현재완료를 사용해 'Have you heard about ~?'이라고 들어 본 적이 있는지 물을 수도 있다.

■ 알고 있는지 물어보는 다양한 표현들

• **A:** You know Samgyetang, don't you? 너는 삼계탕을 알고 있지, 그렇지 않니?
  B: Yes, it's a Korean food. People eat it for their health.
    그래, 그것은 한국 음식이야. 사람들은 건강을 위해 삼계탕을 먹어.

• **A:** Have you heard that Ms. Lee is coming to our school? 이 선생님이 우리 학교에 오신다는 것 들었어?
  B: No, I haven't. 아니, 못 들었어.

• Do you know (that) ice cream is from China? 아이스크림이 중국에서 유래했다는 것을 아니?

• Have you heard about the project? 그 프로젝트에 관해 들어봤니?

• Are you aware that gold medals are made mostly of silver? 금메달이 주로 은으로 만들어진다는 것을 아니?

• Did you hear about the accident? 그 사고에 대해 들었니?

핵심 Check

1. 다음 대화의 밑줄 친 문장과 바꾸어 쓸 수 있는 것을 <u>모두</u> 고르시오.

   A: <u>You know about Yun Dongju, don't you?</u>
   B: Sure.

   ① Do you know about Yun Dongju?
   ② I'm sure I know about Yun Dongju.
   ③ Did you hear from Yun Dongju?
   ④ Have you ever heard about Yun Dongju?
   ⑤ Why don't we know about Yun Dongju?

② 희망 · 기대 표현하기

I'm looking forward to the visit.
나는 그 방문을 기대하고 있어.

- 앞으로 하고 싶은 일에 대한 기대를 표현할 때 'I'm looking forward to ~.'나 'I look forward to ~.'의 표현을 사용한다. 여기서 to는 전치사이므로 뒤에 명사나 동명사가 와야 한다.
  - I'm looking forward to traveling to Korea.
  - I look forward to my birthday party this weekend.
  - **G:** Yubin, I hear you're taking a family trip to Thailand this winter.
    유빈아, 너 이번 겨울에 태국으로 가족 여행을 간다고 들었어.

    B: Yes. I'm looking forward to riding an elephant. 응. 코끼리를 타 보기를 기대하고 있어.

- 'I can't wait to ~'는 원하던 일이 다가오고 있어 빨리하고 싶은 기대감을 나타내는 표현이며, 직역의 의미대로 '~하는 것을 기다릴 수 없다' 또는 '당장 ~하고 싶다, 빨리 ~했으면 좋겠다' 정도로 해석한다. to 뒤에는 동사원형의 형태가 오는데, 뒤에 명사구가 올 경우에는 'I can't wait for+명사(명사구)'의 형태로 쓰기도 한다.
  - I can't wait for my graduation. 내 졸업이 기대된다.

기대를 나타내는 다른 표현들

- I am expecting to 동사원형 ~.
- I am longing to 동사원형 ~.
- I am eager to 동사원형 ~.
- I'm dying to 동사원형 ~.

핵심 Check

2. 다음 대화의 빈칸에 들어갈 말로 <u>어색한</u> 것은?

   A: Do you want to watch *Harry Potter* with me this weekend?
   B: Sure, I'd love to. _____

   ① I can't wait to watch it.
   ② I am longing to watch it.
   ③ I'm dying to watching it.
   ④ I'm looking forward to watching it.
   ⑤ I am eager to watch it.

Listen & Speak 1 A-1

B: Look at Suwon Hawseong. It's huge.

G: It also ❶looks strong.

B: Because ❷it was built to protect the people ❸during wars.

G: Wow. ❹Do you know who built it?

B: Yes. King Jeongjo ❺ordered Jeong Yakyong to direct the building process. ❻You know about Jeong Yakyong, don't you?

G: Yes, I've heard of him. He was a great scientist in Joseon.

B: 수원 화성을 봐. 그것은 거대해.

G: 그것은 또한 튼튼해 보여.

B: 왜냐하면 그것은 전쟁 중에 사람들을 보호하기 위해 지어졌기 때문이야.

G: 우와. 너는 누가 그것을 지었는지 아니?

B: 응. 정조가 정약용에게 건설 과정을 감독할 것을 지시했어. 너는 정약용에 대해 알고 있지, 그렇지 않니?

G: 응. 그에 대해 들어봤어. 그는 조선의 훌륭한 과학자였어.

❶ 'look+형용사'로 '～하게 보이다'라는 뜻이다.
❷ it은 'Suwon Hawseong'을 가리키고, '지어졌다'는 수동태(was built)를 사용한다.
❸ 'during'은 '～ 동안'의 의미로 '특정한 기간'과 함께 사용된다. 반면 'for'는 '숫자로 된 기간'과 함께 사용된다.
❹ 동사 'know'의 목적어 자리에 사용된 간접의문문으로 '의문사 who (주어)+동사(built)' 어순을 취한다.
❺ 'order+목적어+목적보어(to부정사)'로 '～에게 …하라고 명령[지시]하다'로 해석하는 5형식 문장이다.
❻ You know ～, don't you?는 알고 있는지 물어보는 표현이다.

Check(√) True or False

(1) Suwon Hawseong was built to protect the people during wars. T ☐ F ☐

(2) The girl has heard of King Jeongjo. T ☐ F ☐

Listen & Speak 2 A-1

G: ❶I'm planning to go to the Gansong Museum.

B: What is the Gansong Museum?

G: It's a museum ❷built by Gansong Jeon Hyeongpil.

B: I heard that he did great things for the country.

G: Yes. He bought many Korean treasures ❸that some Japanese had taken to Japan.

B: Wow. The museum ❹must be interesting.

G: Yes. ❺I'm looking forward to it!

G: 나는 간송 미술관에 갈 예정이야.

B: 간송 미술관이 뭐야?

G: 간송 전형필에 의해 지어진 미술관이야.

B: 나는 그가 나라를 위해 훌륭한 일들을 했다고 들었어.

G: 응. 그는 몇몇 일본사람들이 일본으로 가져갔었던 한국의 많은 문화재들을 샀어.

B: 우와. 그 미술관은 틀림없이 흥미로울 거야.

G: 응. 나는 그곳을 기대하고 있어!

❶ 'be planning to+동사원형'은 앞으로 할 일에 대한 계획을 나타낼 때 사용하는 표현으로 '～할 예정이다'라는 뜻이다.
❷ 명사 a museum을 수식하는 과거분사로 '지어진'의 의미다.
❸ 목적격 관계대명사절로 선행사 'many Korean treasures'를 수식하는 역할을 한다.
❹ 추측의 조동사로 '～임에 틀림없다'라는 뜻이다.
❺ 앞으로 하고 싶은 일에 대한 기대를 표현할 때 사용하는 표현으로 'to'는 전치사이기 때문에 뒤에 '명사나 동명사'를 사용한다.

Check(√) True or False

(3) The Gansong Museum was built by Jeon Hyeongpil. T ☐ F ☐

(4) Gansong sold Korean treasures to other countries. T ☐ F ☐

Listen & Speak 1 A-2

G: Brian, you know Taegeukgi, ❶don't you?

B: Sure. It's the national flag of Korea, ❷isn't it?

G: That's right. Do you know ❸what the symbols in Taegeukgi mean?

B: No, I don't. Tell me about ❹them.

G: The circle in the middle means harmony and peace.

B: What do the black lines on the four corners mean?

G: They mean four things: sky, fire, water, and earth.

❶ 부가의문문으로 상대방이 알고 있는지 물어보는 표현이다.
❷ be동사의 부가의문문이다.
❸ know의 목적어 자리에 사용된 간접의문문으로 '의문사(what)+주어(the symbols)+동사(mean)' 어순이다.
❹ 앞 문장의 'the symbols in Taegeukgi'를 나타낸다.

Real Life Talk

Andy: Bora, what are you reading?

Bora: I'm reading *Sky, Wind, Star, and Poetry* by Yun Dongju. ❶You know about Yun Dongju, don't you?

Andy: I've heard his name, but I don't know much about him.

Bora: He wrote many beautiful poems ❷when Korea was under Japanese rule. ❸His love for the country and his desire for independence can be felt in his poems.

Andy: Really? I didn't know that. I want ❹to read his poems and learn more about him.

Bora: Great. In fact, ❺I'm planning to visit the Yun Dongju Museum soon. Do you want to come with me?

Andy: Yes, when are you going?

Bora: Next Saturday. It's near Gyeongbok Palace. Can you meet me at the palace at 2 p.m.?

Andy: Sure. Let's meet there.

Bora: Great. ❻I'm really looking forward to the visit.

❶ 'You know ~, don't you?'는 알고 있는지 물어보는 표현이다.
❷ 시간의 부사절 접속사로 '~할 때'로 해석한다.
❸ 문장의 주어는 'His love'와 'his desire'이다. 'can be felt'는 조동사가 있는 수동태로 '느껴질 수 있다'로 해석한다.
❹ want의 목적어로 'to read'와 '(to) learn'이 병렬구조로 연결되어 있다.
❺ '~할 계획이다'라는 의미로 미래의 일에 대한 계획을 말하는 표현이다.
❻ 기대를 나타내는 표현으로 'look forward to+명사/동명사'를 사용한다.

Wrap Up

B: Tomorrow ❶let's put on traditional Korean clothes, *hanbok*, and go to Insadong.

G: Good, but I want to buy gifts for my friends in Germany tomorrow.

B: In Insadong, ❷there are many gift shops.

G: Great. ❸After shopping, what should we eat for lunch?

B: Hmm. ❹You know Samgyetang, don't you?

G: No. What is it?

B: It's a traditional Korean soup. It's delicious and will ❺make you healthy.

G: Sounds good. ❻I'm looking forward to trying it.

❶ 'let's+동사원형'으로 '~하자'라고 제안을 할 때 사용한다.
❷ 'there are+복수명사'로 '~들이 있다'라는 의미다.
❸ 전치사 'After' 뒤에 동명사 'shopping'을 사용한다.
❹ 'You know ~, don't you?'는 알고 있는지 물어보는 표현이다.
❺ 'make+목적어+목적보어(형용사)' 형태로 '…을 ~하게 만들다'라는 의미이다.
❻ 'look forward to+동명사'로 '~하기를 기대하다'라는 뜻이다.

● 다음 우리말과 일치하도록 빈칸에 알맞은 말을 쓰시오.

Listen & Speak 1 A

1. B: Look _____ Suwon Hawseong. It's _____.

   G: It also _____ _____.

   B: _____ it _____ _____ to _____ the people _____ wars.

   G: Wow. Do you know _____ _____ it?

   B: Yes. King Jeongjo _____ Jeong Yakyong _____ _____ the building _____. You know about Jeong Yakyong, _____ _____?

   G: Yes, I've _____ _____ him. He was a great _____ in Joseon.

2. G: Brian, you know Taegeukgi, _____ _____?

   B: Sure. It's the _____ _____ of Korea, _____ it?

   G: That's right. Do you know _____ the _____ in Taegeukgi _____?

   B: No, I don't. Tell me about them.

   G: The _____ in the middle means _____ and _____.

   B: What do the black _____ on the four _____ mean?

   G: They _____ four things: sky, fire, water, and _____.

Listen & Speak 2 A

1. G: I'm _____ _____ _____ to the Gansong Museum.

   B: What is the Gansong Museum?

   G: It's a museum _____ by Gansong Jeon Hyeongpil.

   B: I _____ that he did _____ things for the country.

   G: Yes. He bought many Korean _____ _____ some Japanese _____ _____ to Japan.

   B: Wow. The museum _____ _____ _____.

   G: Yes. I'm _____ _____ _____ it!

2. B: Soyeon, _____ _____ _____ _____ last weekend?

   G: I went to Hyeonchungwon to do _____ _____.

   B: _____ _____ of volunteer work did you do there?

1. B: 수원 화성을 봐. 그것은 거대해.
   G: 그것은 또한 튼튼해 보여.
   B: 왜냐하면 그것은 전쟁 중에 사람들을 보호하기 위해 지어졌기 때문이야.
   G: 우와. 너는 누가 그것을 지었는지 아니?
   B: 응. 정조가 정약용에게 건설 과정을 감독할 것을 지시했어. 너는 정약용에 대해 알고 있지, 그렇지 않니?
   G: 응, 그에 대해 들어봤어. 그는 조선의 훌륭한 과학자였어.

2. G: Brian, 너 태극기를 알고 있지, 그렇지 않니?
   B: 물론이지. 그것은 한국의 국기잖아, 그렇지 않니?
   G: 맞아. 너는 태극기에 있는 상징들이 무엇을 의미하는지 알고 있니?
   B: 아니, 몰라. 그것에 대해 말해 줘.
   G: 가운데 원은 조화와 평화를 의미해.
   B: 네 모서리의 검은 선들은 무엇을 의미하니?
   G: 그것은 하늘, 불, 물 그리고 땅을 의미해.

1. G: 나는 간송 미술관에 갈 예정이야.
   B: 간송 미술관이 뭐야?
   G: 간송 전형필에 의해 지어진 미술관이야.
   B: 나는 그가 나라를 위해 훌륭한 일을 했다고 들었어.
   G: 응. 그는 몇몇 일본 사람들이 일본으로 가져갔던 한국의 많은 문화재들을 샀어.
   B: 우와. 그 미술관은 틀림없이 흥미로울 거야.
   G: 응. 나는 그곳을 기대하고 있어!

2. B: 소연아, 지난 주말에 무엇을 했니?
   G: 나는 봉사 활동을 하러 현충원에 갔어.
   B: 그곳에서 어떤 종류의 봉사 활동을 했어?

G: I _____ around the _____. I felt great _____ for the people _____ died for the country.

B: _____ great. Can I do it, too?

G: Sure. I'm _____ _____ _____ there again next Wednesday. Will you _____ me?

B: Sure. _____ _____ _____ _____ it.

Real Life Talk

Andy: Bora, what are you _____?

Bora: I'm reading *Sky*, *Wind*, *Star*, *and* _____ by Yun Dongju. You _____ about Yun Dongju, _____ _____?

Andy: I've _____ his name, but I don't know much about him.

Bora: He wrote many beautiful _____ _____ Korea was _____ Japanese _____. His love for the country and his _____ for _____ can _____ _____ in his _____.

Andy: Really? I didn't know that. I want _____ _____ his _____ and _____ more about him.

Bora: Great. _____ _____, I'm planning _____ _____ the Yun Dongju Museum soon. Do you want to come with me?

Andy: Yes, _____ are you going?

Bora: Next Saturday. It's _____ Gyeongbok _____. Can you meet me at the _____ at 2 p.m.?

Andy: Sure. _____ meet there.

Bora: Great. I'm really _____ _____ _____ the _____.

Wrap Up

B: Tomorrow let's _____ _____ _____ Korean clothes, *hanbok*, and go to Insadong.

G: Good, but I want to buy gifts _____ my friends in _____ tomorrow.

B: In Insadong, _____ _____ many gift shops.

G: Great. After _____, what should we eat for lunch?

B: Hmm. You _____ Samgyetang, _____ _____?

G: No. What is it?

B: It's a _____ Korean _____. It's _____ and will make you _____.

G: Sounds good. I'm looking forward _____ _____ it.

해석

G: 나는 묘 주변을 청소했어. 나는 나라를 위해 돌아가신 분들에게 깊은 경의를 느꼈어.

B: 대단하게 들린다. 나도 그것을 할 수 있을까?

G: 물론이지. 나는 다음 주 수요일에 그곳에 다시 갈 계획이야. 너도 나와 함께 갈래?

B: 물론이지. 나는 그것을 기대하고 있어.

Andy: 보라, 너 무엇을 읽고 있니?

보라: 윤동주 시인의 「하늘과 바람과 별과 시」를 읽고 있어. 너는 윤동주에 대해 알고 있지, 그렇지 않니?

Andy: 나는 그의 이름을 들어 본 적 있지만 그에 대해 잘 알지는 못해.

보라: 그는 한국이 일본의 통치하에 있을 때 아름다운 시를 많이 썼어. 나라에 대한 그의 사랑과 독립에 대한 염원이 그의 시에서 느껴질 수 있어.

Andy: 정말? 나는 그걸 몰랐어. 나는 그의 시를 읽고 그에 대해 더 많이 배우고 싶어.

보라: 아주 좋아. 사실 나는 곧 윤동주 박물관을 방문할 계획이야. 너도 나와 함께 가길 원하니?

Andy: 응, 언제 갈 거니?

보라: 다음 주 토요일. 그곳은 경복궁 근처에 있어. 오후 2시에 궁에서 만날 수 있니?

Andy: 물론이지. 거기서 만나자.

보라: 좋아. 나는 그 방문을 정말 기대하고 있어.

B: 내일 우리 한국 전통 의상인 한복을 입고 인사동에 가자.

G: 좋아, 그런데 나 내일 독일에 있는 내 친구들을 위한 선물을 사고 싶어.

B: 인사동에 선물 가게가 많아.

G: 잘됐네. 쇼핑하고 나서 점심으로 뭘 먹을까?

B: 흠. 너는 삼계탕에 대해 알고 있지, 그렇지 않니?

G: 아니. 그게 뭐야?

B: 전통적인 한국의 국물 음식이야. 그것은 맛이 좋고 너를 건강하게 만들어 줄 거야.

G: 멋지네. 나는 그것을 먹어보는 것을 기대하고 있어.

01 우리말을 영어로 옮길 때 빈칸에 알맞은 말을 쓰시오.

나는 그 방문이 정말 기대돼.

➡ I'm really _____ _____ _____ the visit.

02 다음 대화의 빈칸에 들어갈 말로 알맞은 것은?

A: _____, don't you?
B: Yes, I heard about it.

① I hope I will visit Dokdo
② You cannot know about Dokdo
③ I'm not quite sure if you know about Dokdo
④ Look at the island in the picture
⑤ You know Dokdo is windy and foggy

03 다음 대화의 빈칸에 들어갈 말로 <u>어색한</u> 표현은?

A: Do you remember our plan to visit the Hanok Village in July?
B: Sure. _____

① I'm looking forward to visiting there.
② I can't wait to visit there.
③ I'm dying to visiting there.
④ I'm expecting to visit there.
⑤ I am longing to visit there.

04 다음 대화의 밑줄 친 말의 의도로 알맞은 것은?

A: <u>You know that Dokdo has two main islands and 89 small islands, don't you?</u>
B: No, I didn't know that.

① 확신 표현하기   ② 알고 있는지 묻기
③ 관심 표현하기   ④ 염려 묻기
⑤ 기대 표현하기

[01~02] 다음 대화를 읽고 물음에 답하시오.

> Seho: Tomorrow (a)let's put on traditional Korean clothes, *hanbok*, and go to Insadong.
>
> Judy: Good, but I want to buy gifts for my friends in Germany tomorrow.
>
> Seho: In Insadong, (b)there are many gift shops.
>
> Judy: Great. (c)After shopping, what should we eat for lunch?
>
> Seho: Hmm. You know Samgyetang, (d)don't you?
>
> Judy: No. What is it?
>
> Seho: It's a traditional Korean soup. It's delicious and will make you healthy.
>
> Judy: Sounds good. I'm looking forward to (e)try it.

01 위 대화의 밑줄 친 (a)~(e) 중, 어법상 어색한 것은?

① (a)   ② (b)   ③ (c)   ④ (d)   ⑤ (e)

 위 대화의 내용과 일치하지 <u>않는</u> 것은?

① They are talking about their plans for tomorrow.

② Judy didn't know there are many gift shops in Insadong.

③ Both Seho and Judy are going to put on *hanbok*.

④ They will eat Samgyetang for dinner.

⑤ Judy can't wait to eat Samgyetang.

03 다음 대화의 (A)~(D)를 알맞은 순서로 배열한 것은?

> B: Soyeon, what did you do last weekend?
>
> G: I went to Hyeonchungwon to do volunteer work.
>
> (A) Sounds great. Can I do it, too?

(B) I cleaned around the tombs. I felt great respect for the people who died for the country.

(C) Sure. I'm planning to go there again next Wednesday. Will you join me?

(D) What kind of volunteer work did you do there?

> B: Sure. I'm looking forward to it.

① (A)–(C)–(B)–(D)   ② (B)–(A)–(C)–(D)

③ (C)–(B)–(A)–(D)   ④ (D)–(B)–(A)–(C)

⑤ (D)–(C)–(A)–(B)

 다음 대화의 빈칸에 들어갈 말로 <u>어색한</u> 것은?

> A: You know about An Junggeun, don't you?
>
> B: _____

① No. I don't know much about him.

② Sure. He made a great effort for Korea's independence.

③ You can go to the An Junggeun Museum and get more information about him.

④ No. I want to learn more about him.

⑤ No, I don't. But I'm looking forward to learning more about him.

05 다음 대화의 밑줄 친 문장과 같은 의미가 되도록 주어진 단어를 이용하여 쓰시오.

> A: Do you remember our plan to make Gimchi in November?
>
> B: Sure. I'm dying to make it.

➡ _____

(look forward)

06 다음 두 사람의 대화가 어색한 것은?

① A: Do you remember our plan to visit the Hanok Village in July?
   B: Sure. I'm looking forward to visiting there.

② A: You know Seho, don't you?
   B: Yes. Isn't he the fastest boy in our school?

③ A: Do you remember our plan to learn the Korean traditional fan dance?
   B: Yes. I'm looking forward to learning it.

④ A: I'm planning to go to the Gansong Museum.
   B: I'd love to, but I'm looking forward to visiting there.

⑤ A: You know Ryu Gwansun, don't you?
   B: Of course. She was an independence activist.

[07~08] 다음 대화를 읽고 물음에 답하시오.

> B: Look at Suwon Hawseong. It's huge.
> G: It also looks strong.
> B: Because it was built to protect the people during wars.
> G: Wow. Do you know who built it?
> B: Yes. (A)정조가 정약용에게 건설 과정을 감독할 것을 지시했어. You know about Jeong Yakyong, don't you?
> G: (B)_____ He was a great scientist in Joseon.

서답형

07 위 대화의 밑줄 친 (A)의 우리말에 맞게 주어진 어구를 이용하여 영어로 쓰시오. (단어 하나를 추가하시오.)

> ordered / direct / Jeong Yakyong / King Jeongjo / the building process

➡ _____

_____

08 위 대화의 빈칸 (B)에 들어갈 말로 알맞은 것을 모두 고르시오.

① I'm looking forward to seeing him.
② Yes, I've heard of him.
③ No. I can't wait to know about him.
④ No, I don't know about him.
⑤ Yes, I saw a program about him on TV.

[09~10] 다음 대화를 읽고 물음에 답하시오.

> G: Brian, (a)you know Taegeukgi, don't you?
> B: Sure. It's the national flag of Korea, (b)isn't it?
> G: That's right. Do you know (c)what do the symbols in Taegeukgi mean?
> B: No, I don't. Tell me about them.
> G: The circle in the middle (d)means harmony and peace.
> B: What do the black lines on the four corners (e)mean?
> G: They mean four things: sky, fire, water, and earth.

09 위 대화의 밑줄 친 (a)~(e) 중 어법상 어색한 것은?

① (a) ② (b) ③ (c) ④ (d) ⑤ (e)

10 위 대화의 내용과 일치하지 않는 것은?

① Brian knows what Taegeukgi is.
② The symbols in Taegeukgi have different meanings.
③ Brian wants to know about the meanings of the symbols in Taegeukgi.
④ Taegeukgi has four lines on each corner.
⑤ The black lines mean sky, fire, water and earth.

[01~02] 다음 대화를 읽고 물음에 답하시오.

Andy: Bora, what are you reading?

Bora: I'm reading *Sky, Wind, Star, and Poetry* by Yun Dongju. You know about Yun Dongju, don't you?

Andy: I've heard his name, but I don't know much about him.

Bora: He wrote many beautiful poems when Korea was under Japanese rule. His love for the country and his desire for independence can be felt in his poems.

Andy: Really? I didn't know that. I want to read his poems and learn more about him.

Bora: Great. In fact, I'm planning to visit the Yun Dongju Museum soon. Do you want to come with me?

Andy: Yes, when are you going?

Bora: Next Saturday. It's near Gyeongbok Palace. Can you meet me at the palace at 2 p.m.?

Andy: Sure. Let's meet there.

Bora: Great. (A)_____

01 위 대화를 읽고 다음 질문에 대한 답을 본문에서 찾아 쓰시오.

Q: What can be felt through Yun Dongju's poems?

➡ _____

_____

02 위 대화의 빈칸 (A)에 들어갈 말을 〈조건〉에 맞게 쓰시오.

┤ 조건 ├
• 'look'을 이용하여 기대나 희망을 나타내는 표현을 쓸 것.
• 현재진행형을 사용하고, 'the visit'을 쓸 것.

➡ _____

03 다음 대화의 빈칸에 들어갈 말로 자연스러운 것을 〈보기〉에서 찾아 문장을 쓰시오.

G: Brian, (A)_____

B: Sure. It's the national flag of Korea, isn't it?

G: That's right. (B)_____

_____

B: No, I don't. Tell me about them.

G: The circle in the middle means harmony and peace.

B: What do the black lines on the four corners mean?

G: (C)_____

┤ 보기 ├

• Do you know what the symbols in Taegeukgi mean?
• you know Taegeukgi, don't you?
• They mean four things: sky, fire, water, and earth.

 대화의 내용상 빈칸에 주어진 〈조건〉에 맞게 영어로 쓰시오.

┤ 조건 ├
• 정약용에 대해 아는지 묻는 표현을 쓸 것.
• 'know'와 '부가의문문'을 사용할 것.

B: Look at Suwon Hawseong. It's huge.

G: It also looks strong.

B: Because it was built to protect the people during wars.

G: Wow. Do you know who built it?

B: Yes. King Jeongjo ordered Jeong Yakyong to direct the building process.

_____

G: Yes, I've heard of him. He was a great scientist in Joseon.

Grammar

1 '과거완료' had + 과거분사

> • I thought about Kim Koo's words in My Wish that I **had read** in the exhibition hall. 나는 전시관에서 읽었던 '나의 소원'에 나오는 김구의 말에 대해 생각했다.
> • When my mom came back home, she found Judy **had watered** the plant. 나의 엄마가 집에 돌아왔을 때, 엄마는 Judy가 화분에 물을 주었던 것을 발견했다.

■ 과거완료시제는 'had + 과거분사' 형태로 표현하며, 과거의 어느 시점을 기준으로, 그 이전에 일어난 동작이나 상태를 나타낸다.

• I lost the cellphone that he **had bought** for me. (나는 그가 사 준 핸드폰을 잃어버렸다.)

■ 과거의 특정 시점을 기준으로 그 이전에 일어난 동작의 완료, 경험, 계속, 결과를 나타낸다.

(1) 완료: '막 ~했었다'는 의미로 과거 이전에 시작된 동작이 과거의 어느 시점에 완료된 일을 나타낸다. 보통 already, yet 등의 부사와 함께 쓰인다.

• They **had arrived** at the base camp before the snow storm began. (그들은 눈보라가 시작되기 전에 베이스 캠프에 도착했다.)

(2) 경험: '~한 적이 있었다'는 의미로 과거 이전부터 과거의 어느 시점까지의 경험을 나타낸다. 보통 never, ever, once, twice, before 등의 부사(구)와 함께 쓰인다.

• She realized David at once, for she **had seen** him before. (그녀는 David을 즉시 알아봤는데, 전에 그를 만난 적이 있었기 때문이었다.)

(3) 결과: '(과거 이전에) ~해서, 그 결과 …했다'는 의미로 과거 이전의 동작이 과거의 어느 시점의 결과에 영향을 미치는 것을 나타낸다.

• Her son **had gone** to the army by the time Emma was well again. (Emma가 다시 건강해질 무렵 그의 아들은 군에 입대했다.)

(4) 계속: '계속 ~하고 있었다'는 의미로 과거 이전부터 과거의 어느 시점까지 계속되는 동작이나 상태를 나타낸다. 보통 since, for 등과 함께 쓰인다.

• Walter **had lived** there for 16 years when he was elected mayor. (Walter는 시장으로 당선되었을 때, 그곳에서 16년간을 살았다.)

■ 부정문은 'had+not+과거분사', 의문문은 'Had+주어+과거분사 ~?', 과거 어느 시점을 기준으로 전부터 진행 중인 동작을 강조할 때, 과거완료진행형 'had+been+V-ing'을 쓴다.

• I was hungry because I **had not eaten** breakfast. (나는 아침을 먹지 않았기 때문에 배가 고팠다.)
• **Had** James **seen** the actor before? (James가 그 배우를 전에 본 적이 있었나요?)
• He **had been preparing** dinner when I saw him. (내가 그를 봤을 때, 그는 저녁식사를 준비하고 있던 중이었다.)

핵심 Check

1. 괄호 안에서 알맞은 단어를 고르시오.

(1) Sally (has / had) lived in Singapore before she moved to Canada.

(2) Judy had never eaten sushi until she (visits / visited) Japan.

2 '목적', '의도'를 나타내는 so that

- Kim Koo always carried Yun's watch in his jacket **so that** he **would** not forget Yun's sacrifice. 김구는 윤의 희생을 잊지 않기 위해서 그의 시계를 항상 재킷에 넣고 다녔다.
- I waved at my sister **so that** she **could** find me. 나는 내 여동생이 나를 찾을 수 있게 그녀에게 손을 흔들었다.

■ so that은 '~하기 위해', '~하고자', '~하도록'의 의미로 '목적'이나 '의도'를 나타낸다. 일반적으로 '주절+so that+주어+can/will(조동사)+동사원형 ~'의 구조로 쓰인다.
- Jinsu got up early **so that** he **could** catch the first train to Barcelona. (진수는 Barcelona로 가는 첫 기차를 타기 위해 일찍 일어났다.)
- Clara tried her best **so that** she **would** not disappoint her fans. (Clara는 자신의 팬들을 실망시키지 않기 위해서 최선을 다했다.)

■ so that은 다양한 표현들로 같은 의미를 나타낼 수 있다.
- She went to Mexico **so that** she **could** learn Spanish. (그녀는 스페인어를 배우러 멕시코에 갔다.)
  = She went to Mexico **in order that** she **could** learn Spanish.
  = She went to Mexico **to learn** Spanish. 〈to부정사의 부사적 용법 – 목적〉
  = She went to Mexico **so as to learn** Spanish.
  = She went to Mexico **in order to learn** Spanish.
- He worked hard **so that he wouldn't** be fired. (그는 해고되지 않으려고 열심히 일했다.)
  = He worked hard **in order that he wouldn't** be fired.
  = He worked hard **(in order) not to** be fired.
  = He worked hard **so as not to** be fired.

■ so that을 기준으로 앞과 뒤 동사의 시제를 일치시킨다.
- Sam **works** hard **so that** he **can** support his family. (Sam은 가족을 부양하기 위해 열심히 일한다.)
- Sam **worked** hard **so that** he **could** support his family.

■ so that이 '그래서'의 의미를 갖는 접속사로 쓰이기도 한다. 대개 so that 앞에 쉼표가 온다.
- Bolt ran every day, **so that** he became a great athlete. (Bolt는 매일 달렸고, 그래서 그는 훌륭한 육상선수가 되었다.)

■ so ~ that 사이에 형용사[부사]가 오면, '너무 ~해서 결국 …하다'라는 뜻이 된다.
- The girl was **so** happy **that** she cried. 그 소녀는 너무 행복해서 울었다.
- The room was **so** dark **that** I couldn't see anything. 방이 너무 어두워서 나는 아무것도 볼 수 없었다.

핵심 Check

2. 괄호 안에서 알맞은 말을 고르시오.

(1) Miranda went to London so (that / where) she could study fashion.

(2) Please turn the volume down (for that / so that) my daughter can sleep.

Grammar 시험대비 기본평가

01 다음 빈칸에 들어갈 말로 알맞은 것은?

> He came back to Sudan in 2001 as he _____.

① promise   ② promises   ③ has promised

④ to promise   ⑤ had promised

02 다음 각 문장의 빈칸에 공통으로 들어갈 말로 알맞은 것은? (대 · 소문자 구분 없음.)

> • Andrew saved much money _____ as to travel around the world.
> • Turn the volume up _____ that we can dance to the music.
> • These are _____ tough that we can't tear them.

① enough   ② too   ③ so

④ such   ⑤ quite

03 다음 밑줄 친 부분 중 어법상 옳은 것을 고르시오.

① Paul <u>has gone</u> to Tokyo before his wife came back.

② I ate the tuna can that I <u>had bought</u> a month before.

③ I <u>had found</u> her purse that she had left in my office.

④ They <u>had lived</u> here for two years until now.

⑤ When <u>had</u> Betty <u>married</u> Chris?

04 다음 두 문장의 의미가 같도록 빈칸에 알맞은 말을 쓰시오.

(1) Mina saved much money to buy the car.

➡ Mina saved much money so _____ she _____ buy the car.

(2) Because it was very hot, Julie turned the air conditioner on.

➡ It was _____ _____ _____ Julie turned the air conditioner on.

(3) Mike will walk fast in order to get there on time.

➡ Mike will walk fast so _____ _____ _____ get there on time.

(4) Judy can't solve the problem because it is very hard.

➡ The problem is _____ _____ Judy _____ solve it.

01 밑줄 친 부분이 어법상 <u>어색한</u> 것은?

① The suspect <u>had</u> already <u>left</u> the room when the police arrived.
② John <u>had broken</u> his arm, so he couldn't play tennis last weekend.
③ Susan asked her friend how to repair the machine which <u>has broken</u> down.
④ I <u>had met</u> him many times before then.
⑤ Amy lost the key that her aunt <u>had given</u> to her.

[02~03] 다음 우리말을 어법상 알맞게 영작한 것을 고르시오.

02

김구는 그의 희생을 잊지 않기 위해서 그의 시계를 항상 가지고 다녔다.

① Kim Koo always carried his watch so that he won't forget his sacrifice.
② Kim Koo carried his watch so always that he could not forget his sacrifice.
③ Kim Koo carried his watch always so what he should not forget his sacrifice.
④ Kim Koo always carried his watch so that he would not forget his sacrifice.
⑤ Kim Koo often carried his watch so he would not forget his sacrifice always.

03

더위를 잊으려고 우리는 얼음을 먹었다.

① We ate the ice not to forget the heat.
② We ate the ice so that we can forget the heat.
③ We ate the ice in order that forget the heat.
④ We ate the ice so cold that we would forget the heat.
⑤ We ate the ice so that we would forget the heat.

[04~05] 다음 밑줄 친 부분 중 어법상 옳은 것을 고르시오.

04 ① Yujin is hungry because she <u>had not eaten</u> anything so far.
② The crow lived in the jungle before it <u>had moved</u> to the city.
③ Their bodies <u>had been</u> in Japan, but Kim Koo brought them to Korea.
④ Mom required that Jane <u>had finished</u> the dishes.
⑤ For the past five years, I <u>had read</u> your books about the origin of space.

05 ① Billy took his umbrella <u>in order for</u> his wife could use it.
② Justin got up early so that he <u>not being</u> late for the contest.
③ The dolphins were <u>so joy that</u> they could jump above the water.
④ Martha has been saving money for 6 months <u>so to</u> buy a new software.
⑤ Lucy exercised regularly <u>in order that</u> she could reduce stress.

06 다음 두 문장의 의미가 같도록 바꿔 쓸 때 적절하지 <u>않은</u> 것은?

① Kate stood up so that her business partner could find her.
= Kate stood up in order for her business partner to find her.

② Ahn left for America so that he would get a better education.
= Ahn left for America so as to get a better education.

③ Bob made cakes so that he would feel happy.
= Bob made cakes to feel happy.

④ Elizabeth exercises regularly in order for her mom not to get worried.
= Elizabeth exercises regularly so that her mom would not get worried.

⑤ Ted left the meeting quite early not to see his rivals.
= Ted left the meeting quite early, so he could not see his rivals.

07 다음 중 밑줄 친 부분의 쓰임이 〈보기〉와 같은 것은?

┤ 보기 ├
I <u>had</u> already <u>solved</u> the quiz when the teacher called my name.

① Kim Koo <u>had</u> not <u>arrived</u> at the airport when the planes landed.
② Sophia <u>had known</u> him for 10 years when she first found him attractive.
③ The Smiths <u>had lived</u> in Seoul for ten years before they moved to Incheon.
④ Grace <u>had</u> never <u>been</u> ill until last year after the accident.
⑤ Koby <u>had played</u> basketball in America for thirty years since then.

08 다음 문장에서 어법상 어색한 단어 한 개를 찾아서 고치시오.

My cousin has been sick in bed for a week when I visited him.

➡ _____

09 다음 중 주어진 문장과 의미가 <u>다른</u> 것은?

The soldiers trained hard so that they would defeat Japan.

① The soldiers trained hard in order that they would defeat Japan.
② The soldiers trained hard to defeat Japan.
③ The soldiers trained hard so as to defeat Japan.
④ The soldiers trained so hard that they defeated Japan.
⑤ The soldiers trained hard in order to defeat Japan.

10 다음 문장의 밑줄 친 so that의 쓰임이 흐름상 어색한 것은?

① The actor wore sunglasses <u>so that</u> he could hide his face.
② Brian's sisters made some dishes <u>so that</u> they could eat together.
③ Yuna practiced hard <u>so that</u> she could win the piano competition.
④ The boy band performed on the street <u>so that</u> many people could recognize them.
⑤ Irene failed the exam <u>so that</u> she had studied harder than before.

[11~12] 다음 중 어법상 옳은 문장은?

11
① April has never eaten the spice until she visited Vietnam.
② Mom can't see the flower now as my sister had picked it.
③ The students have been sitting for half an hour before the class started.
④ When I met her, Sumin had already completed the assignment.
⑤ My sister found the book that I had been given to her.

12
① My history club went to Hyochang Park so as to visit the Kim Koo Museum.
② Betty practices yoga regularly so as to be stay healthy.
③ John spent most of life in order to that he could be a novelist.
④ I study English so that in order to read many books written in English.
⑤ Mina learned French so that she can watch French movies without subtitles.

13 다음 〈보기〉와 같이 두 문장이 같은 의미가 되도록 주어진 단어를 활용하여 다시 쓰시오.

---보기---
I exercise so as to keep in shape. (that, so)
→ I exercise so that I can keep in shape.

(1) Father Lee Taeseok returned to Sudan to help poor people there. (that, in, could, order)
➡ _____

(2) Amy practices every day to join our sports club. (that, so, can)
➡ _____

(3) Clara left for Paris to study fashion. (that, in, could, order)
➡ _____

(4) Thames ran fast in order not to be late for the meeting. (that, would, so)
➡ _____

14 다음 그림을 보고 자연스러운 문장이 되도록 괄호 안에 주어진 어구를 바르게 배열하여 빈칸을 완성하시오.

(1)

➡ Junsu _____. (the pimples, they, that, disappear, squeezed out, would, so)

(2)

➡ Sudong studied hard _____. (that, in order, a, get, he, college scholarship, could, full)

Grammar **133**

 01 다음 우리말과 일치하도록 괄호 안에 주어진 어구를 바르게 배열하여 문장을 완성하시오.

(1) 간송은 몇몇 일본인들이 일본으로 가져갔었던 한국의 많은 문화재들을 샀다.

➡ Gansong _____

_____.

(Japan, taken, bought, to, that, many, Japanese, Korean treasures, had, some).

(2) 이순신은 사람들을 보호할 수 있게 거북선을 만들었다.

➡ Yi Sunsin _____

_____. (the Turtle Ship, could, the people, that, he, protect, made, so).

(3) 그 도둑은 아무도 들을 수 없도록 천천히 걸었다.

➡ The thief _____

_____. (hear, slowly, one, so, walked, could, him, no, that).

02 다음 그림은 학생들이 문화 유산을 조사하고 만든 미니북과 활동 감상문이다. 빈칸에 들어갈 알맞은 말을 괄호 안의 단어와 완료시제를 활용하여 쓰시오.

Before we made this cultural heritage mini book, we _____ (search) for information about the golden crowns of Silla, Bulguksa, *samullori*, and the Nanjungilgi. After we _____ (make) the book, we learned a lesson that it is important to keep our cultural treasures.

 03 다음 문장에서 어법상 <u>어색한</u> 것을 바르게 고쳐 다시 쓰시오.

(1) Could you remind me of the time so order that I won't be late for the party?

➡ _____

_____

_____

(2) Whenever Jane was ill, her mom used to make her a bowl of porridge in order of her to get well.

➡ _____

_____

(3) They are saving money so which they can buy a big house.

➡ _____

_____

(4) Remember my number in order for you can contact me.

➡ _____

_____

_____

(5) The foreigners from Italy went to Gyeongju so that they can see Bulguksa.

➡ _____

_____

(6) Many people joined the New Korean Society so order to support the Independence movement.

➡ _____

_____

04 괄호 안에 주어진 어구와 글자 수 및 조건을 활용하여, 다음 우리말을 영작하시오.

(1) 우리가 팥빙수를 만들 수 있기 위해서는 얼음과 설탕이 필요하다. (that, so, ice, can, patbingsu, sugar, need, 11 단어)

➡ _____

_____

(2) 그녀가 물고기 몇 마리를 잡도록 해주기 위해서 우리는 강으로 갔다. (could, that, catch, go, so, fish, the river, some, 12 단어)

➡ _____

(3) 그 코알라들을 구조하기 위해 한 소방대원이 숲 속으로 뛰어들었다. (she, rescue, firefighter, the woods, that, so, run, could, into, the koalas, 13 단어)

➡ _____

(4) 나의 할머니는 건강을 유지하도록 매일 운동을 합니다. (can, grandma, every day, exercise, healthy, keep, order that, 12 단어)

➡ _____

_____

고난이도

05 다음 우리말을 주어진 〈조건〉에 맞게 영작하시오.

┤ 조건 ├

1. The old man을 포함, 총 19 단어로 쓸 것.
2. 숫자도 영어로 쓸 것.
3. the official, live alone, in, for, until 등을 활용할 것.

그 공무원이 작년에 방문할 때까지 그 노인은 그 집에서 33년간 혼자 살아왔다.

→ The old man _____

_____

_____ .

06 다음 각 문장의 밑줄 친 부분이 과거완료시제의 용법 중 어떤 것에 해당하는지 〈보기〉에서 찾아 기호를 쓰고 우리말로 해석하시오.

┤ 보기 ├

ⓐ 완료 ⓑ 경험 ⓒ 결과 ⓓ 계속

(1) Peter <u>had</u> already <u>left</u> for New York when I got there. ( )

➡ _____

_____

(2) William <u>had lived</u> in Busan for 14 years until last year. ( )

➡ _____

(3) They <u>had waited</u> for the singer for almost a day before the concert started. ( )

➡ _____

(4) Maria <u>had</u> never <u>seen</u> the snow until she came to Korea this winter. ( )

➡ _____

_____

(5) By the time I arrived at the airport, the check-in <u>had</u> already <u>been</u> completed. ( )

➡ _____

(6) When we came home, we found somebody <u>had broken</u> the window. ( )

➡ _____

_____

(7) I didn't recognize the person because I <u>had</u> never <u>met</u> him before. ( )

➡ _____

_____

(8) When the couple woke up, someone <u>had finished</u> making shoes. ( )

➡ _____

My Wish

Last week my history club went to Hyochang Park. We visited the Kim Koo Museum inside the park. At the entrance of the museum, we saw a white statue of Kim Koo. Kim Koo is a great national hero who spent most of his life fighting for the independence of Korea from Japanese rule. In the 1900s, he helped educate young people by building schools. In 1919, when the independence movement had spread throughout the country, he moved to Shanghai, China. There he joined the Government of the Republic of Korea and later became its president.

The exhibition hall in the museum shows a lot of things about Kim Koo's life. While looking around the hall, we stopped at a photo of the Korean Patriotic Organization's members. Kim Koo formed the secret organization in 1931 to fight against Japan. Lee Bongchang and Yun Bonggil belonged to the group. At one place in the hall, we saw two watches under a photo of Kim Koo and Yun Bonggil. In 1932, Kim Koo made a plan to kill Japanese generals in a park in Shanghai.

entrance: 입구
statue: 동상
independence: 독립
Japanese: 일본의
spread: 퍼지다
throughout: ~의 전체에 걸쳐
government: 정부
republic: 공화국
president: 대통령, 의장
exhibition: 전시
hall: 큰 방, 홀, 현관

📎 **확인문제**

● 다음 문장이 본문의 내용과 일치하면 T, 일치하지 않으면 F를 쓰시오.

1 The history club went to Hyochang Park last month. ☐

2 There is the statue of Kim Koo at the entrance of the park. ☐

3 Kim Koo fought for the independence of Korea from Japanese rule. ☐

4 Yun Bonggil was one of the members of the Korean Patriotic Organization. ☐

As the leader of the Korean Patriotic Organization, he directed Yun to
자격을 나타내는 전치사(~로서)
carry out the mission.
direct+목적어+toV: 목적어가 V할 것을 지시하다

When Yun left for the mission, he told Kim, "Sir, you are wearing a
상해에 있는 한 공원에서 일본 장군들을 암살하는 것
very old watch. Mine is new, but I won't need it anymore. Please take
= My watch
my watch, and let me have yours." Kim Koo always carried Yun's
사역동사+목적어+동사원형(목적어가 V하게 시키다)
watch in his jacket so that he would not forget Yun's sacrifice.
~하기 위해서(목적을 나타내는 구문)

After completing the tour of the museum, we moved to the tombs
동명사(전치사 After의 목적어)
of the three heroes, Lee Bongchang, Yun Bonggil, and Baek Jeonggi.
the three heroes와 동격
Their bodies had been in Japan, but after Korea's independence Kim
김구가 그들의 시신을 가지고 온 것은 과거이며 그 전부터 일본에 있었으므로 과거완료
Koo brought them to Hyochang Park. By doing so, he showed his
일본에 있던 시신들을 한국으로 모셔온 것
deep love and respect for the sacrifice of the three heroes.

As I left Hyochang Park, I thought about Kim Koo's words in

My Wish that I had read in the exhibition hall. It was written in
목적격 관계대명사   My Wish
Baekbeomilji.

If God asks me what my wish is, I would say clearly, "It is Korea's
조건의 부사절을 이끄는 접속사(~라면)
Independence." If he asks me what my second wish is, I would say,
간접의문문(의문사+주어+동사)
"It is the independence of my country." If he asks me what my third
wish is, I would say loudly, "It is the complete independence of my
country." That is my answer.

| direct: 지시하다 |
| carry out: 수행하다 |
| patriotic: 애국적인 |
| organization: 조직 |
| member: 구성원, 회원 |
| general: 장군 |
| leader: 지도자 |
| mission: 임무 |
| belong to: ~에 속하다 |
| sacrifice: 희생; 희생하다 |
| tomb: 무덤 |
| god: 하느님, 신 |
| wish: 소원, 소망 |
| clearly: 분명하게, 확실히 |

확인문제

● 다음 문장이 본문의 내용과 일치하면 T, 일치하지 <u>않으면</u> F를 쓰시오.

1 Kim Koo wanted Yun to give his watch to him. ☐

2 Yun thought he wouldn't need his watch anymore. ☐

3 Kim Koo brought the bodies of the three heroes to Hyochang Park before Korea's

independence. ☐

4 The writer read Kim Koo's words in a newspaper. ☐

5 Kim Koo's one and only wish was the complete independence of the country. ☐

● 우리말을 참고하여 빈칸에 알맞은 말을 쓰시오.

My Wish

1 Last week _____ _____ _____ went to Hyochang Park.

2 We _____ the Kim Koo Museum _____ _____ _____ .

3 _____ the _____ of the museum, we saw a white statue of Kim Koo.

4 Kim Koo is _____ _____ _____ _____ who _____ most of his life fighting for the independence of Korea _____ Japanese rule.

5 In the 1900s, he _____ _____ young people _____ _____ schools.

6 _____ 1919, _____ _____ _____ _____ had spread throughout the country, he _____ _____ Shanghai, China.

7 There he _____ the Government of the Republic of Korea and later _____ _____ _____ .

8 _____ _____ _____ in the museum _____ a lot of things about Kim Koo's life.

9 While _____ _____ the hall, we _____ _____ a photo of the Korean _____ _____ members.

10 Kim Koo _____ the secret _____ in 1931 _____ _____ _____ Japan.

11 Lee Bongchang and Yun Bonggil _____ _____ the group.

12 _____ one place in the hall, we _____ _____ _____ under a photo of Kim Koo and Yun Bonggil.

나의 소원

1 지난주에 우리 역사 동아리는 효창 공원에 갔다.

2 우리는 공원 안에 있는 김구 기념관을 방문했다.

3 기념관 입구에서 우리는 하얀색의 김구 조각상을 보았다.

4 김구는 일본 통치로부터 대한의 독립을 위해 싸우는 데 그의 삶 대부분을 보낸 위대한 국민 영웅이다.

5 1900년대에 그는 학교를 설립함으로써 젊은이들을 교육시키는 것을 도왔다.

6 1919년에 3.1 운동이 나라 전체에 걸쳐 퍼져나갔을 때, 그는 중국 상하이로 이동했다.

7 그곳에서 그는 대한민국 임시정부에 합류했고 나중에는 그것의 대표자가 되었다.

8 기념관 안에 있는 전시관은 김구의 삶에 관한 많은 것들을 보여 준다.

9 우리는 전시관을 둘러보면서 한인 애국단의 단원들 사진 앞에 섰다.

10 김구는 일본에 맞서 싸우기 위해 1931년에 비밀 조직을 형성했다.

11 이봉창과 윤봉길이 그 집단에 속해 있었다.

12 전시관의 한 곳에서, 우리는 김구와 윤봉길의 사진 아래에 있는 시계 두 개를 보았다.

13 _____ 1932, Kim Koo _____ _____ _____ kill Japanese generals in a park in Shanghai.

14 As the leader of the Korean _____ _____, he _____ Yun _____ _____ out the mission.

15 When Yun _____ _____ the mission, he told Kim, "Sir, you are _____ _____ _____ _____ _____. _____ is new, but I won't need _____ anymore. Please _____ my watch, and _____ me _____ yours."

16 Kim Koo _____ _____ Yun's watch in his jacket _____ _____ he would not _____ Yun's _____.

17 After _____ the tour of the museum, we _____ _____ the _____ of the three heroes, Lee Bongchang, Yun Bonggil, and Baek Jeonggi.

18 Their bodies _____ _____ in Japan, but after Korea's _____ Kim Koo brought _____ to Hyochang Park.

19 _____ _____ _____, he showed his deep love and respect _____ _____ _____ of the three heroes.

20 _____ I _____ Hyochang Park, I thought about Kim Koo's _____ in My Wish _____ I _____ _____ in the exhibition hall.

21 _____ was _____ _____ _Baekbeomilji._

22 If God asks me _____ _____ _____ _____ _____, I would say clearly, "It is _____ _____."

23 If he asks me _____ _____ _____ _____ is, I would say, "It is the _____ of my country."

24 If he _____ _____ _____ _____ _____ _____, I would say loudly, "It is the _____ of my country." That is my answer.

13 1932년에 김구는 상해에 있는 한 공원에서 일본 장군들을 암살하기 위한 계획을 세웠다.

14 한인 애국단의 지도자로서 그는 윤봉길이 임무를 수행하도록 지시했다.

15 윤봉길이 임무를 위해 떠날 때, 그는 김구에게 말했다. "선생님, 당신은 매우 낡은 시계를 차고 계시는군요. 제 것은 새것이나, 저는 그것이 더 이상 필요하지 않을 것입니다. 부디 제 시계를 가져가시고, 제가 선생님 것을 가지도록 해주십시오."

16 김구는 윤봉길의 희생을 잊지 않기 위해서 윤봉길의 시계를 항상 상의에 넣고 다녔다.

17 기념관 관람을 마치고, 우리는 이봉창, 윤봉길, 그리고 백정기 의사들이 묻힌 삼의사의 묘로 이동했다.

18 그들의 시신은 일본에 있다가 독립이 되고 나서 김구가 그들의 시신을 효창 공원으로 가져왔다.

19 그는 그렇게 함으로써 삼의사들의 희생에 대한 그의 깊은 사랑과 경의를 보여 주었다.

20 내가 효창 공원을 떠날 때, 나는 전시관에서 읽었던 「나의 소원」에 있는 김구의 말을 생각했다.

21 그것은 「백범일지」에 쓰여 있었다.

22 만약 신이 나의 소원이 무엇이냐고 묻는다면, "그것은 대한 독립이오."라고 명확하게 말할 것이다.

23 만약에 그가 나의 두 번째 소원이 무엇이냐고 묻는다면, 나는 "그것은 내 나라의 독립이오."라고 말할 것이다.

24 만약 그가 나의 세 번째 소원이 무엇이냐고 묻는다면, "그것은 내 나라의 완전한 독립이오."라고 큰 소리로 말할 것이다. 그것이 나의 대답이다.

● 우리말을 참고하여 본문을 영작하시오.

1 지난주에 우리 역사 동아리는 효창 공원에 갔다.

➡ _____

2 우리는 공원 안에 있는 김구 기념관을 방문했다.

➡ _____

3 기념관 입구에서 우리는 하얀색의 김구 조각상을 보았다.

➡ _____

4 김구는 일본 통치로부터 대한의 독립을 위해 싸우는 데 그의 삶 대부분을 보낸 위대한 국민 영웅이다.

➡ _____

_____

5 1900년대에 그는 학교를 설립함으로써 젊은이들을 교육시키는 것을 도왔다.

➡ _____

6 1919년에 3.1 운동이 나라 전체에 걸쳐 퍼져나갔을 때, 그는 중국 상하이로 이동했다.

➡ _____

_____

7 그곳에서 그는 대한민국 임시정부에 합류했고 나중에는 그것의 대표자가 되었다.

➡ _____

8 기념관 안에 있는 전시관은 김구의 삶에 관한 많은 것들을 보여 준다.

➡ _____

9 우리는 전시관을 둘러보면서 한인 애국단의 단원들 사진 앞에 섰다.

➡ _____

10 김구는 일본에 맞서 싸우기 위해 1931년에 비밀 조직을 형성했다.

➡ _____

11 이봉창과 윤봉길이 그 집단에 속해 있었다.

➡ _____

12 전시관의 한 곳에서, 우리는 김구와 윤봉길의 사진 아래에 있는 시계 두 개를 보았다.

➡ _____

13 1932년에 김구는 상해에 있는 한 공원에서 일본 장군들을 암살하기 위한 계획을 세웠다.

➡ _____

14 한인 애국단의 지도자로서 그는 윤봉길이 임무를 수행하도록 지시했다.

➡ _____

15 윤봉길이 임무를 위해 떠날 때, 그는 김구에게 말했다. "선생님, 당신은 매우 낡은 시계를 차고 계시는군요. 제 것은 새것이나, 저는 그것이 더 이상 필요하지 않을 것입니다. 부디 제 시계를 가져가시고, 제가 선생님 것을 가지도록 해주십시오."

➡ _____

_____

16 김구는 윤봉길의 희생을 잊지 않기 위해서 윤봉길의 시계를 항상 상의에 넣고 다녔다.

➡ _____

17 기념관 관람을 마치고, 우리는 이봉창, 윤봉길, 그리고 백정기 의사들이 묻힌 삼의사의 묘로 이동했다.

➡ _____

18 그들의 시신은 일본에 있다가 독립이 되고 나서 김구가 그들의 시신을 효창 공원으로 가져왔다.

➡ _____

_____

19 그는 그렇게 함으로써 삼의사들의 희생에 대한 그의 깊은 사랑과 경의를 보여 주었다.

➡ _____

20 내가 효창 공원을 떠날 때, 나는 전시관에서 읽었던 「나의 소원」에 있는 김구의 말을 생각했다.

➡ _____

_____

21 그것은 『백범일지』에 쓰여 있었다.

➡ _____

22 만약 신이 나의 소원이 무엇이냐고 묻는다면, "그것은 대한 독립이오."라고 명확하게 말할 것이다.

➡ _____

23 만약에 그가 나의 두 번째 소원이 무엇이냐고 묻는다면, 나는 "그것은 내 나라의 독립이오."라고 말할 것이다.

➡ _____

24 만약 그가 나의 세 번째 소원이 무엇이냐고 묻는다면, "그것은 내 나라의 완전한 독립이오."라고 큰 소리로 말할 것이다. 그것이 나의 대답이다.

➡ _____

_____

[01~04] 다음 글을 읽고 물음에 답하시오.

Last week my history club went to Hyochang Park. We visited the Kim Koo Museum inside the park. At the entrance of the museum, we saw a white statue of Kim Koo. Kim Koo is a great national hero who spent most of his life fighting for the independence of Korea from Japanese rule. In the 1900s, he helped educate young people (A)_____ building schools. In 1919, when the independence movement had spread throughout the country, he moved to Shanghai, China. There he joined the Government of the Republic of Korea and later became its president.

01 다음 중 빈칸 (A)에 들어갈 말로 가장 적절한 것은?

① about ② by ③ at
④ on ⑤ to

02 Choose the one that is CORRECT about Kim Koo.

① He used to live near Hyochang park.
② He built a museum for independence of Korea.
③ He spent most of his life fighting for Japan.
④ He built schools to educate young people.
⑤ He lived in Korea all his life.

서답형
03 Where is the statue of Kim Koo? Answer in English with eight words.

➡ _____

서답형
04 When did Kim Koo move to Shanghai? Answer in English with six words.

➡ _____

[05~08] 다음 글을 읽고 물음에 답하시오.

The exhibition hall in the museum shows a lot of things about Kim Koo's life. While looking around the hall, we stopped at a photo of the Korean Patriotic Organization's members. Kim Koo formed the secret organization in 1931 to fight against Japan. Lee Bongchang and Yun Bonggil belonged to the group. At one place in the hall, we saw two watches under a photo of Kim Koo and Yun Bonggil. In 1932, Kim Koo made a plan to kill Japanese generals in a park in Shanghai. As the leader of the Korean Patriotic Organization, he directed Yun to carry out the mission.

When Yun left for the mission, he told Kim, "Sir, you are wearing a very old watch. Mine is new, but I won't need it anymore. Please take my watch, and let me have yours." Kim Koo always carried Yun's watch in his jacket so that he would not forget Yun's sacrifice.

05 다음 중 기념관 내 전시관에서 찾아볼 수 있는 것을 모두 고르시오.

① many books about Kim Koo's life
② a photo of the Korean Patriotic Organization's members
③ the statues of Lee Bongchang and Yun Bonggil
④ two watches which belonged to Yun Bonggil and Kim Koo
⑤ a photo of Kim Koo with his family

서답형

06 Where did Kim Koo plan to kill Japanese generals? Answer in English with twelve words.

➡ _____

_____

07 다음 중 위 글을 읽고 답할 수 있는 것은?

① Where was Kim Koo born?

② How many exhibition halls are there in the museum?

③ How many members were there in the Korean Patriotic Organization?

④ What did Kim Koo form in 1931?

⑤ When did Kim Koo and Yun Bonggil take the picture?

중요

08 다음 중 위 글의 내용을 바르게 이해한 사람은?

① Amelia: It is hard to know many things about Kim Koo at the exhibition hall.

② Brian: It is surprising that Kim Koo didn't join the Korean Patriotic Organization.

③ Claire: I'm so sorry Yun didn't leave for the mission.

④ David: Yun was the leader of the Korean Patriotic Organization.

⑤ Ethon: It's so touching that Kim Koo always carried Yun's watch.

[09~11] 다음 글을 읽고 물음에 답하시오.

(A) By doing so, he showed his deep love and respect for the sacrifice of the three heroes.

(B) Their bodies had been in Japan, but after Korea's independence Kim Koo brought them to Hyochang Park.

(C) After completing the tour of the museum, we moved to the tombs of the three heroes, Lee Bongchang, Yun Bonggil, and Baek Jeonggi.

As I left Hyochang Park, I thought about Kim Koo's words in My Wish ⓐ_____ I had read in the exhibition hall. It was written in *Baekbeomilji*.

If God asks me what my wish is, I would say clearly, "It is Korea's Independence." If he asks me what my second wish is, I would say, "It is the independence of my country." If he asks me what my third wish is, I would say loudly, "It is the complete independence of my country." That is my answer.

09 다음 중 빈칸 ⓐ에 들어갈 말로 적절한 것을 모두 고르시오.

① which   ② whose   ③ that

④ what   ⑤ who

중요

10 자연스러운 글이 되도록 (A)~(C)를 바르게 나열한 것은?

① (A)–(C)–(B)   ② (B)–(A)–(C)

③ (B)–(C)–(A)   ④ (C)–(A)–(B)

⑤ (C)–(B)–(A)

서답형

11 주어진 어구를 바르게 나열하여 다음 물음에 대한 답을 완성하시오.

Q: What was written in *Baekbeomilji*?

A: (*Baekbeomilji* / Korea / written / of / independence / in / for / the / Kim Koo's / complete / firm wish / was)

➡ _____

_____

[12~15] 다음 글을 읽고 물음에 답하시오.

Last week my history club went to Hyochang Park. We visited the Kim Koo Museum inside the park. At the entrance of the museum, we saw a white statue of Kim Koo. Kim Koo is a great national hero who spent most of his life fighting for the independence of Korea from Japanese rule. In the 1900s, he helped educate young people by building schools. In 1919, when the independence movement had spread throughout the country, he moved to Shanghai, China. There he joined the Government of the Republic of Korea and later became its president.

서답형
12 위 글의 내용에 맞게 빈칸에 알맞은 말을 쓰시오.

> The history club went to Hyochang Park in order to _____ _____ _____
> _____ _____ _____
> _____.

13 다음 중 효창 공원에서 찾아볼 수 있는 것은?
① the school Kim Koo built for young people
② the pictures of young people taught by Kim Koo
③ a picture of independence movement
④ a large white sculpture of Kim Koo
⑤ a museum Kim Koo built

서답형
14 According to the passage, what did Kim Koo fight for? Answer in English with a full sentence.

➡ _____
_____

중요
15 다음 중 위 글을 읽고 답할 수 없는 것은?
① Where is the Kim Koo Museum?
② What did the writer's history club do last week?
③ How did Kim Koo help educate young people?
④ How did the club go to the Hyochang Park?
⑤ When did the independence movement spread throughout the country?

[16~18] 다음 글을 읽고 물음에 답하시오.

The exhibition hall in the museum shows ① a lot of things about Kim Koo's life. While looking ②after the hall, we stopped ③at a photo of the Korean Patriotic Organization's members. Kim Koo ④formed the secret organization in 1931 to fight against Japan. Lee Bongchang and Yun Bonggil ⑤belonged to the group. At one place in the hall, we saw two watches under a photo of Kim Koo and Yun Bonggil.

16 다음과 같이 풀이되는 말을 위 글에서 찾아 쓰시오.

> a public event at which pictures, sculptures, or other objects of interest are displayed

➡ _____

17 밑줄 친 ①~⑤ 중 글의 흐름상 어색한 것은?

①   ②   ③   ④   ⑤

서답형
18 What were there under a photo of Kim Koo and Yun Bonggil?

➡ _____

[19~21] 다음 글을 읽고 물음에 답하시오.

In 1932, ①Kim Koo made a plan to kill Japanese generals in a park in Shanghai. (A)As the leader of the Korean Patriotic Organization, ②he directed Yun to carry out the mission. When ③he left for the mission, Yun told Kim, "Sir, ④you are wearing a very old watch. Mine is new, but I won't need (B) it anymore. Please take my watch, and let me have yours." Kim Koo always carried Yun's watch in ⑤his jacket so that he would not forget Yun's sacrifice.

19 밑줄 친 ①~⑤ 중 가리키는 것이 <u>다른</u> 하나는?

①   ②   ③   ④   ⑤

20 다음 중 밑줄 친 (A)와 쓰임이 같은 것은?

① They were all dressed as clowns.

② You are as kind as your father.

③ As they were out, I left a message.

④ As you know, Susan is leaving soon.

⑤ We look up to him as a doctor.

서답형
21 밑줄 친 (B)가 의미하는 것을 두 단어의 영어로 쓰시오.

➡ _____

[22~25] 다음 글을 읽고 물음에 답하시오.

After completing the tour of the museum, we moved to the tombs of the three heroes, Lee Bongchang, Yun Bonggil, and Baek Jeonggi. ①Their bodies had been in Japan, but after Korea's ②independence Kim Koo brought them to Hyochang Park. By doing so, he showed his deep love and respect for the ③sacrifice of the three heroes.

As I left Hyochang Park, I thought about Kim Koo's words in My Wish that I had read in the exhibition hall. It was written in *Baekbeomilji*.

If God asks me what my wish is, I would say clearly, "It is Korea's Independence." If he asks me what my second wish is, I would say, "It is the independence of my country." If he asks me what my third wish is, I would say loudly, "It is the ④complement independence of my country." That is my ⑤answer.

22 밑줄 친 ①~⑤ 중 글의 흐름상 <u>어색한</u> 것은?

①   ②   ③   ④   ⑤

23 According to the passage, what did Kim Koo wish most?

① respect from people

② reliance on Japan

③ achieving independence of Korea

④ making Korea a rich country

⑤ making Korea dependent

24 Choose the sentence that is TRUE according to the passage.

① They have just started touring the museum.

② It is uncertain who were buried in the tombs.

③ Kim Koo brought the bodies before Korea's independence.

④ Kim Koo hardly loved the three heroes.

⑤ It was Kim Koo who brought three heroes' bodies into Korea from Japan.

서답형
25 Where are Kim Koo's words written? Answer in English with a full sentence.

➡ _____

[01~05] 다음 글을 읽고 물음에 답하시오.

Last week my history club went to Hyochang Park. We visited the Kim Koo Museum inside the park. At the entrance of the museum, we saw a white statue of Kim Koo. Kim Koo is a great national hero who spent most of his life fighting for the independence of Korea from Japanese rule. In the 1900s, he helped educate young people by building schools. In 1919, when the independence movement had spread throughout the country, he moved to Shanghai, China. (A) There he joined the Government of the Republic of Korea and later became its president.

01 밑줄 친 (A)가 가리키는 것을 위 글에서 찾아 쓰시오.

➡ _____

02 Where did the writer's history club go last week? Answer in English and use the word 'they.'

➡ _____

03 What was there at the entrance of the museum?

➡ _____
_____

04 Where was the Government of the Republic of Korea? Answer in English with a full sentence.

➡ _____

05 위 글의 내용에 맞게 빈칸에 알맞은 말을 쓰시오.

Kim Koo(1876~1949)
He is a great _____ who fought for _____ from Japanese rule.

[06~08] 다음 글을 읽고 물음에 답하시오.

The exhibition hall in the museum shows a lot of things about Kim Koo's life. While looking around the hall, we stopped at a photo of the Korean Patriotic Organization's members. Kim Koo formed the secret organization in 1931 to fight against Japan. Lee Bongchang and Yun Bonggil belonged to the group. At one place in the hall, we saw two watches under a photo of Kim Koo and Yun Bonggil.

06 Whose photo did the writer see?

➡ _____
_____

07 Write the reason why Kim Koo formed the secret organization in 1931. Use the phrase 'It was because' and 'try to.'

➡ _____

08 위 글의 내용에 맞게 빈칸에 알맞은 말을 쓰시오.

A: Do you know who _____ _____ _____ _____ that Kim Koo formed?
B: Yes, I do. Lee Bongchang and Yun Bonggil did.

[09~11] 다음 글을 읽고 물음에 답하시오.

In 1932, Kim Koo made a plan to kill Japanese generals in a park in Shanghai. As the leader of the Korean Patriotic Organization, he directed Yun to carry out the mission.

When Yun left for the mission, he told Kim, "Sir, you are wearing a very old watch. Mine is new, but I won't need it anymore. Please take my watch, and let me have yours." Kim Koo always carried Yun's watch in his jacket so that he would not forget Yun's sacrifice.

09 What was Kim Koo's plan? Answer in English with a full sentence.

➡ _____

_____

10 위 글의 내용에 맞게 빈칸에 들어갈 알맞은 말을 쓰시오.

In 1932, Yun _____ _____ with Kim Koo before he left to carry out the mission Kim Koo directed.

11 Write the reason why Kim Koo always carried Yun's watch in his jacket. Use the phrase 'It was because.'

➡ _____

[12~15] 다음 글을 읽고 물음에 답하시오.

After completing the tour of the museum, we moved to the tombs of the three heroes, Lee Bongchang, Yun Bonggil, and Baek Jeonggi. Their bodies had been in Japan, but after Korea's independence Kim Koo brought them

to Hyochang Park. By (A)doing so, he showed his deep love and respect for the sacrifice of the three heroes.

As I left Hyochang Park, I thought about Kim Koo's words in My Wish that I had read in the exhibition hall. It was written in *Baekbeomilji*.
If God asks me what my wish is, I would say clearly, "It is Korea's Independence." If he asks me what my second wish is, I would say, "It is the independence of my country." If he asks me what my third wish is, I would say loudly, "It is the complete independence of my country." That is my answer.

12 After they completed the tour of the museum, what did they do? Answer in English with a full sentence.

➡ _____

_____

13 밑줄 친 (A)가 의미하는 것을 우리말로 쓰시오.

➡ _____

14 Where did the writer read My Wish? Answer in English with seven words.

➡ _____

15 According to the passage, what was Kim Koo's third wish? Answer in English with a full sentence.

➡ _____

_____

Real Life Talk Step 3

My group members chose An Junggeun because we were impressed by his
choose의 과거형(choose–chose–chosen) · ~에 깊은 인상을 받았다
sacrifice for the country. You can learn more about him by visiting the An
by+Ving: V함으로써
Junggeun Museum or An Junggeun Park.

구문해설 · choose: 선택하다 · sacrifice: ~을 희생하다

해석

우리 그룹은 안중근을 선택했는데, 우리 나라를 위한 희생에 깊은 인상을 받았기 때문입니다. 여러분은 안중근 기념관이나 안중근 공원을 방문함으로써 그에 관하여 더 많은 것을 알 수 있습니다.

Enjoy Writing

Dosan An Changho

An Changho was born in 1878. When he was in his teens, he moved to Seoul
and went to school there. In 1902, he left for America so that he could get
= in Seoul   '목적' ~하기 위해서 = in order that he could
a better education. In America, An helped improve the lives of the Korean
= helped to improve   life의 복수형
people there and became a respected leader. After he had returned to Korea, he
people there = people (who were) there   과거완료시제
founded the New Korean Society in 1907 to fight for Korea's independence.

He also joined the Government of the Republic of Korea in Shanghai in 1919.
타동사(전치사 불필요)
After that, he built a lot of schools to educate people until he died in 1938.
부사적 용법(목적) = so that he could educate   접속사('~할 때까지')

구문해설 · in one's teens: 10대 시절에 · respected: 존경받는 · the New Korean Society: 신민회
· republic: 공화국

도산 안창호

안창호는 1878년에 태어났다. 그가 십 대였을 때, 그는 서울로 이사를 하고 그곳에서 학교를 다녔다. 1902년에 그는 더 나은 교육을 받기 위해서 미국으로 떠났다. 안창호는 미국에서 한국인들의 삶을 개선하는 것을 도왔고, 존경받는 지도자가 되었다. 그가 한국으로 돌아오고 나서, 그는 대한의 독립을 위해 싸우고자 1907년에 신민회를 설립했다. 그는 또한 1919년에 상해의 대한민국 임시정부에 합류했다. 그 후에, 그는 1938년에 죽을 때까지 사람들을 교육하기 위해 많은 학교들을 세웠다.

Project Step 1

A: I want to introduce Bulguksa to foreigners. You know Bulguksa, don't you?
일반동사 긍정문의 부가의문문

B: Yes, I do. It's a temple in Gyeongju.
= Bulguksa

C: Yes. It's one of the most beautiful temples in Korea.
one of the 최상급+복수명사: 가장 ~한 것들 중 하나

D: It also has many treasures like the Dabotop.
many+복수명사   전치사: ~와 같은

구문해설 · introduce: 소개하다 · foreigner: 외국인 · temple: 사원, 절 · treasure: 보물

A: 나는 외국인에게 불국사를 소개하고 싶어. 너는 불국사를 알고 있지, 그렇지 않니?

B: 응. 알고 있어. 그것은 경주에 있는 절이야.

C: 응. 그것은 한국에서 가장 아름다운 절 중 하나야.

D: 그것은 또한 다보탑과 같은 많은 문화재들을 보유하고 있어.

Words & Expressions

01 다음 주어진 두 단어의 관계가 같도록 빈칸에 알맞은 단어를 쓰시오.

independence - dependence : exit - _____

02 다음 문장의 빈칸 (A)와 (B)에 들어갈 단어가 바르게 짝지어진 것은?

• I want to work for international (A) _____ such as the UN.
• There is no love without (B) _____ .

① harmony – rule
② statue – dependence
③ specialist – desire
④ leader – member
⑤ organization – sacrifice

[03~04] 다음 영영풀이에 해당하는 것을 고르시오.

03

a piece of cloth that is usually attached at the end of a pole and represents a country or association

① hall   ② exhibition
③ flag   ④ tomb
⑤ god

04

a series of things that happen one after another for a particular result

① process   ② republic
③ wish   ④ president
⑤ poem

05 다음 빈칸에 주어진 철자를 이용하여 한 단어를 쓰시오.

The museum is staging an e_____ of Picasso's works.

06 다음 밑줄 친 부분의 뜻이 잘못된 것은?

① The main part of the building is crowded with people. (주요한)
② Koreans celebrate Independence Day on August 15th. (독립)
③ The government made a new policy. (정부)
④ He had no desire to discuss the matter further. (안건)
⑤ The queen wears a crown only on certain official events. (왕관)

Conversation

07 다음 대화의 빈칸에 들어갈 말을 주어진 어구를 알맞은 순서로 배열하여 완성하시오.

G: I'm planning to go to the Gansong Museum.
B: What is the Gansong Museum?
G: It's a museum built by Gansong Jeon Hyeongpil.
B: I heard that he did great things for the country.
G: Yes. _____
_____
B: Wow. The museum must be interesting.
G: Yes. I'm looking forward to it!

some Japanese / many Korean treasures / he / had taken / bought / that / to Japan

08 그림을 보고 다음 대화의 빈칸을 완성하시오.

G: I'm making a model of the Turtle Ship. _____ _____ about it, _____ you?

B: Yes, I know about it.

[09~11] 다음 대화를 읽고 물음에 답하시오.

Andy: Bora, what are you reading?

Bora: I'm reading *Sky, Wind, Star, and Poetry* by Yun Dongju. You know about Yun Dongju, don't you?

Andy: I've heard his name, but I don't know much about him. (①)

Bora: He wrote many beautiful poems when Korea was under Japanese rule. His love for the country and his desire for independence can be felt in his poems.

Andy: (②) I want to read his poems and learn more about him.

Bora: Great. (③) In fact, I'm planning to visit the Yun Dongju Museum soon. Do you want to come with me?

Andy: Yes, when are you going?

Bora: Next Saturday. It's near Gyeongbok Palace. (④) Can you meet me at the palace at 2 p.m.?

Andy: Sure. Let's meet there. (⑤)

Bora: Great. I'm really looking forward to the visit.

09 위 대화의 (①)~(⑤) 중 주어진 문장이 들어갈 위치로 알맞은 것은?

Really? I didn't know that.

①   ②   ③   ④   ⑤

10 위 대화를 읽고 다음 물음에 영어로 답하시오.

Q: What are they planning to do next Saturday?

➡ _____

11 위 대화의 내용과 일치하지 않는 것은?

① Bora is reading a poem by Yun Dongju.
② Andy doesn't know much about Yun Dongju.
③ Bora suggested to Andy that he should read many poems by Yun Dongju.
④ Bora may have felt Yun Dongju's love for the country and his desire for independence.
⑤ Andy is looking forward to visiting the Yun Dongju Museum.

Grammar

[12~13] 다음 중 어법상 어색한 문장을 고르시오.

12
① Would you share your recipe so that we can make a good dish like yours?
② Sam learned the computer science so as to develop much better devices.
③ Prepare rice and water so that you can make Juk, the Korean porridge.
④ Tim got up early so as not to miss the bus.
⑤ Isabelle practiced hard so that for her to get a scholarship.

13 ① All my family were really full because we had had lunch.

② Betty had read comic books before she went to bed.

③ Yesterday, my wife lost the necklace that my son had bought for her two days before.

④ When the singer arrived at the show, the opening part had just began.

⑤ Susan wasn't able to recognize him, because she had never seen him before.

14 다음 두 문장의 의미가 같도록 바꿔 쓸 때 적절하지 <u>않은</u> 것은?

① Jenny cleaned the house so that the guests could feel comfortable.

= Jenny cleaned the house for the guests to feel comfortable.

② Robert makes pancakes in order that his five kids can eat.

= Robert makes pancakes so that his five kids can eat.

③ The young college students held the thief tight so that he could not run away.

= The young college students held the thief tight in order not for him to run away.

④ Nancy practiced her movement really hard in order to pass the audition.

= Nancy practiced her movement really hard so that she might pass the audition.

⑤ Daeho went to Tokyo so that he could learn Japanese.

= Daeho went to Tokyo in order to learn Japanese.

15 다음 그림을 보고 괄호 안의 단어를 배열하여 빈칸을 알맞게 채우시오.

(1)

➡ The students are practicing hard _____ _____ _____ _____ _____ a good performance. (show, so, can, they, that)

(2)

➡ Many tourists gathered at the Louvre Museum _____ _____ _____ _____ _____. (the *Mona Lisa*, they, that, so, could, see)

16 다음 괄호 안에서 어법상 알맞은 것을 고르시오.

(1) An Junggeun was sentenced to death after he (had killed / has killed) Ito Hirobumi.

(2) Some of the K-pop fans around the world said that they (have been / had been) learning Korean to understand the lyrics of the songs clearly.

(3) Yesterday I learned that Kim Koo (had made / made) a plan to kill Japanese generals in Shanghai in 1932.

(4) The queen (has gone / had gone) to London before the prince got injured at the car accident.

(5) Sven dropped the carrot that Olaf (had pulled / has pulled) out of the field in the snow.

17 다음 그림을 참고하여 〈보기〉에 주어진 어구를 우리말과 일치하도록 어법상 알맞은 형태로 바꿔 배열하시오. (모든 단어를 한 번 이상 사용할 것.)

> ┌ 보기 ┐
> the rabbit, the ant, the grasshopper, she, he, regretted, reminded, play, sleep, in, that, the middle of, the summer, the race

(1) 토끼는 경주 도중에 잤던 것을 후회했다.
(2) 개미는 베짱이가 여름에 놀았던 것을 일깨워줬다.

(1)

➡ _____

_____

(2)

➡ _____

_____

Reading

[18~20] 다음 글을 읽고 물음에 답하시오.

Last week my history club went to Hyochang Park. ① At the entrance of the museum, we saw a white statue of Kim Koo. ② Kim Koo is a great national hero who spent most of his life fighting for the independence of Korea from Japanese rule. ③ In the 1900s, he helped educate young people by building schools. ④ In 1919,

when the independence movement had spread throughout the country, he moved to Shanghai, China. ⑤ There he joined the Government of the Republic of Korea and later became its president.

18 ①~⑤ 중 주어진 문장이 들어가기에 가장 적절한 곳은?

> We visited the Kim Koo Museum inside the park.

①   ②   ③   ④   ⑤

19 Write the reason why Kim Koo built schools. Use the phrase 'in order to.'

➡ _____

_____

20 다음 중 위 글의 내용과 일치하는 것은?

① The history club went to Hyochang Park a couple of weeks ago.
② The statue of Kim Koo is at the entrance of the park.
③ Kim Koo spent most of his life educating young people.
④ The independence movement spread throughout the country until 1900s.
⑤ Kim Koo joined the Government of the Republic Korea in China.

[21~24] 다음 글을 읽고 물음에 답하시오.

An Changho was born in 1878. When he was in his teens, he moved to Seoul and went to school there. In 1902, he left for America ①so that he could get a better education. In America,

An helped ②improve the lives of the Korean people there and became a ③respecting leader. After he ④had returned to Korea, he founded the New Korean Society in 1907 to fight for Korea's independence. He also joined the Government of the Republic of Korea in Shanghai in 1919. After that, he built a lot of schools ⑤to educate people until he died in 1938.

21 ①~⑤ 중 문맥상 바르지 <u>않은</u> 것은?

①   ②   ③   ④   ⑤

22 다음 중 위 글의 내용과 일치하지 <u>않는</u> 곳을 찾아 바르게 고쳐 쓰시오.

> An Changho was born in Korea and left for America in his twenties. After spending some time in America, he returned to Korea and found the New Korean Society in 1907 in order to fight for Korea's independence.

➡ _____

23 다음 중 위 글을 읽고 답할 수 <u>없는</u> 것은?

① When was An Changho born?
② When did An Changho leave for America?
③ What did An Chanho do in America?
④ How many schools did An Changho build?
⑤ What did An Changho do until he died?

[24~26] 다음 글을 읽고 물음에 답하시오.

The exhibition hall in the museum shows (A) <u>a lot of</u> things about Kim Koo's life. While looking around the hall, we stopped at a photo of the Korean Patriotic Organization's members. Kim Koo formed the secret organization in 1931 to fight against Japan. Lee Bongchang and Yun Bonggil belonged to the group. At one place in the hall, we saw two watches under a photo of Kim Koo and Yun Bonggil. In 1932, Kim Koo made a plan to kill Japanese generals in a park in Shanghai. As the leader of the Korean Patriotic Organization, he directed Yun to carry out the mission.

24 다음 중 밑줄 친 (A)를 대신하여 쓰일 수 <u>없는</u> 것은?

① lots of   ② many
③ a number of   ④ the number of
⑤ plenty of

25 According to the passage, when did Kim Koo form the Korean Patriotic Organization?

➡ _____
    _____

26 According to the passage, choose the sentence that is TRUE.

① The Korean Patriotic Organization was a public organization.
② Kim Koo formed an organization to fight for Japan.
③ Lee Bongchang was the only member of the Korean Patriotic Organization.
④ Kim Koo planned to kill Japanese generals in a park in Korea.
⑤ Kim Koo directed Yun Bonggil to kill Japanese generals.

01 다음 짝지어진 단어의 관계가 같도록 빈칸에 알맞은 말을 쓰시오.

> complete – incomplete : deep – _____

02 다음 영영풀이에 해당하는 단어는?

> a circular ornament made of gold and decorated with jewels that is worn by a king or queen on their head

① device
② clown
③ crown
④ couch
⑤ hall

[03~04] 다음 대화를 읽고 물음에 답하시오.

B: Soyeon, what did you do last weekend?
G: I went to Hyeonchungwon to do volunteer work.
B: What kind of volunteer work did you do there?
G: I cleaned around the tombs. (A)나는 나라를 위해 돌아가신 분들에게 대단한 경의를 느꼈어.
B: Sounds great. Can I do it, too?
G: Sure. I'm planning to go there again next Wednesday. Will you join me?
B: Sure. I'm looking forward to it.

03 위 대화의 밑줄 친 (A)의 우리말에 맞게 주어진 어구를 알맞은 순서로 배열하시오.

> I / for the country / who / felt / for the people / died / great respect

➡ _____

04 위 대화의 내용과 일치하지 <u>않는</u> 것은?

① Soyeon did volunteer work in the museum.
② Soyeon felt respect while doing volunteer work.
③ Soyeon cleaned around the tombs.
④ Soyeon is planning to go there again next Wednesday.
⑤ Both Soyeon and the boy will go to Hyeonchungwon together.

[05~06] 다음 대화를 읽고 물음에 답하시오.

G: Brian, you know Taegeukgi, don't you?
B: Sure. It's the national flag of Korea, isn't it?
G: That's right. (A)_____
B: No, I don't. Tell me about them.
G: The circle in the middle means (B) _____ and peace.
B: What do the black lines on the four corners mean?
G: They mean four things: sky, fire, water, and earth.

05 위 대화의 빈칸 (A)에 들어갈 말로 알맞은 것은?

① What do you know about Taegeukgi?
② Can you draw Taegeukgi?
③ Do you know the origin of Taegeukgi?
④ Do you know what the symbols in Taegeukgi mean?
⑤ Do you know who made Taegeukgi?

06 위 대화의 빈칸 (B)에 들어갈 단어를 <영영풀이>를 참고하여 쓰시오.

<영영풀이>

a situation in which people are peaceful and agree with each other, or when things seem right or suitable together

➡ _____

[07~08] 다음 대화를 읽고 물음에 답하시오.

Andy: Bora, what are you reading?

Bora: I'm reading *Sky, Wind, Star, and Poetry* by Yun Dongju. (A)너는 윤동주에 대해 알고 있지, 그렇지 않니?

Andy: I've heard his name, but I don't know much about him.

Bora: He wrote many beautiful poems when Korea was under Japanese rule. His love for the country and his desire for independence (B)can feel in his poems.

Andy: Really? I didn't know that. I want to read his poems and learn more about him.

Bora: Great. In fact, I'm planning to visit the Yun Dongju Museum soon. Do you want to come with me?

Andy: Yes, when are you going?

Bora: Next Saturday. It's near Gyeongbok Palace. Can you meet me at the palace at 2 p.m.?

Andy: Sure. Let's meet there.

Bora: Great. I'm really looking forward to the visit.

07 위 대화의 밑줄 친 (A)에 맞게 주어진 단어를 활용하여 영작하시오.

about, Yun Dongju

➡ _____

08 위 대화의 밑줄 친 (B)를 알맞은 형태로 고친 것은?

① can feel
② can to be felt
③ can felt
④ can be feeling
⑤ can be felt

09 대화의 밑줄 친 (A)를 문법적으로 맞게 고쳐 쓰시오.

G: I'm planning to go to the Gansong Museum.

B: What is the Gansong Museum?

G: (A)It's a museum was built by Gansong Jeon Hyeongpil.

B: I heard that he did great things for the country.

G: Yes. He bought many Korean treasures that some Japanese had taken to Japan.

B: Wow. The museum must be interesting.

G: Yes. I'm looking forward to it!

➡ _____
_____
_____

10 다음 각 빈칸에 공통으로 들어갈 단어 중 나머지 넷과 성격이 다른 하나는?

① Please turn the light on _____ that we can find the way out.

② Eddy hurried _____ that he wouldn't miss the plane Susan was in.

③ The police officer talked louder _____ that the old lady could understand.

④ Will and Ben woke up early _____ that they could see their daddy off.

⑤ Jacob was _____ busy that he couldn't join our party.

출제율 95%

11 다음 〈보기〉의 문장과 같은 뜻이 되도록 각 괄호 안의 주어진 조건에 맞게 빈칸을 채우시오.

> **보기**
>
> Paula had to read the textbook many times so that she would not forget the contents.

(1) Paula had to read the textbook many
times _____ the contents.
(to부정사의 부사적 용법 활용, 3 단어)

(2) Paula had to read the textbook many
times _____ the contents.
(so as 활용, 5 단어)

(3) Paula had to read the textbook many
times _____ she would
not forget the contents. (in 활용, 3 단어)

출제율 100%

12 다음 중 어법상 올바른 문장을 <u>모두</u> 고르면?

① The grass looked greener than before because it had rained last week.

② Sandy heard that the manager has overworked the day before.

③ Yuna's husband was surprised that she has been elected as a chairwoman.

④ The first period began when I had arrived at the court.

⑤ Jonathan returned the book which he had borrowed from the library.

출제율 95%

13 다음 문장의 빈칸 (a)~(d)에 들어갈 말을 〈보기〉에서 골라 순서대로 나열한 것은?

> • Vicky plays classical music to her son every day (a)_____.
> • Kate has been practicing 500 shots a day for the past 4 years (b)_____.
> • Taylor returned all of the overdue books to the library (c)_____.
> • Clara stopped eating junk food (d)_____.

> **보기**
>
> (A) so that he wouldn't be fined
> (B) so that she could become healthier
> (C) so that he can be a great musician
> (D) so that she can win the gold medal

① (A)-(B)-(C)-(D) ② (A)-(C)-(D)-(B)
③ (B)-(D)-(A)-(C) ④ (C)-(D)-(A)-(B)
⑤ (C)-(A)-(B)-(D)

[14~16] 다음 글을 읽고 물음에 답하시오.

> Last week my history club went to Hyochang Park. We visited the Kim Koo Museum inside the park. At the entrance of the museum, we saw a white statue of Kim Koo. Kim Koo is a great national hero ①who spent most of his life ②fight for the independence of Korea from Japanese rule. In the 1900s, he helped ③educate young people by building schools. In 1919, when the independence movement ④had spread throughout the country, he moved to Shanghai, China. There he ⑤joined the Government of the Republic of Korea and later became its president.

출제율 95%

14 ①~⑤ 중 어법상 바르지 <u>않은</u> 것은?

①   ②   ③   ④   ⑤

출제율 90%

15 주어진 단어를 활용하여 다음 물음에 답하시오. 필요하다면 어휘를 변형하시오.

> **Q:** What did Kim Koo do in the 1900s?
> (build / to / help)

➡ _____

16 다음 중 위 글을 읽고 답할 수 있는 것은?

① Where is Hyochang Park?
② How did they get to Hyochang Park?
③ What is there inside Hyochang Park?
④ Who made the statue of Kim Koo?
⑤ How did Kim Koo build schools?

[17~19] 다음 글을 읽고 물음에 답하시오.

An Changho was born in 1878. ① When he was in his teens, he moved to Seoul and went to school there. ② In America, An helped improve the lives of the Korean people there and became a respected leader. ③ After he had returned to Korea, he founded the New Korean Society in 1907 to fight for Korea's independence. ④ He also joined the Government of the Republic of Korea in Shanghai in 1919. ⑤ After that, he built a lot of schools to educate people until he died in 1938.

17 ①~⑤ 중 주어진 문장이 들어가기에 가장 적절한 곳은?

In 1902, he left for America so that he could get a better education.

①   ②   ③   ④   ⑤

18 According to the passage, what did An Changho do until he died in 1938? Answer in English with a full sentence.

➡ _____

_____

19 다음 중 위 글의 내용과 일치하지 <u>않는</u> 것은?

① An Changho was born in the late 1800s.
② An Changho went to school in Seoul.
③ People in America respected An Changho.
④ An Changho didn't return to Korea again.
⑤ It was An Changho who founded the New Korean Society in 1907.

[20~21] 다음 글을 읽고 물음에 답하시오.

At one place in the hall, we saw two watches under a photo of Kim Koo and Yun Bonggil. In 1932, Kim Koo made a plan (A)<u>to kill</u> Japanese generals in a park in Shanghai. As the leader of the Korean Patriotic Organization, he directed Yun to carry out (B) <u>the mission</u>.

20 다음 중 밑줄 친 (A)와 쓰임이 같은 것은?

① We went into the building <u>to meet</u> them.
② Is there any chance <u>to see</u> you again?
③ It was impossible <u>to get</u> there on time.
④ <u>To make</u> it delicious, I added some sugar.
⑤ He must be generous <u>to give</u> you his watch.

21 밑줄 친 (B)가 의미하는 것을 위 글에서 찾아 우리말로 쓰시오.

➡ _____

01 다음 대화를 읽고 '수원 화성'에 대한 요약문을 완성하시오.

> B: Look at Suwon Hawseong. It's huge.
> G: It also looks strong.
> B: Because it was built to protect the people during wars.
> G: Wow. Do you know who built it?
> B: Yes. King Jeongjo ordered Jeong Yakyong to direct the building process. You know about Jeong Yakyong, don't you?
> G: Yes, I've heard of him. He was a great scientist in Joseon.

➡ Suwon Hwaseong _____ the people during wars. Jeong Yakyong _____ its _____.

02 다음 그림을 보고, 내용에 맞게 〈보기〉에서 알맞은 단어를 하나씩 선택하여 ⓐ~ⓕ의 빈칸에 어법상 알맞은 형태로 써 넣으시오. (A)의 빈칸에는 〈보기〉에 없는 단어 두 개를 이용하여, 내용과 어법에 맞게 써 넣으시오.

| 보기 |
| like   allow   complete   burn |
| use   disappoint |

The principal ⓐ_____ us ⓑ_____ the cooking studio in our school when the exam was over. Half an hour ago, before Annie and I ⓒ_____ the chocolate pie, it ⓓ_____ up. I was so ⓔ_____. I just wanted to give David

delicious food (A)_____ he could ⓕ _____ me.

03 다음 중에서 틀린 문장을 찾아 기호를 쓰고, 바르게 고쳐 문장을 다시 쓰시오.

① The secretary said she had already finished her work before noon.
② The young politician was tired because he had played soccer the day before.
③ Shane refused to go to the theater as he had already watched the movie.
④ I had found out that she lost her bag.
⑤ The repairman said that someone had broken the toilet cover.

➡ _____

04 다음 우리말로 제시한 세 문장을 영작할 때, 〈보기〉의 어구를 사용하여 빈칸에 알맞게 써 넣으시오. (중복 사용 불가)

| 보기 |
| could / my uncle / in order to / had / it / so that / warm / bought / show / my body / which |

(1) 나는 내 몸을 덥힐 수 있도록 뜨거운 커피를 주문했다.
➡ I ordered hot coffee _____ _____.

(2) 우리집 반려동물 토토가 삼촌이 나를 위해 사줬던 스커트를 물어뜯었다.
➡ My pet Toto bit off the skirt _____ _____ for me.

(3) 세호는 어머니에게 보여드리기 위해서 춤 동작들을 연습했다.
➡ Seho practiced the dance movements _____ them to his mom.

An Changho was born in 1878. When he was in his teens, he moved to Seoul and went to school there. (A)In 1902, he left for America so that he could get a better education. In America, An helped improve the lives of the Korean people there and became a respected leader. After he had returned to Korea, he founded the New Korean Society in 1907 to fight for Korea's independence. He also joined the Government of the Republic of Korea in Shanghai in 1919. After that, he built a lot of schools to educate people until he died in 1938.

05 빈칸에 알맞은 말을 써서 밑줄 친 (A)와 같은 의미의 문장을 완성하시오.

= In 1902, he left for America _____
_____ _____ get a better education.
= In 1902, he left for America _____
get a better education.

06 Write the reason why An Changho founded the New Korean Society in 1907. Answer in English with eight words.

➡ _____

_____

07 What did An Changho do in America? Answer in Korean.

➡ _____

After completing the tour of the museum, we moved to the tombs of the three heroes, Lee Bongchang, Yun Bonggil, and Baek Jeonggi. Their bodies had been in Japan, but after Korea's independence Kim Koo brought them to Hyochang Park. By doing so, he showed his deep love and respect for the sacrifice of the three heroes.

As I left Hyochang Park, I thought about Kim Koo's words in My Wish that I had read in the exhibition hall. (A)It was written in *Baekbeomilji*.

If God asks me what my wish is, I would say clearly, "It is Korea's Independence." If he asks me what my second wish is, I would say, "It is the independence of my country." If he asks me what my third wish is, I would say loudly, "It is the complete independence of my country." That is my answer.

08 밑줄 친 (A)가 가리키는 것을 위 글에서 찾아 쓰시오.

➡ _____

09 Where are the tombs of the three heroes now? Answer in English with five words.

➡ _____

10 위 글의 내용에 맞도록 주어진 단어 중에서 골라 빈칸에 알맞게 쓰시오.

(inspire / desire / love / crisis)

Kim Koo's words in My Wish make us feel his _____ for the independence of Korea and his _____ for the country.

01 다음은 독도에 관한 사실이다. 이 사실을 아는지 묻는 표현을 〈보기〉처럼 쓰시오.

> • Dokdo has two main islands and 89 small islands.
> • Dokdo is windy and foggy.
> • There is a rock on Dokdo that looks like Korea.

┤ 보기 ├

> A: You know that Dokdo has two main islands and 89 small islands, don't you?
> B: Yes, I heard about it.

02 다음 그림과 각 그림에 주어진 단어들을 활용하여, so that을 사용한 문장을 어법에 맞게 자유롭게 영작하시오.

(passing, rescue, shout, cry,   (birds, look, watch, observe,
boat, ship, yell, help)   telescope, tool)

(1) _____

(2) _____

03 김좌진 장군에 대한 대화문을 참고하여 다음 글을 완성하시오.

> Q: When was he born?
> A: He was born in 1889.
> Q: Who was he?
> A: He was a Korean general who fought against Japanese rule.
> Q: What did he do to defeat Japan?
> A: He gathered and trained soldiers.
> Q: How did his efforts turn out to be?
> A: His efforts paid off at Cheongsanri, where his soldiers earned one of their greatest victories against Japan.

> Kim Jwajin was born in Hong Seong _____. He was a Korean general _____. When Korea was under Japanese rule, he _____ _____ to defeat Japan. His efforts paid off at Cheongsanri, _____ _____.

단원별 모의고사

01 다음 단어에 대한 영어 설명이 <u>어색한</u> 것은?

① desire: a strong wish or feeling

② treasure: what is highly valued

③ look forward to: to feel pleased and excited about something that is going to happen

④ mission: any work that someone believes it is their duty to do

⑤ state: a sculptured figure of a person, animal, etc. in bronze, stone, wood, etc.

02 다음 짝지어진 단어의 관계가 같도록 빈칸에 알맞은 말을 쓰시오.

> educate – teach : reign – _____

03 다음 영영풀이에 해당하는 단어를 고르시오.

> to place a dead body in the ground, to put something in the ground and cover it

① bury   ② spread   ③ kill

④ mean   ⑤ direct

04 다음 중 짝지어진 대화가 <u>어색한</u> 것은?

① A: Do you remember our plan to go to the War Memorial?

B: Sure. I'm looking forward to going there.

② A: What kind of volunteer work did you do there?

B: I cleaned around the tombs.

③ A: I'm planning to go to the Gansong Museum.

B: What is the Gansong Museum?

④ A: Have you ever heard about An Junggeun?

B: No, I haven't. He was an independence activist.

⑤ A: I'm planning to visit the Hangeul Museum next week. Do you want to join me?

B: I'd love to. I'm looking forward to visiting there.

[05~06] 다음 대화를 읽고 물음에 답하시오.

B: Tomorrow let's put on traditional Korean clothes, hanbok, and go to Insadong.

G: Good, but I want to buy gifts for my friends in Germany tomorrow.

B: In Insadong, there are many gift shops.

G: Great. After shopping, what should we eat for lunch?

B: Hmm. (A)_____

G: No. What is it?

B: It's a traditional Korean soup. It's delicious and will make you healthy.

G: Sounds good. (B)<u>I'm looking forward to trying it.</u>

05 위 대화의 빈칸 (A)에 들어갈 말로 알맞지 <u>않은</u> 것은? (2개)

① Have you ever heard about Samgyetang?

② Do you know how to cook Samgyetang?

③ You know Samgyetang, don't you?

④ Why don't you eat Samgyetang?

⑤ Did you hear about Samgyetang?

06 위 대화의 밑줄 친 (B)와 같은 의미가 되도록 'die'를 이용하여 기대의 표현을 쓰시오.

➡ _____

[07~08] 다음 대화를 읽고 물음에 답하시오.

Andy: Bora, what are you reading?

Bora: I'm reading *Sky, Wind, Star, and Poetry* by Yun Dongju. (a)You know about Yun Dongju, don't you?

Andy: I've heard his name, but I don't know much about him.

Bora: He wrote many beautiful poems (b)when Korea was under Japanese rule. His love for the country and his desire for independence can be felt in his poems.

Andy: Really? I didn't know (c)that. I want to read his poems and learn more about him.

Bora: Great. In fact, (d)I'm planning to visit the Yun Dongju Museum soon. Do you want to come with me?

Andy: Yes, when are you going?

Bora: Next Saturday. It's near Gyeongbok Palace. Can you meet me at the palace at 2 p.m.?

Andy: Sure. Let's meet there.

Bora: Great. (e)I'm really looking forward to the visit.

07 위 대화의 밑줄 친 (a)~(e)에 대한 설명 중 잘못된 것은?

① (a): 상대방이 알고 있는지 물어보는 표현이다.

② (b): '한국이 일본의 통치하에 있을 때'의 뜻으로 'when'은 부사절 접속사다.

③ (c): 지시대명사로 앞 문장의 '나라에 대한 그의 사랑과 독립에 대한 염원이 그의 시에서 느껴진 다'는 문장을 대신한다.

④ (d): 미래의 계획을 말하는 표현으로 'be going to+동사원형' 구문을 이용하여 바꿔 쓸 수 있다.

⑤ (e): 앞으로 하고 싶은 일에 대한 기대를 표현하는 것으로 'to' 다음에는 명사나 동사원형이 와야 한다.

08 위 대화를 읽고 답할 수 <u>없는</u> 질문은?

① What is Bora reading?

② Who wrote the poem *Sky, Wind, Star, and Poetry*?

③ What can be felt through Yun Dongju's poems?

④ How many poems does Bora want to read?

⑤ What are they planning to do next Saturday?

09 다음 대화의 빈칸 (A)와 (B)에 공통으로 들어갈 말로 알맞은 것은?

G: I'm planning to go to the Gansong Museum.

B: What is the Gansong Museum?

G: It's a museum built by Gansong Jeon Hyeongpil.

B: I heard (A)_____ he did great things for the country.

G: Yes. He bought many Korean treasures (B)_____ some Japanese had taken to Japan.

B: Wow. The museum must be interesting.

G: Yes. I'm looking forward to it!

① that   ② what
③ which   ④ who
⑤ when

10 다음 대화의 (A)와 (B)가 가리키는 것을 제시된 단어 수에 맞게 찾아 쓰시오.

G: Brian, you know Taegeukgi, don't you?

B: Sure. It's the national flag of Korea, isn't it?

G: That's right. Do you know what the symbols in Taegeukgi mean?

B: No, I don't. Tell me about (A)them.

G: The circle in the middle means harmony and peace.

B: What do the black lines on the four corners mean?

G: (B)They mean four things: sky, fire, water, and earth.

➡ (A) _____ (4 단어)

(B) _____ (3 단어)

[11~12] 다음 대화를 읽고 물음에 답하시오.

(A)

B: Look at Suwon Hawseong. It's huge.

G: It also looks strong.

B: Because it (1)_____ to protect the people during wars.

G: Wow. Do you know who (2)_____ it?

B: Yes. King Jeongjo ordered Jeong Yakyong to direct the building process. (a) _____ Jeong Yakyong, don't you?

G: Yes, I've heard of him. He was a great scientist in Joseon.

(B)

G: I'm planning to go to the Gansong Museum.

B: What is the Gansong Museum?

G: It's a museum (3)_____ by Gansong Jeon Hyeongpil.

B: I heard that he did great things for the country.

G: Yes. He bought many Korean treasures that some Japanese had taken to Japan.

B: Wow. The museum must be interesting.

G: Yes. (b)_____ to it!

11 위 대화의 빈칸 (1)~(3)에 'build'를 활용하여 알맞게 써 넣으시오.

➡ (1)_____ (2)_____ (3)_____

12 위 대화 (A)의 빈칸 (a)는 '알고 있는지 묻는 표현'을, (B)의 빈칸 (b)는 '기대, 희망'을 나타내는 표현을 각각 쓰시오.

➡ (a)_____ (b) _____

13 다음 주어진 우리말을 영작한 것으로 옳지 <u>않은</u> 것은?

Bradley는 부자가 되기 위해 밤낮으로 일했다.

① Bradley worked day and night so as to become rich.

② Bradley worked day and night in order that he became rich.

③ Bradley worked day and night so that he could become rich.

④ Bradley worked day and night to be rich.

⑤ Bradley worked day and night in order to be rich.

14 다음 두 문장을 한 문장으로 만들 때 빈칸에 들어갈 말로 가장 알맞은 것은?

• There was a yellow dust storm all day long.

• The cars were covered with thick dust.

→ The cars were covered with thick dust because _____.

① there is a yellow dust storm all day long

② there has come a yellow dust storm all day long

③ there has been a yellow dust storm all day long

④ there had been a yellow dust storm all day long

⑤ there had been being a yellow dust storm all day long

15 다음 중 밑줄 친 부분의 쓰임이 나머지 넷과 <u>다른</u> 것은?

① Smith will send you his phone number <u>so that</u> you can contact him anytime.

② Frank hurried to the radio station <u>so that</u> he wouldn't be late for the program.

③ Minju did her best <u>so that</u> her research team could find another galaxy.

④ Dave answered loudly, <u>so that</u> the teacher heard him clearly.

⑤ John turned off the radio <u>so that</u> his wife could focus on the book better.

16 다음 각 그림을 보고, 주어진 어구를 알맞게 배열하여 영작하되, 과거완료시제를 반드시 포함하시오. (동사는 변형 가능)

(1) Pinocchio, the goddess, say, lie, that

➡ _____

(2) Pooh, the hive, after, touch, by bees, be stung, he

➡ _____

_____

[17~18] 다음 글을 읽고 물음에 답하시오.

Last week my history club went to Hyochang Park. We visited the Kim Koo Museum inside the park. At the entrance of the museum, we saw a white statue of Kim Koo. Kim Koo is ①<u>a great national hero</u> who spent most of his life ②<u>fighting for</u> the independence of Korea from Japanese rule. In the 1900s, he helped ③<u>educate young people</u> by building schools. In 1919, when the independence movement had spread throughout the country, he ④<u>moved</u> to Shanghai, China. There he ⑤<u>left</u> the Government of the Republic of Korea and later became its president.

17 위 글의 내용과 일치하지 <u>않는</u> 것은?

① The writer is a member of the history club.

② The Kim Koo Museum is located in Hyochang Park.

③ There was a time when Korea was ruled by Japan.

④ Kim Koo lived in Korea all his life.

⑤ The Government of the Republic of Korea was in Shanghai.

18 ①~⑤ 중 글의 흐름상 <u>어색한</u> 것은?

①   ②   ③   ④   ⑤

[19~22] 다음 글을 읽고 물음에 답하시오.

The exhibition hall in the museum shows a lot of things about Kim Koo's life. While looking around the hall, we stopped at a photo of the Korean Patriotic Organization's members. Kim Koo formed the secret organization in 1931 to fight against Japan.

Lee Bongchang and Yun Bonggil belonged to the group. At one place in the hall, we saw two watches under a photo of Kim Koo and Yun Bonggil. In 1932, Kim Koo made a plan to kill Japanese generals in a park in Shanghai. As the leader of the Korean Patriotic Organization, he directed Yun to (A) carry out the mission.

When Yun left for the mission, he told Kim, "(B)Sir, you are wearing a very old watch. Mine is new, but I won't need it anymore. Please take my watch, and let me have yours." Kim Koo always carried Yun's watch in his jacket so that he would not forget Yun's sacrifice.

19 Choose the sentence that is TRUE about the Korean Patriotic Organization.

① It was founded by Lee Bongchang.

② It was an open organization.

③ It was formed in 1932.

④ Its purpose was to fight against Japan.

⑤ Yun Bonggil didn't know about the organization.

20 다음 중 밑줄 친 (A)를 대신하여 쓰일 수 있는 것은?

① ignore   ② perform

③ introduce   ④ practice

⑤ threat

21 다음 중 윤봉길이 밑줄 친 (B)와 같이 말한 이유로 가장 적절한 것은?

① his interest in Kim Koo's old watch

② his firm opinion to buy a new watch

③ his strong will to devote his life to the mission

④ his deep respect fot Kim Koo

⑤ his natural spirit of helping other people

22 According to the passage, what does the exhibition hall show?

➡ _____

[23~24] 다음 글을 읽고 물음에 답하시오.

An Changho was born in 1878. When he was in his teens, he moved to Seoul and went to school there. In 1902, he left for America so that he could get a better education. In America, An helped improve the lives of the Korean people there and became a respected leader. After he had returned to Korea, he founded the New Korean Society in 1907 to fight for Korea's independence. He also joined the Government of the Republic of Korea in Shanghai in 1919. After that, he built a lot of schools to educate people until he died in 1938.

23 위 글의 내용에 맞게 주어진 문장을 바르게 나열하시오.

ⓐ He returned to Korea.

ⓑ He joined the Government of the Republic of Korea.

ⓒ He went to America to get a better education.

ⓓ He founded the New Korean Society.

ⓔ He studied in Seoul.

ⓕ He became a respected leader by helping people in America.

➡ _____

24 What did An Changho do in order to fight for Korea's independence? Answer in English with a full sentence.

➡ _____
_____

MEMO

INSIGHT
on the textbook
교과서 파헤치기

※ 다음 영어를 우리말로 쓰시오.

01	enough	22	recommend
02	analyze	23	poet
03	attend	24	veterinarian
04	figure	25	mail carrier
05	calm	26	select
06	cast	27	greenery
07	personality	28	strength
08	detail	29	microphone
09	developer	30	audition
10	highly	31	stethoscope
11	florist	32	performance
12	analyst	33	gardener
13	weakness	34	realistic
14	include	35	by -ing
15	among	36	come true
16	resource	37	care for
17	conduct	38	be happy with ~
18	reduce	39	belong to
19	specialist	40	make the best use of
20	handle	41	It seems that ~
21	creature	42	I'm sure that ~
		43	dream of ~

※ 다음 우리말을 영어로 쓰시오.

01 성격 _____

02 분석하다 _____

03 출연자들 _____

04 힘, 강점 _____

05 청진기 _____

06 지휘하다, 처신하다 _____

07 수의사 _____

08 약함, 약점 _____

09 세부, 세목 _____

10 선택하다, 고르다 _____

11 정원사 _____

12 전문가 _____

13 개발자 _____

14 마이크 _____

15 매우, 대단히 _____

16 ~ 중에서 _____

17 플로리스트, 화초 연구가 _____

18 오디션을 보다 _____

19 화초, 푸른 잎 _____

20 분석가 _____

21 다루다 _____

22 포함하다 _____

23 진정시키다, 평온하게 하다 _____

24 책임 _____

25 현실적인 _____

26 전통의, 전통적인 _____

27 추천하다 _____

28 공연 _____

29 생물, 생명체 _____

30 자원 _____

31 줄이다, 완화하다 _____

32 언젠가 _____

33 기술자 _____

34 충분히; 충분한 _____

35 ~을 보살피다 _____

36 (단체, 조직에) 소속하다, 속하다 _____

37 ~을 꿈꾸다 _____

38 ~에 만족하다 _____

39 실현되다 _____

40 ~함으로써 _____

41 ~처럼 보이다, ~일 것 같다 _____

42 ~을 확신하다 _____

43 ~을 최대한 활용하다 _____

※ 다음 영영풀이에 알맞은 단어를 <보기>에서 골라 쓴 후, 우리말 뜻을 쓰시오.

1 _____ : the actors in a film, play, or show: _____

2 _____ : facts or information that can be analysed: _____

3 _____ : to take things and put them together: _____

4 _____ : to bring a person or thing to a state or place: _____

5 _____ : to be a member of an organization: _____

6 _____ : your job or duty to deal with something or someone: _____

7 _____ : someone whose job is to analyze and examine something: _____

8 _____ : a person whose job is to pay out and take in money in a bank: _____

9 _____ : green plants or branches, especially when cut and used as decoration:

   _____

10 _____ : the type of person you are, shown by the way you behave, feel, and

   think: _____

11 _____ : a useful or valuable possession or quality of a country, organization, or

   person: _____

12 _____ : to study or examine something in detail, in order to discover more about

   it: _____

13 _____ : to contain something as a part of something else, or to make something

   part of something else: _____

14 _____ : to give a short performance in order to show that you are suitable for a

   part in a film, play, show, etc.: _____

15 _____ : a person or company that creates new products, especially computer

   products such as software: _____

16 _____ : to protect someone or something and provide the things they need,

   especially someone who is young, old or ill: _____

보기			
resource	data	belong to	greenery
include	analyst	responsibility	analyze
care for	lead	collect	bank teller
personality	cast	developer	audition

※ 다음 우리말과 일치하도록 빈칸에 알맞은 말을 쓰시오.

Listen & Speak 1 A

1. **B:** Anne, I'm _____ to visit the _____ _____ to see my uncle. He is a _____ _____.

   G: Oh, I want _____ _____ a police officer _____.

   B: You _____? Me, _____. I have _____ _____ _____ _____ a police officer _____ I was ten.

   G: Can I come _____ you, Matt? I want to meet your uncle and _____ him _____.

   B: Sure. What _____ you _____ _____ _____ _____?

   G: I want to ask him _____ I need _____ _____ _____ _____ a police officer.

   B: I see. I'm _____ he _____ _____ _____ _____ meet you.

2. **M:** What's _____, Jisu?

   G: I want to be an _____, but my _____ _____ is not good _____.

   M: Hmm... _____ _____ _____ _____ is not just about _____ good _____.

   G: What should I _____ _____ _____ _____ an _____?

   M: Read _____ _____ _____ books _____ _____ good stories and _____ _____ every day.

   G: Okay, I'll do so.

   M: I'm _____ _____ _____ _____ you can be a good animator _____ you _____ _____ _____.

   G: Thank you very much.

Listen & Speak 1 B

- **A:** I'm _____ in _____. _____ job would be _____ for me?

  B: I'm quite _____ that an app _____ could be a good job for you.

- **A:** I'm _____ _____ _____. _____ _____ would _____ _____ _____ _____ me?

  B: I'm _____ _____ that a writer could _____ _____ _____ _____ _____ you.

해석

1. **B:** Anne, 나는 우리 삼촌을 보러 경찰서에 갈 예정이야. 그는 경찰관이거든.

   G: 오, 나는 언젠가 경찰관이 되고 싶어.

   B: 그래? 나도야. 나는 10살 때부터 경찰관이 되는 것을 꿈꿔왔어.

   G: 내가 너와 함께 갈 수 있을까, Matt? 나 너희 삼촌을 만나서 몇 가지 물어보고 싶어.

   B: 물론이지. 무엇을 물어볼 거니?

   G: 나는 경찰관이 되기 위해 내가 무엇을 해야 하는지 물어보고 싶어.

   B: 알겠어. 나는 그가 널 만나고 싶어 할 거라고 확신해.

2. **M:** 무슨 문제 있니, 지수야?

   G: 저는 만화 영화 제작자가 되고 싶은데, 그리기 실력이 좋은 편이 아니에요.

   M: 음... 만화 영화 제작자가 되는 것은 단순히 그림을 잘 그린다고 되는 것만은 아니란다.

   G: 만화 영화 제작자가 되기 위해서 제가 무엇을 해야 하나요?

   M: 좋은 이야기를 만들기 위해 책을 많이 읽고, 그림 그리는 것을 매일 연습하렴.

   G: 알겠어요. 그렇게 할게요.

   M: 나는 네가 열심히 노력하면 훌륭한 만화 영화 제작자가 될 수 있다고 아주 확신해.

   G: 정말 감사해요.

- **A:** 나는 기술에 관심이 있어? 어떤 직업이 나에게 맞을까?

  B: 나는 앱 개발자가 너에게 좋은 직업이 될 수 있을 거라고 아주 확신해.

- **A:** 나는 쓰기에 관심이 있어. 어떤 직업이 나에게 맞을까?

  B: 나는 작가가 너에게 좋은 직업이 될 수 있을 거라고 아주 확신해.

1. **G:** I'm _____ _____ _____ you, Mr. Han. Could you please tell me _____ _____ _____?

 M: Okay. I _____ travelers to _____ _____ in China and give them _____ about where they should _____.

 G: What _____ do you do?

 M: I tell them about _____ _____ and _____ food in China.

 G: _____ _____ to me _____ _____ _____ about China is very important. Are you _____ _____ your job?

 M: Yes. I really love _____ _____.

2. **B:** Did you _____ the report about your _____ _____?

 G: Yes, I did. I _____ about my role model, Ms. Shin. I want to _____ _____ her.

 B: What _____ she _____?

 G: She teaches people _____ _____ _____. She _____ _____ them _____ stress and _____ _____.

 B: Good. _____ _____ _____ she helps _____ _____ _____ their mind _____ body healthy.

 G: Yes, and I think it's great.

Listen & Speak 2 B

- **A:** I want to be a radio _____ _____. What would help me _____ one?

 B: It _____ _____ me _____ your own stories would be _____.

- **A:** I want to be a _____ _____. What would _____ _____ _____ one?

 B: It _____ to me _____ _____ _____ _____ at a hospital would _____ _____.

Real Life Talk

Bora: What are you _____ _____ in _____ the things on this list?

Jessie: I'm most _____ _____ _____ outside and playing sports.

1. **G:** 만나 뵙게 되어 반갑습니다, Mr. Han. 당신이 어떤 일을 하시는지 말해 주실 수 있나요?
 M: 그래. 나는 중국에 있는 다양한 장소로 여행객들을 안내하고 그들이 방문해야 할 곳에 대한 정보를 제공해.
 G: 그 외에 또 어떤 일을 하시나요?
 M: 나는 그들에게 중국의 대중문화와 전통 음식에 대해 말해 줘.
 G: 중국에 대해 많이 아는 것이 매우 중요한 것 같네요. 당신의 직업에 만족하시나요?
 M: 응. 나는 내 직업을 정말 사랑해.

2. **B:** 네 롤 모델에 관한 기사 다 썼니?
 G: 응, 다 썼어. 나는 나의 롤 모델인 신 씨에 관해 썼어. 나는 그녀처럼 되고 싶어.
 B: 그녀는 무슨 일을 하니?
 G: 그녀는 사람들에게 스트레칭하는 방법을 가르쳐. 그녀는 또한 그들이 스트레스를 완화하여 평온해지도록 도와 줘.
 B: 좋구나. 그녀가 사람들의 몸과 마음을 둘 다 건강하게 유지하도록 돕는 것 같아.
 G: 맞아, 그리고 나는 그것이 훌륭하다고 생각해.

- **A:** 나는 라디오 방송 작가가 되고 싶어. 내가 그것이 되는 데 뭐가 도움이 될까?
 B: 너 자신만의 이야기를 쓰는 것이 도움이 될 것 같아.
- **A:** 나는 사회복지사가 되고 싶어. 내가 그것이 되는 데 뭐가 도움이 될까?
 B: 병원에서 아이들에게 책을 읽어 주는 것이 도움이 될 것 같아.

보라: 너는 이 목록에 있는 것들 중에서 무엇에 가장 관심이 있니?
Jessie: 나는 밖에서 일하는 것과 스포츠 하는 것에 가장 관심이 있어.

Bora: What are you _____ _____ in _____ the things on this list?

Jessie: I'm most interested in _____ outside and _____ sports.

Bora: Well, _____ _____ _____ _____ _____ y o u _____ _____ the _____ type.

Jessie: What do you _____?

Bora: Most people _____ _____ one of six _____ _____. _____ is _____ the _____.

Jessie: Oh, that's _____. _____ _____ _____ jobs do they _____ for realistic types?

Bora: A farmer, a _____ _____, a soccer player, _____ _____ _____.

Jessie: Oh, I have always wanted _____ _____ a soccer player.

Bora: That's good. _____ _____ _____ you could become a great _____ _____.

Communication Task Step 2

A: I have _____ _____, _____ _____, 1 I, and _____ _____.

B: It _____ _____ me that you _____ _____ Type S.

C: Yes. _____ _____ are _____ for Type S are teacher, nurse, _____ or _____.

A: Cool. I _____ _____ _____ to be a teacher.

D: That _____ great. I'm _____ _____ _____ _____ be a good teacher.

Wrap Up 1

B: Hello, what _____ you _____, Sumi?

G: I'm _____ _____ a good _____ on the Internet. I need it for my family dinner today.

B: That is nice. Do you _____ _____?

G: Yes, I try _____ _____ every weekend. I want to be a _____ _____.

B: What are you doing to _____ your dream _____ _____?

G: I'm _____ a cooking class. I try _____ _____ _____ new and _____ dishes.

B: _____ _____ _____ you could be a _____ _____.

보라: 음, 내 생각에 너는 현실적인 타입에 속하는 것 같아.

Jessie: 무슨 의미야?

보라: 대부분의 사람들은 여섯 가지 성격 유형 중 한 가지에 속해. 현실적인 타입도 그중 하나야.

Jessie: 오, 재미있다. 현실적인 타입의 사람들에게 그들이 추천하는 직업은 뭐야?

보라: 농부, 경찰관, 축구 선수 같은 거야.

Jessie: 오, 나는 항상 축구 선수가 되고 싶어 해 왔어.

보라: 멋지다. 나는 네가 훌륭한 축구 선수가 될 수 있을 거라고 아주 확신해.

A: 나는 S가 3개, A가 2개, I가 1개, E가 1개 있어.

B: 너는 S 타입에 속해 있는 것 같아.

C: 응. S 타입에게 추천되는 직업은 선생님, 간호사, 사서, 상담사야.

A: 멋지다. 나는 항상 선생님이 되고 싶었어.

D: 그거 멋지네. 나는 네가 좋은 선생님이 될 수 있다고 아주 확신해.

B: 안녕, 뭐 하고 있니, 수미야?

G: 나는 인터넷으로 좋은 요리법을 찾아보고 있어. 나는 오늘 우리 가족의 저녁 식사를 위해 그것이 필요해.

B: 그거 멋지네. 너는 요리를 자주 하니?

G: 응, 나는 매주 주말에 요리를 하려고 노력해. 나는 언젠가 요리사가 되고 싶어.

B: 네 꿈을 이루기 위해서 무엇을 하고 있니?

G: 나는 요리 수업을 듣고 있어. 새롭고 창의적인 요리를 생각해 내기 위해 노력해.

B: 나는 네가 좋은 요리사가 될 것이라고 아주 확신해.

※ 다음 우리말에 맞도록 대화를 영어로 쓰시오.

 해석

Listen & Speak 1 A

1. B: _____
   _____

   G: _____

   B: _____

   G: _____

   B: _____

   G: _____

   B: _____

2. M: _____

   G: _____

   M: _____

   G: _____

   M: _____

   G: _____

   M: _____

   G: _____

Listen & Speak 1 B

• A: _____

  B: _____

• A: _____

  B: _____

1. B: Anne, 나는 우리 삼촌을 보러 경찰서에 갈 예정이야. 그는 경찰관이거든.
   G: 오, 나는 언젠가 경찰관이 되고 싶어.
   B: 그래? 나도야. 나는 10살 때부터 경찰관이 되는 것을 꿈꿔왔어.
   G: 내가 너와 함께 갈 수 있을까, Matt? 나 너희 삼촌을 만나서 몇 가지 물어보고 싶어.
   B: 물론이지. 무엇을 물어볼 거니?
   G: 나는 경찰관이 되기 위해 내가 무엇을 해야 하는지 물어보고 싶어.
   B: 알겠어. 나는 그가 널 만나고 싶어 할 거라고 확신해.

2. M: 무슨 문제 있니, 지수야?
   G: 저는 만화 영화 제작자가 되고 싶은데, 그리기 실력이 좋은 편이 아니에요.
   M: 음... 만화 영화 제작자가 되는 것은 단순히 그림을 잘 그린다고 되는 것만은 아니란다.
   G: 만화 영화 제작자가 되기 위해서 제가 무엇을 해야 하나요?
   M: 좋은 이야기를 만들기 위해 책을 많이 읽고, 그림 그리는 것을 매일 연습하렴.
   G: 알겠어요. 그렇게 할게요.
   M: 나는 네가 열심히 노력하면 훌륭한 만화 영화 제작자가 될 수 있다고 아주 확신해.
   G: 정말 감사해요.

• A: 나는 기술에 관심이 있어? 어떤 직업이 나에게 맞을까?
  B: 나는 앱 개발자가 너에게 좋은 직업이 될 수 있을 거라고 아주 확신해.
• A: 나는 쓰기에 관심이 있어. 어떤 직업이 나에게 맞을까?
  B: 나는 작가가 너에게 좋은 직업이 될 수 있을 거라고 아주 확신해.

Listen & Speak 2 A

1. G: _____

   M: _____

   _____

   G: _____

   M: _____

   G: _____

   _____

   M: _____

2. B: _____

   G: _____

   B: _____

   G: _____

   _____

   B: _____

   G: _____

Listen & Speak 2 B

- A: _____

  B: _____

- A: _____

  B: _____

Real Life Talk

Bora: _____

Jessie: _____

1. G: 만나 뵙게 되어 반갑습니다, Mr. Han. 당신이 어떤 일을 하시는지 말해 주실 수 있나요?
   M: 그래. 나는 중국에 있는 다양한 장소로 여행객들을 안내하고 그들이 방문해야 할 곳에 대한 정보를 제공해.
   G: 그 외에 또 어떤 일을 하시나요?
   M: 나는 그들에게 중국의 대중문화와 전통 음식에 대해 말해 줘.
   G: 중국에 대해 많이 아는 것이 매우 중요한 것 같네요. 당신의 직업에 만족하시나요?
   M: 응. 나는 내 직업을 정말 사랑해.

2. B: 네 롤 모델에 관한 기사 다 썼니?
   G: 응, 다 썼어. 나는 나의 롤 모델인 신 씨에 관해 썼어. 나는 그녀처럼 되고 싶어.
   B: 그녀는 무슨 일을 하니?
   G: 그녀는 사람들에게 스트레칭하는 방법을 가르쳐. 그녀는 또한 그들이 스트레스를 완화하여 평온해지도록 도와 줘.
   B: 좋구나. 그녀가 사람들의 몸과 마음을 둘 다 건강하게 유지하도록 돕는 것 같아.
   G: 맞아, 그리고 나는 그것이 훌륭하다고 생각해.

- A: 나는 라디오 방송 작가가 되고 싶어. 내가 그것이 되는 데 뭐가 도움이 될까?
  B: 너 자신만의 이야기를 쓰는 것이 도움이 될 것 같아.
- A: 나는 사회복지사가 되고 싶어. 내가 그것이 되는 데 뭐가 도움이 될까?
  B: 병원에서 아이들에게 책을 읽어 주는 것이 도움이 될 것 같아.

보라: 너는 이 목록에 있는 것들 중에서 무엇에 가장 관심이 있니?
Jessie: 나는 밖에서 일하는 것과 스포츠 하는 것에 가장 관심이 있어.

Bora: _____

Jessie: _____

Bora: _____

_____

Jessie: _____

_____

Bora: _____

Jessie: _____

Bora: _____

보라: 음, 내 생각에 너는 현실적인 타입에 속하는 것 같아.

Jessie: 무슨 의미야?

보라: 대부분의 사람들은 여섯 가지 성격 유형 중 한 가지에 속해. 현실적인 타입도 그중 하나야.

Jessie: 오, 재미있다. 현실적인 타입의 사람들에게 그들이 추천하는 직업은 뭐야?

보라: 농부, 경찰관, 축구 선수 같은 거야.

Jessie: 오, 나는 항상 축구 선수가 되고 싶어 해 왔어.

보라: 멋지다. 나는 네가 훌륭한 축구 선수가 될 수 있을 거라고 아주 확신해.

Communication Task Step 2

A: _____

B: _____

C: _____

_____

A: _____

D: _____

A: 나는 S가 3개, A가 2개, I가 1개, E가 1개 있어.

B: 너는 S 타입에 속해 있는 것 같아.

C: 응. S 타입에게 추천되는 직업은 선생님, 간호사, 사서, 상담사야.

A: 멋지다. 나는 항상 선생님이 되고 싶었어.

D: 그거 멋지네. 나는 네가 좋은 선생님이 될 수 있다고 아주 확신해.

Wrap Up 1

B: _____

G: _____

_____

B: _____

G: _____

B: _____

G: _____

B: _____

B: 안녕, 뭐 하고 있니, 수미야?

G: 나는 인터넷으로 좋은 요리법을 찾아보고 있어. 나는 오늘 우리 가족의 저녁 식사를 위해 그것이 필요해.

B: 그거 멋지네. 너는 요리를 자주 하니?

G: 응, 나는 매주 주말에 요리를 하려고 노력해. 나는 언젠가 요리사가 되고 싶어.

B: 네 꿈을 이루기 위해서 무엇을 하고 있니?

G: 나는 요리 수업을 듣고 있어. 새롭고 창의적인 요리를 생각해 내기 위해 노력해.

B: 나는 네가 좋은 요리사가 될 것이라고 아주 확신해.

※ 다음 우리말과 일치하도록 빈칸에 알맞은 것을 골라 쓰시오.

The World of Wonderful Jobs

Florist

1 Hi, I am Tom. A _____ is someone _____ beautiful things _____ flowers.

   A. with   B. who   C. florist   D. creates

2 _____ _____ a florist, you _____ to know many _____ about flowers.

   A. need   B. to   C. things   D. become

3 I _____ a high school _____ florists and _____.

   A. for   B. attended   C. gardeners

4 It was at this school that I learned _____ _____ grow and _____ _____ different types of flowers.

   A. how   B. for   C. to   D. care

5 These _____, florists can do a _____ _____ things.

   A. lot   B. days   C. different   D. of

6 I design _____ _____ sometimes and I _____ shops _____ flowers.

   A. sets   B. decorate   C. movie   D. with

7 I am happy when I create _____ _____ with _____ flowers and _____.

   A. fresh   B. something   C. greenery   D. colorful

8 _____ you like plants and the arts, I _____ _____ you _____ a florist.

   A. recommend   B. highly   C. become   D. if

Sport Data Analyst

9 I am Emma. I am a _____ _____ _____.

   A. data   B. sport   C. analyst

10 It _____ _____ a difficult job, _____ _____?

   A. like   B. doesn't   C. sounds   D. it

11 _____ _____, it is a lot of fun. I _____ _____ a baseball team.

   A. fact   B. for   C. in   D. work

12 My job is to _____ _____ games and _____ a computer program to _____ data.

   A. recorded   B. collect   C. run   D. watch

플로리스트

1 안녕하세요. 저는 Tom입니다. 플로리스트란 꽃으로 아름다운 것들을 창조하는 사람입니다.

2 플로리스트가 되기 위해서 여러분은 꽃에 관해 많은 것을 알 필요가 있습니다.

3 나는 플로리스트와 정원사를 양성하는 고등학교에 다녔습니다.

4 제가 다양한 종류의 꽃을 기르고 다루는 방법을 배운 곳이 바로 이 학교에서였습니다.

5 오늘날, 플로리스트는 많은 다양한 일을 할 수 있습니다.

6 나는 때때로 영화 세트장을 디자인하고 꽃으로 상점을 꾸밉니다.

7 나는 싱싱한 꽃과 화초로 다채로운 무언가를 창조해 낼 때 행복합니다.

8 만약 당신이 식물과 예술을 좋아한다면, 나는 당신에게 플로리스트가 될 것을 강력히 추천합니다.

스포츠 데이터 분석가

9 나는 Emma입니다. 나는 스포츠 데이터 분석가입니다.

10 어려운 직업처럼 들리죠, 그렇지 않나요?

11 사실, 그것은 매우 재미있습니다. 나는 야구팀을 위해서 일합니다.

12 나의 일은 녹화된 경기를 보고 자료를 수집하기 위해 컴퓨터 프로그램을 실행하는 것입니다.

13 Then, I _____ the data to _____ my team's _____ and _____.

    A. weaknesses   B. strengths   C. analyze   D. show

14 _____ the team _____ their strengths and weaknesses, they can _____ _____ next time.

    A. better   B. understands   C. do   D. if

15 _____ I was young, I _____ _____ a _____ fan of baseball.

    A. big   B. since   C. been   D. have

16 Now, in my _____, I _____ baseball games _____ the _____.

    A. time   B. work   C. all   D. watch

17 This is a _____ job for me _____ _____ baseball games is my _____!

    A. watching   B. perfect   C. hobby   D. because

Director of a Musical Theater

18 Hi, I am Chris. _____ a _____ of a musical _____, I do a _____ of things.

    A. theater   B. as   C. director   D. lot

19 I _____ the actors and I _____ _____ good, strong _____.

    A. for   B. audition   C. look

20 After _____ the _____, I teach them the songs for _____.

    A. scene   B. selecting   C. each   D. cast

21 Then, I _____ the _____ and orchestra _____ for _____.

    A. together   B. put   C. practice   D. cast

22 _____ the _____, I am in the orchestra _____ and _____.

    A. conduct   B. during   C. performance   D. area

23 It's my _____ to have _____ song _____ the same _____ every time.

    A. played   B. responsibility   C. way   D. each

13 그러고 나서, 나는 내 팀의 강점과 약점을 보여 주기 위해서 그 자료들을 분석합니다.

14 만약 팀이 자신들의 강점과 약점을 이해하면, 그들은 다음번에 더 잘할 수 있습니다.

15 어렸을 때부터, 나는 야구의 열혈 팬이었습니다.

16 지금, 나는 일하는 중에 내내 야구를 봅니다.

17 야구 경기를 보는 것은 나의 취미이기 때문에 이것은 나에게 완벽한 직업입니다!

뮤지컬 극장 감독

18 안녕하세요. 나는 Chris입니다. 뮤지컬 극장 감독으로서 나는 많은 것들을 합니다.

19 나는 배우들을 대상으로 오디션을 실시하고, 훌륭하고 강한 목소리를 찾아냅니다.

20 배역에 맞는 배우를 고른 뒤에, 나는 그들에게 각 장면을 위한 노래를 가르칩니다.

21 그리고 나서, 나는 배우와 오케스트라를 함께 연습시킵니다.

22 공연 동안에, 나는 오케스트라석에 있고 지휘를 합니다.

23 각각의 노래가 매번 동일하게 연주되도록 만드는 것은 나의 책임입니다.

24 I _____ the musicians and the singers _____ _____ the show _____.

    A. keep   B. direct   C. together   D. to

25 _____ and _____ is not just about _____ my arms _____!

    A. waving   B. directing   C. around   D. conducting

Ocean Scientist

26 My name is Yeji. I am an ocean _____. Ocean science is a _____ _____.

    A. big   B. scientist   C. field

27 It _____ _____ of the oceans and the _____ _____ in them.

    A. creatures   B. studies   C. includes   D. living

28 _____ other things, I _____ _____ many kinds of fish _____ in the seas near Korea.

    A. have   B. living   C. among   D. studied

29 It is the _____ _____ in a fish _____ _____ me.

    A. interests   B. growth   C. ring   D. that

30 _____ _____ at it, I can find _____ when and where the fish was _____.

    A. born   B. looking   C. by   D. out

31 All the information I get from fish is _____ _____ understand sea _____ and _____ the oceans better.

    A. to   B. manage   C. used   D. resources

32 My job is important _____ it makes _____ _____ _____ of nature possible.

    A. best   B. because   C. use   D. the

24 나는 공연을 제대로 진행하기 위해 연주자들과 가수들을 감독합니다.

25 지휘하고 감독하는 것은 단지 내 팔을 흔드는 것만이 아닙니다!

해양 과학자

26 나는 예지입니다. 나는 해양 과학자입니다. 해양 과학은 거대한 분야입니다.

27 그것은 바다와 그 안에 살고 있는 생물에 관한 연구를 포함합니다.

28 여러 가지 중에서 나는 한국 주변의 바다에 살고 있는 많은 종류의 물고기를 연구해 왔습니다.

29 나의 흥미를 끄는 것은 바로 물고기 안에 있는 나이테입니다.

30 나이테를 살펴봄으로써. 나는 언제 어디서 그 물고기가 태어났는지 알아낼 수 있습니다.

31 내가 물고기에서 얻은 모든 정보는 바다의 자원을 이해하고 바다를 더 잘 관리하기 위해 사용됩니다.

32 내 직업은 자연을 가장 잘 활용할 수 있게 한다는 점에서 중요합니다.

※ 다음 우리말과 일치하도록 빈칸에 알맞은 말을 쓰시오.

The World of Wonderful Jobs

Florist

1 Hi, I am Tom. A _____ is someone _____ _____ beautiful things _____ flowers.

2 _____ _____ a florist, you _____ _____ _____ _____ _____ about flowers.

3 I _____ a high school _____ florists and _____.

4 It was _____ _____ _____ that I learned _____ _____ _____ and _____ _____ different types of flowers.

5 _____ _____, florists can do _____ _____ things.

6 I design _____ _____ sometimes and I _____ shops _____ _____.

7 I am happy when I create _____ _____ _____ fresh flowers and _____.

8 If you like _____ and the arts, I _____ _____ you become a florist.

Sport Data Analyst

9 I am Emma. I am a _____ _____ _____.

10 It _____ _____ a difficult job, _____ _____?

11 _____ _____, it is _____ _____ _____ _____. I work for a baseball team.

12 My job is _____ _____ _____ _____ and _____ a computer program _____ _____ data.

플로리스트

1 안녕하세요. 저는 Tom입니다. 플로리스트란 꽃으로 아름다운 것들을 창조하는 사람입니다.

2 플로리스트가 되기 위해서 여러분은 꽃에 관해 많은 것을 알 필요가 있습니다.

3 나는 플로리스트와 정원사를 양성하는 고등학교에 다녔습니다.

4 제가 다양한 종류의 꽃을 기르고 다루는 방법을 배운 곳이 바로 이 학교에서였습니다.

5 오늘날, 플로리스트는 많은 다양한 일을 할 수 있습니다.

6 나는 때때로 영화 세트장을 디자인하고 꽃으로 상점을 꾸밉니다.

7 나는 싱싱한 꽃과 화초로 다채로운 무언가를 창조해 낼 때 행복합니다.

8 만약 당신이 식물과 예술을 좋아한다면. 나는 당신에게 플로리스트가 될 것을 강력히 추천합니다.

스포츠 데이터 분석가

9 나는 Emma입니다. 나는 스포츠 데이터 분석가입니다.

10 어려운 직업처럼 들리죠, 그렇지 않나요?

11 사실, 그것은 매우 재미있습니다. 나는 야구팀을 위해서 일합니다.

12 나의 일은 녹화된 경기를 보고 자료를 수집하기 위해 컴퓨터 프로그램을 실행하는 것입니다.

13 Then, I _____ the data _____ _____ my team's strengths and _____.

14 If the team _____ their _____ and weaknesses, they can _____ _____ next time.

15 _____ I was young, I _____ _____ a big fan of baseball.

16 Now, in my work, I watch _____ _____ _____ _____.

17 This is a _____ _____ for me _____ _____ _____ is my _____!

Director of a Musical Theater

18 Hi, I am Chris. _____ a director of _____ , I do _____ _____ _____ things.

19 I _____ the actors and I _____ _____ good, strong _____.

20 After _____ _____ _____, I teach them the songs _____ _____ _____ _____.

21 Then, I _____ the _____ and orchestra _____ for practice.

22 _____ the _____, I am in the orchestra area and _____.

23 It's _____ _____ to have _____ song _____ the _____ _____ every time.

13 그리고 나서. 나는 내 팀의 강점과 약점을 보여 주기 위해서 그 자료들을 분석합니다.

14 만약 팀이 자신들의 강점과 약점을 이해하면. 그들은 다음번에 더 잘할 수 있습니다.

15 어렸을 때부터. 나는 야구의 열혈 팬이었습니다.

16 지금. 나는 일하는 중에 내내 야구를 봅니다.

17 야구 경기를 보는 것은 나의 취미이기 때문에 이것은 나에게 완벽한 직업입니다!

뮤지컬 극장 감독

18 안녕하세요. 나는 Chris입니다. 뮤지컬 극장 감독으로서 나는 많은 것들을 합니다.

19 나는 배우들을 대상으로 오디션을 실시하고, 훌륭하고 강한 목소리를 찾아냅니다.

20 배역에 맞는 배우를 고른 뒤에. 나는 그들에게 각 장면을 위한 노래를 가르칩니다.

21 그리고 나서. 나는 배우와 오케스트라를 함께 연습시킵니다.

22 공연 동안에. 나는 오케스트라석에 있고 지휘를 합니다.

23 각각의 노래가 매번 동일하게 연주되도록 만드는 것은 나의 책임입니다.

24 I _____ the musicians and the singers _____ _____ the show _____.

25 _____ and _____ is not just about _____ my arms around!

Ocean Scientist

26 My name is Yeji. I am an _____ _____. Ocean science is _____ _____ _____.

27 It _____ studies of the _____ and the _____ _____ _____ _____.

28 _____ other things, I _____ _____ many kinds of fish _____ in the seas near Korea.

29 It is _____ _____ in a fish _____ _____ me.

30 _____ _____ at it, I can _____ _____ when and where the fish _____ _____.

31 All the information _____ _____ _____ fish _____ _____ _____ _____ sea resources and _____ the _____ _____.

32 My job is important _____ it _____ _____ _____ _____ _____ nature possible.

---

24 나는 공연을 제대로 진행하기 위해 연주자들과 가수들을 감독합니다.

25 지휘하고 감독하는 것은 단지 내 팔을 흔드는 것만이 아닙니다!

해양 과학자

26 나는 예지입니다. 나는 해양 과학자입니다. 해양 과학은 거대한 분야입니다.

27 그것은 바다와 그 안에 살고 있는 생물에 관한 연구를 포함합니다.

28 여러 가지 중에서 나는 한국 주변의 바다에 살고 있는 많은 종류의 물고기를 연구해 왔습니다.

29 나의 흥미를 끄는 것은 바로 물고기 안에 있는 나이테입니다.

30 나이테를 살펴봄으로써, 나는 언제 어디서 그 물고기가 태어났는지 알아낼 수 있습니다.

31 내가 물고기에서 얻은 모든 정보는 바다의 자원을 이해하고 바다를 더 잘 관리하기 위해 사용됩니다.

32 내 직업은 자연을 가장 잘 활용할 수 있게 한다는 점에서 중요합니다.

※ 다음 문장을 우리말로 쓰시오.

The World of Wonderful Jobs

Florist

1 Hi, I am Tom. A florist is someone who creates beautiful things with flowers.
➡ _____

2 To become a florist, you need to know many things about flowers.
➡ _____

3 I attended a high school for florists and gardeners.
➡ _____

4 It was at this school that I learned how to grow and care for different types of flowers.
➡ _____

5 These days, florists can do a lot of different things.
➡ _____

6 I design movie sets sometimes and I decorate shops with flowers.
➡ _____

7 I am happy when I create something colorful with fresh flowers and greenery.
➡ _____

8 If you like plants and the arts, I highly recommend you become a florist.
➡ _____

Sport Data Analyst

9 I am Emma. I am a sport data analyst.
➡ _____

10 It sounds like a difficult job, doesn't it?
➡ _____

11 In fact, it is a lot of fun. I work for a baseball team.
➡ _____

12 My job is to watch recorded games and run a computer program to collect data.
➡ _____

13 Then, I analyze the data to show my team's strengths and weaknesses.
➡ _____

14 If the team understands their strengths and weaknesses, they can do better next time.
➡ _____

15 Since I was young, I have been a big fan of baseball.
➡ _____

16 Now, in my work, I watch baseball games all the time.
➡ _____

17 This is a perfect job for me because watching baseball games is my hobby!
➡ _____

Director of a Musical Theater

18 Hi, I am Chris. As a director of a musical theater, I do a lot of things.
➡ _____

19 I audition the actors and I look for good, strong voices.
➡ _____

20 After selecting the cast, I teach them the songs for each scene.
➡ _____

21 Then, I put the cast and orchestra together for practice.
➡ _____

22 During the performance, I am in the orchestra area and conduct.
➡ _____

23 It's my responsibility to have each song played the same way every time.
➡ _____

24 I direct the musicians and the singers to keep the show together.
➡ _____

25 Conducting and directing is not just about waving my arms around!
➡ _____

Ocean Scientist

26 My name is Yeji. I am an ocean scientist. Ocean science is a big field.
➡ _____

27 It includes studies of the oceans and the creatures living in them.
➡ _____

28 Among other things, I have studied many kinds of fish living in the seas near Korea.
➡ _____

29 It is the growth ring in a fish that interests me.
➡ _____

30 By looking at it, I can find out when and where the fish was born.
➡ _____

31 All the information I get from fish is used to understand sea resources and manage the oceans better.
➡ _____

32 My job is important because it makes the best use of nature possible.
➡ _____

Step4

※ 다음 괄호 안의 단어들을 우리말에 맞도록 바르게 배열하시오.

The World of Wonderful Jobs

Florist

1 (hi, / am / I / Tom. // florist / a / someone / is / creates / who / things / beautiful / flowers. / with)

➡ _____

➡ _____

2 (become / to / florist, / a / need / you / know / to / things / many / flowers. / about)

➡ _____

3 (attended / I / a / school / high / florists / for / gardeners. / and)

➡ _____

4 (was / it / this / at / school / that / learned / I / to / how / grow / and / for / care / types / different / flowers. / of)

➡ _____

5 (days, / these / can / florists / do / lot / a / of / things. / different)

➡ _____

6 (design / I / sets / movie / sometimes / and / decorate / I / with / shops / flowers.)

➡ _____

7 (am / I / when / happy / create / I / something / with / colorful / flowers / fresh / greenery. / and)

➡ _____

➡ _____

8 (you / if / like / and / plants / arts, / the / highly / I / you / recommend / become / florist. / a)

➡ _____

Sport Data Analyst

9 (am / I / Emma. // am / I / sport / a / analyst. / data)

➡ _____

10 (sounds / it / a / like / job, / difficult / it? / doesn't)

➡ _____

11 (fact, / in / is / it / lot / a / fun. / of // I / for / work / baseball / team. / a)

➡ _____

12 (job / my / to / is / recorded / watch / games / and / a / run / computer / program / collect / to / data.)

➡ _____

플로리스트

1 안녕하세요. 저는 Tom입니다. 플로리스트란 꽃으로 아름다운 것들을 창조하는 사람입니다.

2 플로리스트가 되기 위해서 여러분은 꽃에 관해 많은 것을 알 필요가 있습니다.

3 나는 플로리스트와 정원사를 양성하는 고등학교에 다녔습니다.

4 제가 다양한 종류의 꽃을 기르고 다루는 방법을 배운 곳이 바로 이 학교에서였습니다.

5 오늘날, 플로리스트는 많은 다양한 일을 할 수 있습니다.

6 나는 때때로 영화 세트장을 디자인하고 꽃으로 상점을 꾸밉니다.

7 나는 싱싱한 꽃과 화초로 다채로운 무언가를 창조해 낼 때 행복합니다.

8 만약 당신이 식물과 예술을 좋아한다면, 나는 당신에게 플로리스트가 될 것을 강력히 추천합니다.

스포츠 데이터 분석가

9 나는 Emma입니다. 나는 스포츠 데이터 분석가입니다.

10 어려운 직업처럼 들리죠, 그렇지 않나요?

11 사실, 그것은 매우 재미있습니다. 나는 야구팀을 위해서 일합니다.

12 나의 일은 녹화된 경기를 보고 자료를 수집하기 위해 컴퓨터 프로그램을 실행하는 것입니다.

13 (then, / analyze / I / data / the / show / to / team's / my / strengths / weaknesses. / and)

➡ _____

14 (the / if / team / understands / strengths / their / weaknesses, / and / can / they / better / do / time. / next)

➡ _____
_____

15 (I / since / young, / was / have / I / been / big / a / fan / baseball. / of)

➡ _____

16 (now, / my / in / work, / watch / I / games / baseball / the / all / time.)

➡ _____

17 (is / this / a / perfect / for / job / me / watching / because / games / baseball / my / is / hobby!)

➡ _____
_____

Director of a Musical Theater

18 (hi, / am / I / Chris. // a / as / director / a / of / theater, / musical / do / I / lot / a / things. / of)

➡ _____

19 (audition / I / actors / the / and / look / I / good, / for / voices. / strong)

➡ _____

20 (selecting / after / cast, / the / teach / I / them / songs / the / each / for / scene.)

➡ _____

21 (then, / put / I / cast / the / and / together / orchestra / practice. / for)

➡ _____

22 (the / during / performace, / am / I / in / orchestra / the / and / area / conduct.)

➡ _____

23 (my / it's / responsibility / have / to / song / each / played / same / the / every / way / time.)

➡ _____

_____

24 (direct / I / musicians / the / and / singers / the / keep / to / show / the / together.)

➡ _____

25 (directing / and / conducting / is / just / not / waving / about / arms / my / around!)

➡ _____

Ocean Scientist

26 (name / my / Yeji. / is // am / I / ocean / an / scientist. // science / ocean / a / is / field. / big)

➡ _____

27 (includes / it / of / studies / the / oceans / the / and / living / creatures / them. / in)

➡ _____

28 (other / among / things, / have / I / kinds / many / studied / of / living / fish / the / in / seas / Korea. / near)

➡ _____

_____

29 (is / it / growth / the / ring / a / in / fish / interests / that / me.)

➡ _____

30 (looking / by / it, / at / can / I / out / find / where / and / when / fish / the / born. / was)

➡ _____

31 (the / all / information / get / I / fish / from / used / is / to / sea / understand / manage / and / resources / oceans / the / better.)

➡ _____

_____

32 (job / my / is / because / important / makes / it / best / the / use / nature / of / possible.)

➡ _____

23 각각의 노래가 매번 동일하게 연주되도록 만드는 것은 나의 책임입니다.

24 나는 공연을 제대로 진행하기 위해 연주자들과 가수들을 감독합니다.

25 지휘하고 감독하는 것은 단지 내 팔을 흔드는 것만이 아닙니다!

해양 과학자

26 나는 예지입니다. 나는 해양 과학자입니다. 해양 과학은 거대한 분야입니다.

27 그것은 바다와 그 안에 살고 있는 생물에 관한 연구를 포함합니다.

28 여러 가지 중에서 나는 한국 주변의 바다에 살고 있는 많은 종류의 물고기를 연구해 왔습니다.

29 나의 흥미를 끄는 것은 바로 물고기 안에 있는 나이테입니다.

30 나이테를 살펴봄으로써, 나는 언제 어디서 그 물고기가 태어났는지 알아낼 수 있습니다.

31 내가 물고기에서 얻은 모든 정보는 바다의 자원을 이해하고 바다를 더 잘 관리하기 위해 사용됩니다.

32 내 직업은 자연을 가장 잘 활용할 수 있게 한다는 점에서 중요합니다.

※ 다음 우리말을 영어로 쓰시오.

The World of Wonderful Jobs

Florist

1 ▶ 안녕하세요. 저는 Tom입니다. 플로리스트란 꽃으로 아름다운 것들을 창조하는 사람입니다.

➡ _____

2 ▶ 플로리스트가 되기 위해서 여러분은 꽃에 관해 많은 것을 알 필요가 있습니다.

➡ _____

3 ▶ 나는 플로리스트와 정원사를 양성하는 고등학교에 다녔습니다.

➡ _____

4 ▶ 제가 다양한 종류의 꽃을 기르고 다루는 방법을 배운 곳이 바로 이 학교에서였습니다.

➡ _____

5 ▶ 오늘날, 플로리스트는 많은 다양한 일을 할 수 있습니다.

➡ _____

6 ▶ 나는 때때로 영화 세트장을 디자인하고 꽃으로 상점을 꾸밉니다.

➡ _____

7 ▶ 나는 싱싱한 꽃과 화초로 다채로운 무언가를 창조해 낼 때 행복합니다.

➡ _____

8 ▶ 만약 당신이 식물과 예술을 좋아한다면, 나는 당신에게 플로리스트가 될 것을 강력히 추천합니다.

➡ _____

Sport Data Analyst

9 ▶ 나는 Emma입니다. 나는 스포츠 데이터 분석가입니다.

➡ _____

10 ▶ 어려운 직업처럼 들리죠, 그렇지 않나요?

➡ _____

11 ▶ 사실, 그것은 매우 재미있습니다. 나는 야구팀을 위해서 일합니다.

➡ _____

12 ▶ 나의 일은 녹화된 경기를 보고 자료를 수집하기 위해 컴퓨터 프로그램을 실행하는 것입니다.

➡ _____

13 ▶ 그러고 나서, 나는 내 팀의 강점과 약점을 보여 주기 위해서 그 자료들을 분석합니다.

➡ _____

14 ▶ 만약 팀이 자신들의 강점과 약점을 이해하면, 그들은 다음번에 더 잘할 수 있습니다.

➡ _____

15 ▶ 어렸을 때부터, 나는 야구의 열혈 팬이었습니다.

➡ _____

16 지금, 나는 일하는 중에 내내 야구를 봅니다.
➡ _____

17 야구 경기를 보는 것은 나의 취미이기 때문에 이것은 나에게 완벽한 직업입니다!
➡ _____

Director of a Musical Theater

18 안녕하세요. 나는 Chris입니다. 뮤지컬 극장 감독으로서 나는 많은 것들을 합니다.
➡ _____

19 나는 배우들을 대상으로 오디션을 실시하고, 훌륭하고 강한 목소리를 찾아냅니다.
➡ _____

20 배역에 맞는 배우를 고른 뒤에, 나는 그들에게 각 장면을 위한 노래를 가르칩니다.
➡ _____

21 그러고 나서, 나는 배우와 오케스트라를 함께 연습시킵니다.
➡ _____

22 공연 동안에, 나는 오케스트라 석에 있고 지휘를 합니다.
➡ _____

23 각각의 노래가 매번 동일하게 연주되도록 만드는 것은 나의 책임입니다.
➡ _____

24 나는 공연을 제대로 진행하기 위해 연주자들과 가수들을 감독합니다.
➡ _____

25 지휘하고 감독하는 것은 단지 내 팔을 흔드는 것만이 아닙니다!
➡ _____

Ocean Scientist

26 나는 예지입니다. 나는 해양 과학자입니다. 해양 과학은 거대한 분야입니다.
➡ _____

27 그것은 바다와 그 안에 살고 있는 생물에 관한 연구를 포함합니다.
➡ _____

28 여러 가지 중에서 나는 한국 주변의 바다에 살고 있는 많은 종류의 물고기를 연구해 왔습니다.
➡ _____

29 나의 흥미를 끄는 것은 바로 물고기 안에 있는 나이테입니다.
➡ _____

30 나이테를 살펴봄으로써, 나는 언제 어디서 그 물고기가 태어났는지 알아낼 수 있습니다.
➡ _____

31 내가 물고기에서 얻은 모든 정보는 바다의 자원을 이해하고 바다를 더 잘 관리하기 위해 사용됩니다.
➡ _____

32 내 직업은 자연을 가장 잘 활용할 수 있게 한다는 점에서 중요합니다.
➡ _____

※ 다음 우리말과 일치하도록 빈칸에 알맞은 말을 쓰시오.

Enjoy Writing C

1. My _____ _____.

2. I like food from _____ _____ _____ and I _____ _____ _____ _____.

3. I can also _____ _____ _____ _____ and _____.

4. _____ _____ _____, it is a chef _____ I want to be _____ I _____ _____ _____.

5. _____ _____ my dream, I will read magazines _____ _____.

6. Also, I will go to France _____ _____ _____ _____ _____.

7. _____ _____ _____ is my dad.

8. He _____ _____ of new _____ and then cooks these new dishes for us.

9. I want to _____ _____ _____ _____ by people _____ _____ _____.

1. 내 꿈의 직업
2. 나는 전 세계 음식을 좋아하고 요리를 잘한다.
3. 나는 또한 음식을 맛있고 아름다워 보이게 만들 수 있다.
4. 이러한 이유로 내가 자라서 되고 싶은 것은 요리사이다.
5. 내 꿈을 이루기 위해, 나는 요리에 관한 잡지를 읽을 것이다.
6. 또한 나는 프랑스에 가서 다양한 요리 기술을 익힐 것이다.
7. 내 롤 모델은 나의 아빠이다.
8. 그는 항상 새로운 요리법을 생각해 내시고 우리를 위해 이러한 요리를 만들어 주신다.
9. 나는 내 이름이 내 음식을 좋아하는 사람들에게 기억되도록 하고 싶다.

Project

1. HELP _____!!

2. Do you _____ _____?

3. If your answer is yes, _____ is you that we _____ _____ _____.

4. Please join us _____ _____ and _____ _____.

5. _____ more information, _____ _____ _____ at www. robots.com.

1. 사람 구합니다!
2. 로봇을 좋아하시나요?
3. 당신의 답이 예스라면, 당신이 바로 우리가 찾는 사람입니다.
4. 우리와 함께 로봇을 훈련시키고, 고쳐 보세요.
5. 더 자세한 사항은 우리 웹사이트 www.robots.com을 방문해 주세요.

Project Step 3

1. _____ you _____ _____ _____ and _____ robots?

2. If _____, we're sure that you'll be _____ _____ _____ _____.

3. _____ _____ _____, _____ our websites.

1. 당신은 로봇을 훈련시키고 수리하는 것을 잘하나요?
2. 만약 그렇다면, 우리는 당신이 좋은 로봇 전문가가 될 것이라고 확신합니다.
3. 더 많은 정보를 위해서, 우리 웹사이트를 방문하세요.

※ 다음 우리말을 영어로 쓰시오.

Enjoy Writing C

1. 내 꿈의 직업
➡ _____

2. 나는 전 세계 음식을 좋아하고 요리를 잘한다.
➡ _____

3. 나는 또한 음식을 맛있고 아름다워 보이게 만들 수 있다.
➡ _____

4. 이러한 이유로 내가 자라서 되고 싶은 것은 요리사이다.
➡ _____

5. 내 꿈을 이루기 위해, 나는 요리에 관한 잡지를 읽을 것이다.
➡ _____

6. 또한 나는 프랑스에 가서 다양한 요리 기술을 익힐 것이다.
➡ _____

7. 내 롤 모델은 나의 아빠이다.
➡ _____

8. 그는 항상 새로운 요리법을 생각해 내시고 우리를 위해 이러한 요리를 만들어 주신다.
➡ _____

9. 나는 내 이름이 내 음식을 좋아하는 사람들에게 기억되도록 하고 싶다.
➡ _____

Project

1. 사람 구합니다!
➡ _____

2. 로봇을 좋아하시나요?
➡ _____

3. 당신의 답이 예스라면, 당신이 바로 우리가 찾는 사람입니다.
➡ _____

4. 우리와 함께 로봇을 훈련시키고, 고쳐보세요.
➡ _____

5. 더 자세한 사항은 우리 웹사이트 www.robots.com을 방문해 주세요.
➡ _____

Project Step 3

1. 당신은 로봇을 훈련시키고 수리하는 것을 잘하나요?
➡ _____

2. 만약 그렇다면, 우리는 당신이 좋은 로봇 전문가가 될 것이라고 확신합니다.
➡ _____

3. 더 많은 정보를 위해서, 우리 웹사이트를 방문하세요.
➡ _____

※ 다음 영어를 우리말로 쓰시오.

01	score	22	creative
02	alert	23	mistake
03	birth	24	intend
04	comment	25	guess
05	contact	26	limit
06	advantage	27	posting
07	detox	28	refreshed
08	uncomfortable	29	respect
09	addiction	30	copyright
10	disadvantage	31	outdoor
11	enjoyable	32	pain
12	form	33	suggest
13	necessary	34	cause
14	noisy	35	in fact
15	half	36	for free
16	dangerous	37	on the other hand
17	reduce	38	put aside
18	citizen	39	right away
19	post	40	set up
20	focus	41	for a while
21	instead	42	stay away from
		43	figure out

※ 다음 우리말을 영어로 쓰시오.

01 중독 _____

02 출생, 탄생 _____

03 불편한 _____

04 야기하다, 원인이 되다 _____

05 제한하다 _____

06 게시하다 _____

07 차단하다, 막다 _____

08 줄이다 _____

09 저작권 _____

10 알람소리, 경보 _____

11 상쾌한 _____

12 장점, 유리함 _____

14 존중하다, 존경하다 _____

15 시끄러운 _____

16 단점, 약점, 불리한 점 _____

17 즐거운 _____

18 실수 _____

19 집중하다 _____

20 발언, 논평, 비평 _____

21 만들다, 형성시키다 _____

22 ~할 작정이다 _____

23 제안하다 _____

24 시민 _____

25 연락하다 _____

26 필요한 _____

27 반, 절반 _____

28 옥외의, 야외의 _____

29 고통 _____

30 창의적인 _____

31 위험한 _____

32 해독 _____

33 비밀번호 _____

34 기기, 장치 _____

35 잠시 동안 _____

36 치우다 _____

37 ~ 와 같은 _____

38 ~에서 떨어져 있다, ~을 멀리하다 _____

39 사실 _____

40 치우다 _____

41 무료로 _____

42 알아내다, 계산하다 _____

43 반면에 _____

※ 다음 영영풀이에 알맞은 단어를 <보기>에서 골라 쓴 후, 우리말 뜻을 쓰시오.

1 _____ : an act of being born: _____

2 _____ : one of two equal parts of something: _____

3 _____ : a right to sell a book, music, film, etc.: _____

4 _____ : a thing that is regarded as representing for another: _____

5 _____ : something that may help one to gain favorable result: _____

6 _____ : something that you say about someone or something: _____

7 _____ : a warning to people to be prepared to deal with something dangerous: _____

8 _____ : a mechanical object that is made for a particular purpose: _____

9 _____ : to plan to do something, to have an action planned in your mind: _____

10 _____ : an inability to stop doing or using something, especially something harmful: _____

11 _____ : a spoken or written piece of information that you send to someone: _____

12 _____ : to communicate with someone by calling or sending them a letter, email, etc.: _____

13 _____ : an action, decision, or judgment that produces an unwanted or unintentional result: _____

14 _____ : storing pictures, sound, etc. in a number of small signals or showing them in numbers: _____

15 _____ : a period when you stop taking unhealthy or harmful foods, drinks, or drugs into your body for a period: _____

16 _____ : talk between two or more people in which thoughts, feelings, and ideas are expressed, or questions are asked and answered: _____

보기			
digital	symbol	alert	comment
intend	message	contact	half
detox	mistake	device	advantage
addiction	birth	conversation	copyright

※ 다음 우리말과 일치하도록 빈칸에 알맞은 말을 쓰시오.

Listen & Speak 1 A

1. G: You _____ _____, Peter.

   B: I played computer games _____ _____, _____ last night I _____ _____ _____ _____ _____ four hours.

   G: _____ computer games too much _____ _____ _____ _____ _____ _____ _____.

   B: I know, Jenny, but I _____ _____ it. I think I'm _____ to it.

   G: If I _____ you, I _____ _____ a daily plan _____ _____ game time.

   B: That's a good idea. Thanks.

2. W: Tony, you _____ too _____ _____ _____ your smartphone.

   B: My friends _____ _____ on SNS _____ every day, so I _____ _____ _____, Mom.

   W: _____ _____ _____ _____ _____, I would _____ _____ _____ _____ to your friends.

   B: _____ activities?

   W: Yes. You can do _____ _____ _____ great activities _____ _____ soccer or skating.

   B: All _____. I will _____ them today.

Listen & Speak 2 A

1. G: James, what _____ you _____?

   B: I'm _____ some of the pictures _____ I _____ _____ Sarah today.

   G: Did you ask Sarah _____ you _____ _____ them online?

   B: No, but I think it's okay _____ she _____ _____ in the pictures.

   G: You're _____ _____ _____ _____ someone's pictures _____ _____.

   B: Oh, maybe you're right. I'll _____ Sarah and ask her _____ _____.

1. G: 너 피곤해 보인다, Peter.
   B: 나 늦게까지 게임을 해서, 어젯밤에 4시간도 못 잤어.
   G: 컴퓨터 게임을 너무 많이 하는 건 네 건강에 좋지 않아.
   B: 나도 알아, Jenny, 그런데 멈출 수가 없어. 난 그것에 중독된 것 같아.
   G: 만약 내가 너라면, 게임 시간을 제한하기 위해 일일 계획을 짤 거야.
   B: 그거 좋은 생각이네. 고마워.

2. W: Tony, 너 스마트 폰에 너무 많은 시간을 보내는구나.
   B: 제 친구들은 거의 매일 SNS에서 만나기 때문에, 저도 어쩔 수 없어요, 엄마.
   W: 만약 내가 너라면, 친구들에게 야외 활동을 하자고 제안할 거야.
   B: 야외 활동이요?
   W: 응. 너는 축구나 스케이트 타기 등과 같은 많은 멋진 활동을 할 수 있어.
   B: 알겠어요. 오늘 제안해 볼게요.

1. G: James, 뭐 하고 있니?
   B: 나 오늘 Sarah와 함께 찍은 사진들 중 몇 장을 올리고 있어.
   G: 네가 그걸 온라인에 올려도 될지 Sarah에게 물어봤니?
   B: 아니, 그렇지만 그녀가 사진들 속에서 멋져 보이기 때문에 괜찮을 것 같아.
   G: 너는 다른 사람들의 사진을 물어보지 않고 올리면 안 돼.
   B: 오, 네 말이 맞을지 몰라. 내가 지금 당장 Sarah에게 전화해서 물어볼게.

2. G: David, _____ _____ this new movie on the computer.

B: _____ the computer?

G: Yes. I have a website we can _____ it from _____ _____.

B: You're not _____ _____ _____ movies _____ that website, Catherine. It's _____ the _____.

G: Really? I didn't know that.

B: _____ _____ _____ _____ to the movie theater, _____?

G: Okay. _____ go.

2. G: David, 컴퓨터로 이 신작 영화 보자.
B: 컴퓨터로?
G: 응. 우리가 그것을 무료로 내려 받을 수 있는 웹 사이트가 있어.
B: 너는 그런 웹 사이트에서 영화를 내려 받으면 안 돼, Catherine. 그건 법에 어긋나.
G: 정말? 그런지 몰랐어.
B: 대신, 우리 영화관에 가는 건 어떨까?
G: 좋아. 가자.

Real Life Talk

Bora: Seho, look! Somebody _____ _____ _____ your SNS. I don't think you _____ _____.

Seho: Really? Who did this?

Bora: I think someone _____ _____ your _____.

Seho: _____ _____ I _____?

Bora: If I _____ you, I would _____ my _____.

Seho: I think I _____.

Bora: Is your password _____ _____ _____?

Seho: I _____ my _____ _____.

Bora: That is not good. _____ _____, it is a big mistake. You'_____ _____ _____ _____ _____ your _____ _____ when you _____ _____ _____.

Seho: Okay, I see. I will _____ it to a _____ _____.

보라: 세호야, 봐! 누군가 네 SNS에 이상한 것을 올렸어. 나는 네가 그것들을 올렸다고 생각하지 않아.
세호: 정말? 누가 그랬지?
보라: 내 생각에 누군가 네 비밀번호를 알아낸 것 같아.
세호: 어떻게 해야 하지?
보라: 내가 너라면 비밀번호를 바꾸겠어.
세호: 내 생각에도 그래야 할 것 같아.
보라: 네 비밀번호는 추측하기 쉽니?
세호: 내 생일 날짜를 사용했어.
보라: 그것은 좋지 않아. 사실 그건 큰 실수야. 비밀번호를 만들 때 개인 정보를 사용하지 말아야 해.
세호: 그래, 알았어. 그걸 더 강한 것으로 바꿀 거야.

Wrap Up

B: What are you _____, Sohee?

G: I'm _____ a _____ about the restaurant I visited today.

B: Those are great pictures. Did you _____ all of them?

G: No. I _____ the pictures _____ someone's _____.

B: Then you'_____ _____ _____ _____ _____ _____ _____ them on your blog.

G: _____ _____?

B: _____ only the blog _____ has the _____ _____ _____ them.

G: Oh, I see.

B: 뭐 하고 있니, 소희야?
G: 나는 오늘 방문했던 식당에 관한 게시 글을 쓰고 있어.
B: 멋진 사진들이네. 그것들을 네가 다 찍었니?
G: 아니. 누군가의 블로그에서 사진들을 가져왔어.
B: 그럼 너는 그것들을 네 블로그에 게시하면 안 돼.
G: 왜 안 돼?
B: 왜냐하면 그 블로그 주인만이 그것들을 사용할 권리가 있거든.
G: 오, 알겠어.

※ 다음 우리말에 맞도록 대화를 영어로 쓰시오.

Listen & Speak 1 A

1. G: _____

   B: _____

   _____

   G: _____

   B: _____

   G: _____

   B: _____

2. W: _____

   B: _____

   W: _____

   B: _____

   W: _____

   B: _____

Listen & Speak 2 A

1. G: _____

   B: _____

   G: _____

   B: _____

   G: _____

   B: _____

2. G: _____

   B: _____

   G: _____

   B: _____

   _____

   G: _____

   B: _____

   G: _____

해석

1. G: 너 피곤해 보인다, Peter.
   B: 나 늦게까지 게임을 해서, 어젯밤에 4시간도 못 잤어.
   G: 컴퓨터 게임을 너무 많이 하는 건 네 건강에 좋지 않아.
   B: 나도 알아, Jenny, 그런데 멈출 수가 없어. 난 그것에 중독된 것 같아.
   G: 만약 내가 너라면, 게임 시간을 제한하기 위해 일일 계획을 짤 거야.
   B: 그거 좋은 생각이네. 고마워.

2. W: Tony, 너 스마트 폰에 너무 많은 시간을 보내는구나.
   B: 제 친구들은 거의 매일 SNS에서 만나기 때문에, 저도 어쩔 수 없어요, 엄마.
   W: 만약 내가 너라면, 친구들에게 야외 활동을 하자고 제안할 거야.
   B: 야외 활동이요?
   W: 응. 너는 축구나 스케이트 타기 등과 같은 많은 멋진 활동을 할 수 있어.
   B: 알겠어요. 오늘 제안해 볼게요.

1. G: James, 뭐 하고 있니?
   B: 나 오늘 Sarah와 함께 찍은 사진들 중 몇 장을 올리고 있어.
   G: 네가 그걸 온라인에 올려도 될지 Sarah에게 물어봤니?
   B: 아니, 그렇지만 그녀가 사진들 속에서 멋져 보이기 때문에 괜찮을 것 같아.
   G: 너는 다른 사람들의 사진을 물어보지 않고 올리면 안 돼.
   B: 오, 네 말이 맞을지 몰라. 내가 지금 당장 Sarah에게 전화해서 물어볼게.

2. G: David, 컴퓨터로 이 신작 영화 보자.
   B: 컴퓨터로?
   G: 응. 우리가 그것을 무료로 내려 받을 수 있는 웹 사이트가 있어.
   B: 너는 그런 웹 사이트에서 영화를 내려 받으면 안 돼, Catherine. 그건 법에 어긋나.
   G: 정말? 그런지 몰랐어.
   B: 대신, 우리 영화관에 가는 건 어떨까?
   G: 좋아. 가자.

Real Life Talk

Bora: _____
_____

Seho: _____

Bora: _____

Seho: _____

Bora: _____

Seho: _____

Bora: _____

Seho: _____

Bora: _____
_____

Seho: _____

보라: 세호야, 봐! 누군가 네 SNS에 이상한 것을 올렸어. 나는 네가 그것들을 올렸다고 생각하지 않아.

세호: 정말? 누가 그랬지?

보라: 내 생각에 누군가 네 비밀번호를 알아낸 것 같아.

세호: 어떻게 해야 하지?

보라: 내가 너라면 비밀번호를 바꾸겠어.

세호: 내 생각에도 그래야 할 것 같아.

보라: 네 비밀번호는 추측하기 쉽니?

세호: 내 생일 날짜를 사용했어.

보라: 그것은 좋지 않아. 사실 그건 큰 실수야. 비밀번호를 만들 때 개인 정보를 사용하지 말아야 해.

세호: 그래, 알았어. 그걸 더 강한 것으로 바꿀 거야.

Wrap Up

B: _____

G: _____

B: _____

G: _____

B: _____

G: _____

B: _____

G: _____

B: 뭐 하고 있니, 소희야?

G: 나는 오늘 방문했던 식당에 관한 게시 글을 쓰고 있어.

B: 멋진 사진들이네. 그것들을 네가 다 찍었니?

G: 아니. 누군가의 블로그에서 사진들을 가져왔어.

B: 그럼 너는 그것들을 네 블로그에 게시하면 안 돼.

G: 왜 안 돼?

B: 왜냐하면 그 블로그 주인만이 그것들을 사용할 권리가 있거든.

G: 오, 알겠어.

※ 다음 우리말과 일치하도록 빈칸에 알맞은 것을 골라 쓰시오.

Time for Digital Detox

1 Hi, students! _____ you _____ _____ in the morning, what is the _____ thing you do?

A. first   B. up   C. when   D. wake

2 Do you _____ SNS _____ _____ your _____?

A. postings   B. read   C. smartphone   D. on

3 _____ your smartphone is not _____ you. _____ do you _____?

A. feel   B. imagine   C. near   D. how

4 Students, please _____ _____ _____ the list that are _____ for you.

A. on   B. check   C. true   D. items

5 _____ you _____ your smartphone?

A. addicted   B. are   C. to

6 _____ my smartphone, I _____ _____.

A. feel   B. without   C. uncomfortable

7 I _____ my smartphone _____ the _____.

A. into   B. take   C. bathroom

8 It is _____ enjoyable to _____ time _____ my smartphone _____ with friends.

A. than   B. spend   C. more   D. on

9 I often _____ SNS _____ _____ _____.

A. while   B. check   C. studying   D. postings

10 I _____ to _____ the time I spend _____ my smartphone, but I _____.

A. fail   B. reduce   C. try   D. on

11 I check my smartphone _____ _____ I hear the _____ of an _____.

A. alert   B. right   C. sound   D. after

12 I have my smartphone _____ _____ me _____ I'm _____.

A. while   B. next   C. eating   D. to

13 What is your _____? Did you check _____ _____ _____?

A. half   B. score   C. than   D. more

14 If _____, you may have a _____ _____ smartphone _____.

A. with   B. so   C. addiction   D. problem

15 Smartphone _____ _____ you to _____ too much _____ on your smartphone.

A. causes   B. addiction   C. spend   D. time

16 Also, you cannot _____ on your _____ and may have a _____ in your _____.

A. pain   B. studies   C. neck   D. focus

17 Then now is the time _____ _____ digital detox.

A. to   B. for   C. start   D. you

디지털 디톡스를 할 시간

1 안녕하세요, 학생 여러분! 여러분은 아침에 일어났을 때, 가장 먼저 하는 일이 무엇인가요?

2 스마트폰으로 SNS 게시물을 읽나요?

3 스마트폰이 여러분 근처에 있지 않다고 상상해 보세요. 기분이 어떤가요?

4 학생 여러분, 이 목록에서 여러분에게 맞는 항목들을 표시해 보세요.

5 너는 스마트폰에 중독되었는가?

6 나는 스마트폰이 없으면, 불편함을 느낀다.

7 나는 스마트폰을 화장실에 가져간다.

8 나는 친구들과 함께 시간을 보내는 것보다 스마트폰을 하면서 보내는 시간이 더 즐겁다.

9 나는 공부하면서 SNS 게시물을 종종 확인한다.

10 나는 스마트폰을 사용하는 시간을 줄이려고 노력하지만, 실패한다.

11 나는 알림음을 듣자마자 스마트폰을 확인한다.

12 나는 식사 중에 스마트폰을 옆에 둔다.

13 여러분의 점수는 어떤가요? 절반보다 더 많이 표시했나요?

14 만약 그렇다면, 여러분은 스마트폰 중독의 문제를 가지고 있을지도 모릅니다.

15 스마트폰 중독은 여러분이 스마트폰에 너무 많은 시간을 보내게 만듭니다.

16 또한 여러분은 학업에 집중할 수 없고 목에 통증이 있을지도 모릅니다.

17 그렇다면 지금 여러분은 디지털 디톡스를 시작할 시간입니다.

18 Digital detox means _____ _____ from digital devices, _____ as smartphones and computers, for a _____.

A. while　　　B. away　　　C. such　　　D. staying

19 Digital detox will help you a _____. You can enjoy _____ _____ the _____ digital world.

A. noisy　　　B. from　　　C. freedom　　　D. lot

20 You can _____ more on your _____. Sometimes you can feel _____ and have new, _____ ideas.

A. work　　　B. creative　　　C. refreshed　　　D. focus

21 Digital detox will also _____ you _____ more time _____ _____.

A. others　　　B. help　　　C. with　　　D. spend

22 _____ _____ a smartphone, _____, is not _____.

A. however　　　B. without　　　C. easy　　　D. living

23 So, it is _____ for you to _____ some _____ for _____ your smartphone.

A. rules　　　B. necessary　　　C. set　　　D. using

24 You then _____ _____ _____ the rules.

A. to　　　B. need　　　C. follow

25 Now, please _____ groups and, in your group, _____ _____ for _____ your smartphone.

A. create　　　B. form　　　C. using　　　D. rules

<By Yerim, Yongmin, and Hojin>

26 We will _____ _____ our smartphones _____ _____.

A. off　　　B. studying　　　C. turn　　　D. while

27 We will not _____ our _____ _____ the _____.

A. into　　　B. take　　　C. bathroom　　　D. smarphones

28 We will _____ our smartphones _____ _____ the bedroom and not _____ them at night.

A. of　　　B. keep　　　C. out　　　D. use

<By Jina, Hosung, and Minsu>

29 More Time for Outside Activities – We will _____ more time _____ _____ our smartphones.

A. without　　　B. spend　　　C. outside　　　D. playing

30 Fewer SNS Messages – We will _____ _____ SNS _____ our smartphones.

A. fewer　　　B. on　　　C. post　　　D. messages

<By Jiho, Sohee, and Yumin>

31 If I _____ you, I would _____ my time on my smartphone _____ _____.

A. reduce　　　B. half　　　C. were　　　D. by

32 If I were you, I _____ _____ all _____.

A. alerts　　　B. turn　　　C. would　　　D. off

33 You did a good job, students! If we had no smartphones, our _____ would be more _____, but too much _____ of a smartphone is _____.

A. dangerous　　　B. lives　　　C. use　　　D. difficult

34 _____ digital detox, you can _____ a _____ smartphone _____.

A. wise　　　B. with　　　C. become　　　D. user

18 디지털 디톡스는 스마트폰과 컴퓨터 같은 디지털 기기들로부터 잠시 동안 떨어져 있는 것을 의미합니다.

19 디지털 디톡스는 여러분을 많이 도와줄 것입니다. 여러분은 시끄러운 디지털 세계로부터 자유를 즐길 수 있습니다.

20 여러분은 하는 일에 더욱 집중할 수 있습니다. 종종 여러분은 상쾌함을 느끼고 새롭고 창의적인 아이디어를 얻을 수 있습니다.

21 디지털 디톡스는 또한 여러분이 다른 사람들과 더 많은 시간을 보내도록 도와줄 것입니다.

22 하지만 스마트폰 없이 사는 것은 쉽지 않습니다.

23 그러므로 여러분은 스마트폰을 사용하기 위한 몇 가지 규칙을 정할 필요가 있습니다.

24 그리고 나서 여러분은 그 규칙들을 따라야 합니다.

25 자, 조를 형성하고, 여러분의 조에서, 스마트폰을 사용하기 위한 규칙을 만들어 보세요.

〈예림, 용민, 호진으로부터〉

26 우리는 공부하는 동안 스마트폰을 끌 것이다.

27 우리는 화장실에 스마트폰을 가져가지 않을 것이다.

28 우리는 밤에 스마트폰을 침실 밖에 두고 사용하지 않을 것이다.

〈지나, 호성, 민수로부터〉

29 야외 활동을 위한 더 많은 시간 – 우리는 스마트폰 없이 밖에서 노는 데 더 많은 시간을 보낼 것이다.

30 SNS는 더 적게 – 우리는 스마트폰에 SNS 메시지를 더 적게 올릴 것이다.

〈지호, 소희, 유민〉

31 만약 내가 너라면, 나는 스마트폰에 쓰는 시간을 절반으로 줄일 것이다.

32 만약 내가 너라면, 모든 알림을 끌 것이다.

33 잘했어요, 학생 여러분! 만약 스마트폰이 없다면 우리의 삶이 더 힘들겠지만, 스마트폰을 너무 많이 사용하는 것은 위험합니다.

34 디지털 디톡스와 함께, 여러분은 현명한 스마트폰 사용자가 될 수 있습니다.

※ 다음 우리말과 일치하도록 빈칸에 알맞은 말을 쓰시오.

Time for Digital Detox

1 Hi, students! _____ you _____ _____ _____ _____ _____ _____, _____ is the first thing you do?

2 Do you _____ SNS _____ _____ your smartphone?

3 _____ your smartphone _____ not _____ you. _____ do you feel?

4 Students, please _____ _____ on the list _____ _____ true for you.

5 _____ you _____ _____ your smartphone?

6 _____ my smartphone, I _____ _____.

7 I _____ my smartphone _____ the _____.

8 It is _____ _____ _____ spend time _____ my smartphone _____ _____ friends.

9 I often _____ SNS _____ _____ _____.

10 I try to _____ the time _____ _____ _____ my smartphone, but I _____.

11 I check my smartphone _____ _____ _____ I hear the sound of _____ _____.

12 I have my smartphone _____ _____ me _____ I'm eating.

13 _____ is your _____? Did you _____ _____ _____ _____?

14 If so, you may _____ a problem _____ smartphone _____.

15 Smartphone addiction _____ _____ _____ _____ too much time _____ your smartphone.

16 _____, you cannot _____ _____ your _____ and may _____ _____ _____ _____ your _____.

17 Then now is the time _____ _____ _____ _____ _____ _____.

디지털 디톡스를 할 시간

1 안녕하세요, 학생 여러분! 여러분은 아침에 일어났을 때, 가장 먼저 하는 일이 무엇인가요?

2 스마트폰으로 SNS 게시물을 읽나요?

3 스마트폰이 여러분 근처에 있지 않다고 상상해 보세요. 기분이 어떤가요?

4 학생 여러분, 이 목록에서 여러분에게 맞는 항목들을 표시해 보세요.

5 너는 스마트폰에 중독되었는가?

6 나는 스마트폰이 없으면, 불편함을 느낀다.

7 나는 스마트폰을 화장실에 가져간다.

8 나는 친구들과 함께 시간을 보내는 것보다 스마트폰을 하면서 보내는 시간이 더 즐겁다.

9 나는 공부하면서 SNS 게시물을 종종 확인한다.

10 나는 스마트폰을 사용하는 시간을 줄이려고 노력하지만, 실패한다.

11 나는 알림음을 듣자마자 스마트폰을 확인한다.

12 나는 식사 중에 스마트폰을 옆에 둔다.

13 여러분의 점수는 어떤가요? 절반보다 더 많이 표시했나요?

14 만약 그렇다면, 여러분은 스마트폰 중독의 문제를 가지고 있을지도 모릅니다.

15 스마트폰 중독은 여러분이 스마트폰에 너무 많은 시간을 보내게 만듭니다.

16 또한 여러분은 학업에 집중할 수 없고 목에 통증이 있을지도 모릅니다.

17 그렇다면 지금 여러분은 디지털 디톡스를 시작할 시간입니다.

18 Digital detox _____ _____ _____ digital devices, such as smartphones and computers, _____ a while.

19 Digital detox will _____ you _____ _____. You can enjoy _____ _____ the _____ digital world.

20 You can _____ more _____ your work. Sometimes you can _____ _____ and have new, _____ _____.

21 Digital detox will also _____ you _____ more time _____ _____.

22 _____ without a smartphone, _____ _____ not easy.

23 So, it is _____ _____ _____ _____ some rules _____ _____ your smartphone.

24 You then _____ _____ _____ the rules.

25 Now, please _____ groups and, in your group, _____ _____ _____ your smartphone.

<By Yerim, Yongmin, and Hojin>

26 We will _____ _____ our smartphones _____ _____.

27 We will not _____ our smartphones _____ the bathroom.

28 We will _____ our smartphones _____ _____ _____ and not use _____ at night.

<By Jina, Hosung, and Minsu>

29 _____ _____ _____ Outside Activities – We will _____ _____ _____ _____ _____ _____ our smartphones.

30 _____ SNS Messages – We will _____ _____ SNS messages _____ our smartphones.

<By Jiho, Sohee, and Yumin>

31 If _____ _____ you, I _____ _____ my time _____ my smartphone _____ _____.

32 If _____ _____ you, I _____ turn _____ all alerts.

33 You did a good job, students! If we _____ no smartphones, our lives _____ _____ _____ _____ _____, but _____ _____ use of a smartphone is _____.

34 _____ digital detox, you can become a _____ _____.

---

18 디지털 디톡스는 스마트폰과 컴퓨터 같은 디지털 기기들로부터 잠시 동안 떨어져 있는 것을 의미합니다.

19 디지털 디톡스는 여러분을 많이 도와줄 것입니다. 여러분은 시끄러운 디지털 세계로부터 자유를 즐길 수 있습니다.

20 여러분은 하는 일에 더욱 집중할 수 있습니다. 종종 여러분은 상쾌함을 느끼고 새롭고 창의적인 아이디어를 얻을 수 있습니다.

21 디지털 디톡스는 또한 여러분이 다른 사람들과 더 많은 시간을 보내도록 도와줄 것입니다.

22 하지만 스마트폰 없이 사는 것은 쉽지 않습니다.

23 그러므로 여러분은 스마트폰을 사용하기 위한 몇 가지 규칙을 정할 필요가 있습니다.

24 그리고 나서 여러분은 그 규칙들을 따라야 합니다.

25 자, 조를 형성하고, 여러분의 조에서, 스마트폰을 사용하기 위한 규칙을 만들어 보세요.

〈예림, 용민, 호진으로부터〉

26 우리는 공부하는 동안 스마트폰을 끌 것이다.

27 우리는 화장실에 스마트폰을 가져가지 않을 것이다.

28 우리는 밤에 스마트폰을 침실 밖에 두고 사용하지 않을 것이다.

〈지나, 호성, 민수로부터〉

29 야외 활동을 위한 더 많은 시간 – 우리는 스마트폰 없이 밖에서 노는 데 더 많은 시간을 보낼 것이다.

30 SNS는 더 적게 – 우리는 스마트폰에 SNS 메시지를 더 적게 올릴 것이다.

〈지호, 소희, 유민〉

31 만약 내가 너라면, 나는 스마트폰에 쓰는 시간을 절반으로 줄일 것이다.

32 만약 내가 너라면, 모든 알림을 끌 것이다.

33 잘했어요, 학생 여러분! 만약 스마트폰이 없다면 우리의 삶이 더 힘들겠지만, 스마트폰을 너무 많이 사용하는 것은 위험합니다.

34 디지털 디톡스와 함께, 여러분은 현명한 스마트폰 사용자가 될 수 있습니다.

※ 다음 문장을 우리말로 쓰시오.

1 Hi, students! When you wake up in the morning, what is the first thing you do?
➡ _____

2 Do you read SNS postings on your smartphone?
➡ _____

3 Imagine your smartphone is not near you. How do you feel?
➡ _____

4 Students, please check items on the list that are true for you.
➡ _____

5 Are you addicted to your smartphone?
➡ _____

6 Without my smartphone, I feel uncomfortable.
➡ _____

7 I take my smartphone into the bathroom.
➡ _____

8 It is more enjoyable to spend time on my smartphone than with friends.
➡ _____

9 I often check SNS postings while studying.
➡ _____

10 I try to reduce the time I spend on my smartphone, but I fail.
➡ _____

11 I check my smartphone right after I hear the sound of an alert.
➡ _____

12 I have my smartphone next to me while I'm eating.
➡ _____

13 What is your score? Did you check more than half?
➡ _____

14 If so, you may have a problem with smartphone addiction.
➡ _____

15 Smartphone addiction causes you to spend too much time on your smartphone.
➡ _____

16 Also, you cannot focus on your studies and may have a pain in your neck.
➡ _____

17 Then now is the time for you to start digital detox.
➡ _____

18 Digital detox means staying away from digital devices, such as smartphones and computers, for a while.
➡ _____

19 Digital detox will help you a lot. You can enjoy freedom from the noisy digital world.

➡ _____

20 You can focus more on your work. Sometimes you can feel refreshed and have new, creative ideas.

➡ _____

21 Digital detox will also help you spend more time with others.

➡ _____

22 Living without a smartphone, however, is not easy.

➡ _____

23 So, it is necessary for you to set some rules for using your smartphone.

➡ _____

24 You then need to follow the rules.

➡ _____

25 Now, please form groups and, in your group, create rules for using your smartphone.

➡ _____

By Yerim, Yongmin, and Hojin

26 We will turn off our smartphones while studying.

➡ _____

27 We will not take our smartphones into the bathroom.

➡ _____

28 We will keep our smartphones out of the bedroom and not use them at night.

➡ _____

By Jina, Hosung, and Minsu

29 More Time for Outside Activities – We will spend more time playing outside without our smartphones.

➡ _____

30 Fewer SNS Messages – We will post fewer SNS messages on our smartphones.

➡ _____

By Jiho, Sohee, and Yumin

31 If I were you, I would reduce my time on my smartphone by half.

➡ _____

32 If I were you, I would turn off all alerts.

➡ _____

33 You did a good job, students! If we had no smartphones, our lives would be more difficult, but too much use of a smartphone is dangerous.

➡ _____

_____

34 With digital detox, you can become a wise smartphone user.

➡ _____

※ 다음 괄호 안의 단어들을 우리말에 맞도록 바르게 배열하시오.

Time for Digital Detox

1 (students! / hi, // you / when / up / wake / the / in / morning, / is / what / first / the / thing / do? / you)
➡ _____
_____

2 (you / do / SNS / read / postings / on / smartphone? / your)
➡ _____

3 (your / imagine / smarphone / not / is / you. / near // do / how / feel? / you)
➡ _____

4 (please / students, / items / check / the / on / that / list / true / are / you. / for)
➡ _____

5 (you / are / to / addicted / smartphone? / your)
➡ _____

6 (my / without / smartphone, / feel / I / uncomfortable.)
➡ _____

7 (take / I / smarphone / my / the / bathroom. / into)
➡ _____

8 (is / it / enjoyable / more / spend / to / time / my / on / smartphone / with / friends. / than)
➡ _____

9 (often / I / check / postings / SNS / studying. / while)
➡ _____

10 (try / I / reduce / to / time / the / spend / I / my / on / smartphone, / I / but / fail.)
➡ _____

11 (check / I / smartphone / my / after / right / hear / I / sound / the / of / alert. / an)
➡ _____

12 (have / I / smartphone / my / to / next / while / me / eating. / I'm)
➡ _____

13 (is / what / score? / your // you / did / more / check / half? / than)
➡ _____

14 (so, / if / may / you / have / problem / a / with / addiction. / smartphone)
➡ _____

15 (addiction / smartphone / you / causes / spend / to / much / too / on / time / smartphone. / your)
➡ _____

16 (you / also, / focus / cannot / your / on / studies / may / and / a / have / in / pain / neck. / your)
➡ _____

17 (now / then / the / is / for / time / you / start / to / detox. / digital)
➡ _____

디지털 디톡스를 할 시간

1 안녕하세요, 학생 여러분! 여러분은 아침에 일어났을 때, 가장 먼저 하는 일이 무엇인가요?

2 스마트폰으로 SNS 게시물을 읽나요?

3 스마트폰이 여러분 근처에 있지 않다고 상상해 보세요. 기분이 어떤가요?

4 학생 여러분, 이 목록에서 여러분에게 맞는 항목들을 표시해 보세요.

5 너는 스마트폰에 중독되었는가?

6 나는 스마트폰이 없으면, 불편함을 느낀다.

7 나는 스마트폰을 화장실에 가져간다.

8 나는 친구들과 함께 시간을 보내는 것보다 스마트폰을 하면서 보내는 시간이 더 즐겁다.

9 나는 공부하면서 SNS 게시물을 종종 확인한다.

10 나는 스마트폰을 사용하는 시간을 줄이려고 노력하지만, 실패한다.

11 나는 알림음을 듣자마자 스마트폰을 확인한다.

12 나는 식사 중에 스마트폰을 옆에 둔다.

13 여러분의 점수는 어떤가요? 절반보다 더 많이 표시했나요?

14 만약 그렇다면, 여러분은 스마트폰 중독의 문제를 가지고 있을지도 모릅니다.

15 스마트폰 중독은 여러분이 스마트폰에 너무 많은 시간을 보내게 만듭니다.

16 또한 여러분은 학업에 집중할 수 없고 목에 통증이 있을지도 모릅니다.

17 그렇다면 지금 여러분은 디지털 디톡스를 시작할 시간입니다.

18 (detox / digital / staying / means / from / away / devices, / digital / as / such / and / smartphones / for / computers, / while. / a)
➡ _____

19 (detox / digital / help / will / a / you / lot. // can / you / freedom / enjoy / from / noisy / the / world. / digital)
➡ _____

20 (can / you / more / focus / on / work. / your // you / sometimes / feel / can / and / refreshed / new, / have / ideas. / creative)
➡ _____

21 (detox / digital / also / will / you / help / more / spend / with / time / others.)
➡ _____

22 (without / living / smartphone, / a / is / however, / easy. / not)
➡ _____

23 (it / so, / is / for / necessary / you / set / to / rules / some / using / for / smartphone. / your)
➡ _____

24 (then / you / to / need / follow / rules. / the)
➡ _____

25 (please / now, / groups / form / and, / your / in / group, / rules / create / for / using / smartphone. / your)
➡ _____

By Yerim, Yongmin, and Hojin
26 (will / we / off / turn / smartphones / our / studying. / while)
➡ _____

27 (will / we / take / not / smartphones / our / into / bathroom. / the)
➡ _____

28 (will / we / our / keep / out / smartphones / of / bedroom / the / and / use / not / them / night. / at)
➡ _____

By Jina, Hosung, and Minsu
29 (Time / More / for / Activities / Outside / – / will / we / more / spend / playing / time / without / outside / smartphones. / our)
➡ _____

30 (SNS / Fewer / Messages / – / will / we / fewer / post / messages / SNS / our / on / smartphones.)
➡ _____

By Jiho, Sohee, and Yumin
31 (I / if / you, / were / would / I / my / time / reduce / my / on / by / smartphone / half.)
➡ _____

32 (I / if / you, / were / would / I / off / alerts. / turn / all)
➡ _____

33 (did / you / good / a / students! / job, / we / if / no / had / smartphones, / lives / our / be / would / more / but / difficult, / much / too / of / use / is / smartphone / a / dangerous.)
➡ _____

34 (digital / with / detox, / can / you / a / become / smartphone / wise / user.)
➡ _____

18 디지털 디톡스는 스마트폰과 컴퓨터 같은 디지털 기기들로부터 잠시 동안 떨어져 있는 것을 의미합니다.

19 디지털 디톡스는 여러분을 많이 도와줄 것입니다. 여러분은 시끄러운 디지털 세계로부터 자유를 즐길 수 있습니다.

20 여러분은 하는 일에 더욱 집중할 수 있습니다. 종종 여러분은 상쾌함을 느끼고 새롭고 창의적인 아이디어를 얻을 수 있습니다.

21 디지털 디톡스는 또한 여러분이 다른 사람들과 더 많은 시간을 보내도록 도와줄 것입니다.

22 하지만 스마트폰 없이 사는 것은 쉽지 않습니다.

23 그러므로 여러분은 스마트폰을 사용하기 위한 몇 가지 규칙을 정할 필요가 있습니다.

24 그리고 나서 여러분은 그 규칙들을 따라야 합니다.

25 자, 조를 형성하고, 여러분의 조에서, 스마트폰을 사용하기 위한 규칙을 만들어 보세요.

〈예림, 용민, 호진으로부터〉

26 우리는 공부하는 동안 스마트폰을 끌 것이다.

27 우리는 화장실에 스마트폰을 가져가지 않을 것이다.

28 우리는 밤에 스마트폰을 침실 밖에 두고 사용하지 않을 것이다.

〈지나, 호성, 민수로부터〉

29 야외 활동을 위한 더 많은 시간 – 우리는 스마트폰 없이 밖에서 노는 데 더 많은 시간을 보낼 것이다.

30 SNS는 더 적게 – 우리는 스마트폰에 SNS 메시지를 더 적게 올릴 것이다.

〈지호, 소희, 유민〉

31 만약 내가 너라면, 나는 스마트폰에 쓰는 시간을 절반으로 줄일 것이다.

32 만약 내가 너라면, 모든 알림을 끌 것이다.

33 잘했어요, 학생 여러분! 만약 스마트폰이 없다면 우리의 삶이 더 힘들겠지만, 스마트폰을 너무 많이 사용하는 것은 위험합니다.

34 디지털 디톡스와 함께, 여러분은 현명한 스마트폰 사용자가 될 수 있습니다.

※ 다음 우리말을 영어로 쓰시오.

1 안녕하세요, 학생 여러분! 여러분은 아침에 일어났을 때, 가장 먼저 하는 일이 무엇인가요?
➡ _____

2 스마트폰으로 SNS 게시물을 읽나요?
➡ _____

3 스마트폰이 여러분 근처에 있지 않다고 상상해 보세요. 기분이 어떤가요?
➡ _____

4 학생 여러분, 이 목록에서 여러분에게 맞는 항목들을 표시해 보세요.
➡ _____

5 너는 스마트폰에 중독되었는가?
➡ _____

6 나는 스마트폰이 없으면, 불편함을 느낀다.
➡ _____

7 나는 스마트폰을 화장실에 가져간다.
➡ _____

8 나는 친구들과 함께 시간을 보내는 것보다 스마트폰을 하면서 보내는 시간이 더 즐겁다.
➡ _____

9 나는 공부하면서 SNS 게시물을 종종 확인한다.
➡ _____

10 나는 스마트폰을 사용하는 시간을 줄이려고 노력하지만, 실패한다.
➡ _____

11 나는 알림음을 듣자마자 스마트폰을 확인한다.
➡ _____

12 나는 식사 중에 스마트폰을 옆에 둔다.
➡ _____

13 여러분의 점수는 어떤가요? 절반보다 더 많이 표시했나요?
➡ _____

14 만약 그렇다면, 여러분은 스마트폰 중독의 문제를 가지고 있을지도 모릅니다.
➡ _____

15 스마트폰 중독은 여러분이 스마트폰에 너무 많은 시간을 보내게 만듭니다.
➡ _____

16 또한 여러분은 학업에 집중할 수 없고 목에 통증이 있을지도 모릅니다.
➡ _____

17 그렇다면 지금 여러분은 디지털 디톡스를 시작할 시간입니다.
➡ _____

18 디지털 디톡스는 스마트폰과 컴퓨터 같은 디지털 기기들로부터 잠시 동안 떨어져 있는 것을 의미합니다.
➡ _____

19 디지털 디톡스는 여러분을 많이 도와줄 것입니다. 여러분은 시끄러운 디지털 세계로부터 자유를 즐길 수 있습니다.

➡ _____

20 여러분은 하는 일에 더욱 집중할 수 있습니다. 종종 여러분은 상쾌함을 느끼고 새롭고 창의적인 아이디어를 얻을 수 있습니다.

➡ _____

21 디지털 디톡스는 또한 여러분이 다른 사람들과 더 많은 시간을 보내도록 도와줄 것입니다.

➡ _____

22 하지만 스마트폰 없이 사는 것은 쉽지 않습니다.

➡ _____

23 그러므로 여러분은 스마트폰을 사용하기 위한 몇 가지 규칙을 정할 필요가 있습니다.

➡ _____

24 그러고 나서 여러분은 그 규칙들을 따라야 합니다.

➡ _____

25 자, 조를 형성하고, 여러분의 조에서, 스마트폰을 사용하기 위한 규칙을 만들어 보세요.

➡ _____

By Yerim, Yongmin, and Hojin

26 우리는 공부하는 동안 스마트폰을 끌 것이다.

➡ _____

27 우리는 화장실에 스마트폰을 가져가지 않을 것이다.

➡ _____

28 우리는 밤에 스마트폰을 침실 밖에 두고 사용하지 않을 것이다.

➡ _____

By Jina, Hosung, and Minsu

29 야외 활동을 위한 더 많은 시간 – 우리는 스마트폰 없이 밖에서 노는 데 더 많은 시간을 보낼 것이다.

➡ _____

30 SNS는 더 적게 – 우리는 스마트폰에 SNS 메시지를 더 적게 올릴 것이다.

➡ _____

By Jiho, Sohee, and Yumin

31 만약 내가 너라면, 나는 스마트폰에 쓰는 시간을 절반으로 줄일 것이다.

➡ _____

32 만약 내가 너라면, 모든 알림을 끌 것이다.

➡ _____

33 잘했어요, 학생 여러분! 만약 스마트폰이 없다면 우리의 삶이 더 힘들겠지만, 스마트폰을 너무 많이 사용하는 것은 위험합니다.

➡ _____

34 디지털 디톡스와 함께, 여러분은 현명한 스마트폰 사용자가 될 수 있습니다.

➡ _____

Step1

※ 다음 우리말과 일치하도록 빈칸에 알맞은 말을 쓰시오.

Enjoy Writing C

1. _____ No Smartphones

2. There _____ _____ some _____ and some _____ _____ there _____ no smartphones.

3. First, _____ some advantages.

4. _____ we _____ smartphones, we _____ _____ _____ more often.

5. _____, we _____ neck pain.

6. _____, there _____ _____ some _____.

7. _____ there were no smartphones, it _____ _____ be easy _____ people.

8. Also, it _____ _____ so long _____ _____ _____ _____ _____.

1. 만약 스마트폰이 없다면
2. 만약 스마트폰이 없다면 몇몇 장점과 단점이 있을 것이다.
3. 첫째로 몇 가지 장점을 이야기해 보자.
4. 만약 우리가 스마트폰을 가지고 있지 않다면, 우리는 밖에서 더 자주 놀 것이다.
5. 게다가, 우리는 목통증의 위험이 없을 것이다.
6. 반면에 몇 가지 단점도 있을 것이다.
7. 만약 스마트폰이 없다면, 우리는 사람들에게 연락하는 것이 쉽지 않을 것이다.
8. 또한 우리가 정보를 찾는 데 시간이 많이 걸릴 것이다.

Project 2

1. _____ is necessary _____ digital _____!

2. _____ there were no _____ or _____, our lives _____ _____ _____ _____.

3. So, _____ is very important _____ _____ _____ digital devices _____ as a digital citizen.

4. I _____ _____ and _____ on SNS.

5. I never _____ anyone.

6. I _____ _____ _____.

7. I _____.

8. I _____ too _____.

1. 우리는 디지털 시민이 될 필요가 있다!
2. 만약 인터넷이나 SNS가 없다면, 우리의 삶은 더 힘들 것이다.
3. 그래서 우리는 디지털 시민으로서 디지털 기기들을 현명하게 사용하는 것이 중요하다.
4. 나는 SNS에서 내 자신과 다른 사람들을 존중한다.
5. 나는 절대 내 비밀번호를 누구와도 공유하지 않는다.
6. 나는 친절한 말을 쓴다.
7. 나는 나쁜 말을 절대 쓰지 않는다.
8. 나는 온라인에서 너무 많은 시간을 보내지 않는다.

Project 3

1. It's very important _____ _____ a digital citizen.

2. Our group will _____ you _____.

3. Please _____.

1. 모두가 디지털 시민이 되는 것은 매우 중요해.
2. 우리 모둠이 디지털 시민이 무엇을 하는지 보여줄게.
3. 재미있게 봐.

구석구석 지문 Test

※ 다음 우리말을 영어로 쓰시오.

Enjoy Writing C

1. 만약 스마트폰이 없다면
   ➡ _____

2. 만약 스마트폰이 없다면 몇몇 장점과 단점이 있을 것이다.
   ➡ _____

3. 첫째로 몇 가지 장점을 이야기해 보자.
   ➡ _____

4. 만약 우리가 스마트폰을 가지고 있지 않다면, 우리는 밖에서 더 자주 놀 것이다.
   ➡ _____

5. 게다가, 우리는 목통증의 위험이 없을 것이다.
   ➡ _____

6. 반면에 몇 가지 단점도 있을 것이다.
   ➡ _____

7. 만약 스마트폰이 없다면, 우리는 사람들에게 연락하는 것이 쉽지 않을 것이다.
   ➡ _____

8. 또한 우리가 정보를 찾는 데 시간이 많이 걸릴 것이다.
   ➡ _____

Project 2

1. 우리는 디지털 시민이 될 필요가 있다!
   ➡ _____

2. 만약 인터넷이나 SNS가 없다면, 우리의 삶은 더 힘들 것이다.
   ➡ _____

3. 그래서 우리는 디지털 시민으로서 디지털 기기들을 현명하게 사용하는 것이 중요하다.
   ➡ _____

4. 나는 SNS에서 내 자신과 다른 사람들을 존중한다.
   ➡ _____

5. 나는 절대 내 비밀번호를 누구와도 공유하지 않는다.
   ➡ _____

6. 나는 친절한 말을 쓴다.
   ➡ _____

7. 나는 나쁜 말을 절대 쓰지 않는다.
   ➡ _____

8. 나는 온라인에서 너무 많은 시간을 보내지 않는다.
   ➡ _____

Project 3

1. 모두가 디지털 시민이 되는 것은 매우 중요해.
   ➡ _____

2. 우리 모둠이 디지털 시민이 무엇을 하는지 보여줄게.
   ➡ _____

3. 재미있게 봐.
   ➡ _____

※ 다음 영어를 우리말로 쓰시오.

01 burial

02 respect

03 rule

04 sacrifice

05 desire

06 zip code

07 secret

08 general

09 government

10 harmony

11 educate

12 specialist

13 spread

14 feed

15 movement

16 throughout

17 entrance

18 protect

19 reader

20 main

21 mission

22 tomb

23 organization

24 palace

25 treasure

26 patriotic

27 foggy

28 president

29 independence

30 direct

31 statue

32 bury

33 republic

34 complete

35 exhibition

36 belong to

37 put on

38 hear of

39 be in need

40 carry out

41 look like+명사

42 so that+주어+동사

43 look forward to+명사/동명사

※ 다음 우리말을 영어로 쓰시오.

01 묻다, 매장하다 _____

02 비밀; 비밀의 _____

03 바람, 갈망 _____

04 존경, 경의 _____

05 정부 _____

06 통치, 지배 _____

07 교육시키다 _____

08 매장, 장례식 _____

09 안개 낀 _____

10 장군 _____

11 희생; 희생하다 _____

12 시 _____

13 독립 _____

14 궁전 _____

15 주된, 주요한 _____

16 묘, 무덤 _____

17 감독하다. 지휘[총괄]하다 _____

18 보물 _____

19 먹이를 주다, 먹이다 _____

20 애국적인 _____

21 조각상 _____

22 보호하다 _____

23 퍼지다, 퍼뜨리다 _____

24 우편 번호 _____

25 입구 _____

26 끝내다; 완전한 _____

27 지도자, 리더 _____

28 조직, 기구 _____

29 전문가 _____

30 조화 _____

31 전시회 _____

32 임무 _____

33 공화국 _____

34 ~의 도처에, ~ 내내 _____

35 (정치적, 사회적) 운동 _____

36 ~을 입다 _____

37 ~에 속하다 _____

38 ~을 수행하다 _____

39 ~처럼 보이다 _____

40 ~가 필요하다 _____

41 ~에 관해 듣다 _____

42 ~하기 위해서 _____

43 ~을 기대하다 _____

※ 다음 영영풀이에 알맞은 단어를 <보기>에서 골라 쓴 후, 우리말 뜻을 쓰시오.

1 _____ : what is highly valued: _____

2 _____ : a country governed by elected representatives: _____

3 _____ : a public display of art works, pictures or other interesting things: _____

4 _____ : any work that someone believes it is their duty to do: _____

5 _____ : a large house that is the official home of a king and queen: _____

6 _____ : a group of people working together for a purpose of being organized: _____

7 _____ : to place a dead body in the ground, to put something in the ground and cover it: _____

8 _____ : a series of things that happen one after another for a particular result: _____

9 _____ : giving up of something valuable for a specific purpose: _____

10 _____ : a sculptured figure of a person animal, etc. in bronze, stone, wood, etc.: _____

11 _____ : the act of putting a dead body into the ground, or the ceremony connected with this: _____

12 _____ : a large stone structure or underground room where someone, especially an important person, is buried: _____

13 _____ : a large outdoor area with fairground rides, shows, and other entertainments: _____

14 _____ : a circular ornament made of gold and decorated with jewels that is worn by a king or queen on their head: _____

15 _____ : a piece of writing that uses beautiful words that imply deep meanings and sounds rhythmical when you read: _____

16 _____ : a piece of cloth that is usually attached at the end of a pole and represents a country or association: _____

보기

poem	statue	republic	mission
sacrifice	crown	bury	process
flag	tomb	treasure	exhibition
burial	amusement park	palace	organization

※ 다음 우리말과 일치하도록 빈칸에 알맞은 말을 쓰시오.

Listen & Speak 1 A

1. **B:** _____ _____ Suwon Hawseong. It's _____.

   G: It also _____ _____.

   B: _____ it _____ _____ _____ _____ the people _____ wars.

   G: Wow. Do you know _____ _____ it?

   B: Yes. King Jeongjo _____ Jeong Yakyong _____ _____ the building _____. You know about Jeong Yakyong, _____ _____?

   G: Yes, I've _____ _____ him. He was a _____ _____ in Joseon.

2. **G:** Brian, you know Taegeukgi, _____ _____?

   B: Sure. It's the _____ _____ of Korea, _____ _____?

   G: That's right. Do you know _____ the _____ in Taegeukgi _____?

   B: No, I don't. _____ _____ about _____.

   G: The _____ in the middle _____ _____ and _____.

   B: What do the black _____ on the four _____ _____?

   G: They _____ four things: sky, fire, water, and _____.

Listen & Speak 2 A

1. **G:** I'm _____ _____ _____ to the Gansong Museum.

   B: What is the Gansong Museum?

   G: It's a _____ _____ _____ Gansong Jeon Hyeongpil.

   B: I _____ that he did _____ _____ for the country.

   G: Yes. He _____ many Korean _____ _____ some Japanese _____ _____ to Japan.

   B: Wow. The museum _____ _____ _____.

   G: Yes. I'm _____ it!

2. **B:** Soyeon, _____ _____ _____ _____ last weekend?

   G: I went to Hyeonchungwon _____ _____ _____ _____.

   B: _____ _____ volunteer work did you do there?

해석

1. B: 수원 화성을 봐, 그것은 거대해.
   G: 그것은 또한 튼튼해 보여.
   B: 왜냐하면 그것은 전쟁 중에 사람들을 보호하기 위해 지어졌기 때문이야.
   G: 우와. 너는 누가 그것을 지었는지 아니?
   B: 응. 정조가 정약용에게 건설 과정을 감독할 것을 지시했어. 너는 정약용에 대해 알고 있지, 그렇지 않니?
   G: 응, 그에 대해 들어봤어. 그는 조선의 훌륭한 과학자였어.

2. G: Brian, 너 태극기를 알고 있지, 그렇지 않니?
   B: 물론이지. 그것은 한국의 국기잖아, 그렇지 않니?
   G: 맞아. 너는 태극기에 있는 상징들이 무엇을 의미하는지 알고 있니?
   B: 아니, 몰라. 그것에 대해 말해 줘.
   G: 가운데 원은 조화와 평화를 의미해.
   B: 네 모서리의 검은 선들은 무엇을 의미하니?
   G: 그것은 하늘, 불, 물 그리고 땅을 의미해.

1. G: 나는 간송 미술관에 갈 예정이야.
   B: 간송 미술관이 뭐야?
   G: 간송 전형필에 의해 지어진 미술관이야.
   B: 나는 그가 나라를 위해 훌륭한 일들을 했다고 들었어.
   G: 응. 그는 몇몇 일본 사람들이 일본으로 가져갔던 한국의 많은 문화재들을 샀어.
   B: 우와. 그 미술관은 틀림없이 흥미로울 거야.
   G: 응. 나는 그곳을 기대하고 있어!

2. B: 소연아, 지난 주말에 무엇을 했니?
   G: 나는 봉사 활동을 하러 현충원에 갔어.
   B: 그곳에서 어떤 종류의 봉사 활동을 했어?

G: I _____ _____ the _____. I felt great _____ for the people _____ _____ for the country.

B: _____ great. Can I do it, _____?

G: Sure. I'm _____ _____ _____ there again next Wednesday. Will you _____ me?

B: Sure. _____ _____ _____ _____ it.

Real Life Task

Andy: Bora, what are you _____?

Bora: I'm reading *Sky, Wind, Star, and* _____ by Yun Dongju. You _____ about Yun Dongju, _____ _____?

Andy: I've _____ his name, but I don't know _____ about him.

Bora: He wrote many beautiful _____ _____ Korea was _____ Japanese _____. His love for the country and his _____ for _____ can _____ _____ in his _____.

Andy: Really? I didn't know that. I want _____ _____ his and _____ _____ about him.

Bora: Great. _____ _____, I'm _____ the Yun Dongju Museum soon. Do you want to come with me?

Andy: Yes, _____ are you _____?

Bora: Next Saturday. It's _____ Gyeongbok _____. Can you meet me at the _____ _____ 2 p.m.?

Andy: Sure. _____ there.

Bora: Great. I'm really _____ the _____.

Wrap Up

B: Tomorrow _____ _____ Korean clothes, *hanbok*, and go to Insadong.

G: Good, but I want to buy _____ _____ my friends in _____ tomorrow.

B: In Insadong, _____ _____ many _____ _____.

G: Great. After _____, what should we eat _____ _____?

B: Hmm. You _____ Samgyetang, _____?

G: No. What is it?

B: It's a _____ Korean _____. It's _____ and will _____ _____ _____.

G: Sounds good. I'm _____ _____ _____ _____ it.

G: 나는 묘 주변을 청소했어. 나는 나라를 위해 돌아가신 분들에게 깊은 경의를 느꼈어.

B: 대단하게 들린다. 나도 그것을 할 수 있을까?

G: 물론이지. 나는 다음 주 수요일에 그곳에 다시 갈 계획이야. 너도 나와 함께 갈래?

B: 물론이지. 나는 그것을 기대하고 있어.

Andy: 보라, 너 무엇을 읽고 있니?

보라: 윤동주 시인의 「하늘과 바람과 별과 시」를 읽고 있어. 너는 윤동주에 대해 알고 있지, 그렇지 않니?

Andy: 나는 그의 이름을 들어 본 적 있지만 그에 대해 잘 알지는 못해.

보라: 그는 한국이 일본의 통치하에 있을 때 아름다운 시를 많이 썼어. 나라에 대한 그의 사랑과 독립에 대한 염원이 그의 시에서 느껴질 수 있어.

Andy: 정말? 나는 그걸 몰랐어. 나는 그의 시를 읽고 그에 대해 더 많이 배우고 싶어.

보라: 아주 좋아. 사실 나는 곧 윤동주 박물관을 방문할 계획이야. 너도 나와 함께 가길 원하니?

Andy: 응, 언제 갈 거니?

보라: 다음 주 토요일에. 그곳은 경복궁 근처에 있어. 오후 2시에 궁에서 만날 수 있니?

Andy: 물론이지. 거기서 만나자.

보라: 좋아. 나는 그 방문을 정말 기대하고 있어.

B: 내일 우리 한국 전통 의상인 한복을 입고 인사동에 가자.

G: 좋아, 그런데 나 내일 독일에 있는 내 친구들을 위한 선물을 사고 싶어.

B: 인사동에 선물 가게가 많아.

G: 잘됐네. 쇼핑하고 나서 점심으로 뭘 먹을까?

B: 흠. 너는 삼계탕에 대해 알고 있지, 그렇지 않니?

G: 아니. 그게 뭐야?

B: 전통적인 한국의 국물 음식이야. 그것은 맛이 좋고 너를 건강하게 만들어 줄 거야.

G: 멋지네. 나는 그것을 먹어보는 것을 기대하고 있어.

※ 다음 우리말에 맞도록 대화를 영어로 쓰시오.

Listen & Speak 1 A

1. B: _____

    G: _____

    B: _____

    G: _____

    B: _____

    G: _____

2. G: _____

    B: _____

    G: _____

    B: _____

    G: _____

    B: _____

    G: _____

Listen & Speak 2 A

1. G: _____

    B: _____

    G: _____

    B: _____

    G: _____

    B: _____

    G: _____

2. B: _____

    G: _____

    B: _____

해석

1. B: 수원 화성을 봐, 그것은 거대해.
   G: 그것은 또한 튼튼해 보여.
   B: 왜냐하면 그것은 전쟁 중에 사람들을 보호하기 위해 지어졌기 때문이야.
   G: 우와. 너는 누가 그것을 지었는지 아니?
   B: 응. 정조가 정약용에게 건설 과정을 감독할 것을 지시했어. 너는 정약용에 대해 알고 있지, 그렇지 않니?
   G: 응, 그에 대해 들어봤어. 그는 조선의 훌륭한 과학자였어.

2. G: Brian, 너 태극기를 알고 있지, 그렇지 않니?
   B: 물론이지. 그것은 한국의 국기잖아, 그렇지 않니?
   G: 맞아. 너는 태극기에 있는 상징들이 무엇을 의미하는지 알고 있니?
   B: 아니, 몰라. 그것에 대해 말해 줘.
   G: 가운데 원은 조화와 평화를 의미해.
   B: 네 모서리의 검은 선들은 무엇을 의미하니?
   G: 그것은 하늘, 불, 물 그리고 땅을 의미해.

1. G: 나는 간송 미술관에 갈 예정이야.
   B: 간송 미술관이 뭐야?
   G: 간송 전형필에 의해 지어진 미술관이야.
   B: 나는 그가 나라를 위해 훌륭한 일들을 했다고 들었어.
   G: 응. 그는 몇몇 일본 사람들이 일본으로 가져갔었던 한국의 많은 문화재들을 샀어.
   B: 우와. 그 미술관은 틀림없이 흥미로울 거야.
   G: 응. 나는 그곳을 기대하고 있어!

2. B: 소연아, 지난 주말에 무엇을 했니?
   G: 나는 봉사 활동을 하러 현충원에 갔어.
   B: 그곳에서 어떤 종류의 봉사 활동을 했어?

G: _____
_____
B: _____
G: _____
B: _____

G: 나는 묘 주변을 청소했어. 나는 나라를 위해 돌아가신 분들에게 깊은 경의를 느꼈어.
B: 대단하게 들린다. 나도 그것을 할 수 있을까?
G: 물론이지. 나는 다음 주 수요일에 그곳에 다시 갈 계획이야. 너도 나와 함께 갈래?
B: 물론이지. 나는 그것을 기대하고 있어.

Real Life Task

Andy: _____
Bora: _____
_____
Andy: _____
Bora: _____
_____
_____
Andy: _____
Bora: _____
_____
Andy: _____
Bora: _____
_____
Andy: _____
Bora: _____

Andy: 보라, 너 무엇을 읽고 있니?
보라: 윤동주 시인의 「하늘과 바람과 별과 시」를 읽고 있어. 너는 윤동주에 대해 알고 있지, 그렇지 않니?
Andy: 나는 그의 이름을 들어 본 적 있지만 그에 대해 잘 알지는 못해.
보라: 그는 한국이 일본의 통치하에 있을 때 아름다운 시를 많이 썼어. 나라에 대한 그의 사랑과 독립에 대한 염원이 그의 시에서 느껴질 수 있어.
Andy: 정말? 나는 그걸 몰랐어. 나는 그의 시를 읽고 그에 대해 더 많이 배우고 싶어.
보라: 아주 좋아. 사실 나는 곧 윤동주 박물관을 방문할 계획이야. 너도 나와 함께 가길 원하니?
Andy: 응, 언제 갈 거니?
보라: 다음 주 토요일에. 그곳은 경복궁 근처에 있어. 오후 2시에 궁에서 만날 수 있니?
Andy: 물론이지. 거기서 만나자.
보라: 좋아. 나는 그 방문을 정말 기대하고 있어.

Wrap Up

B: _____
G: _____
B: _____
G: _____
B: _____
G: _____
B: _____
G: _____

B: 내일 우리 한국 전통 의상인 한복을 입고 인사동에 가자.
G: 좋아, 그런데 나 내일 독일에 있는 내 친구들을 위한 선물을 사고 싶어.
B: 인사동에 선물 가게가 많아.
G: 잘됐네. 쇼핑하고 나서 점심으로 뭘 먹을까?
B: 흠. 너는 삼계탕에 대해 알고 있지, 그렇지 않니?
G: 아니. 그게 뭐야?
B: 전통적인 한국의 국물 음식이야. 그것은 맛이 좋고 너를 건강하게 만들어 줄 거야.
G: 멋지네. 나는 그것을 먹어보는 것을 기대하고 있어.

※ 다음 우리말과 일치하도록 빈칸에 알맞은 것을 골라 쓰시오.

My Wish

1 _____ _____ my history club _____ _____ Hyochang Park.

A. went   B. last   C. to   D. week

2 We _____ the Kim Koo Museum _____ the _____.

A. inside   B. visited   C. park

3 At the _____ of the _____, we _____ a white _____ of Kim Koo.

A. statue   B. entrance   C. saw   D. museum

4 Kim Koo is a great _____ _____ who spent most of his life _____ for the _____ of Korea from Japanese rule.

A. fighting   B. hero   C. national   D. independence

5 In the 1900s, he _____ _____ young people _____ _____ schools.

A. educate   B. building   C. helped   D. by

6 In 1919, when the independence _____ had _____ _____ the country, he _____ to Shanghai, China.

A. throughout   B. movement   C. moved   D. spread

7 There he _____ the Government of the Republic of Korea and _____ _____ its _____.

A. later   B. joined   C. president   D. became

8 The _____ hall in the museum _____ a _____ of things about Kim Koo's _____.

A. life   B. exhibition   C. lot   D. shows

9 _____ _____ _____ the hall, we _____ at a photo of the Korean Patriotic Organization's members.

A. stopped   B. looking   C. while   D. around

10 Kim Koo _____ the _____ organization in 1931 to _____ _____ Japan.

A. against   B. secret   C. fight   D. formed

11 Lee Bongchang and Yun Bonggil _____ _____ the _____.

A. to   B. group   C. belonged

12 At one _____ in the _____, we saw two _____ _____ a photo of Kim Koo and Yun Bonggil.

A. under   B. place   C. watches   D. hall

나의 소원

1 지난주에 우리 역사 동아리는 효창 공원에 갔다.

2 우리는 공원 안에 있는 김구 기념관을 방문했다.

3 기념관 입구에서 우리는 하얀색의 김구 조각상을 보았다.

4 김구는 일본 통치로부터 대한의 독립을 위해 싸우는 데 그의 삶 대부분을 보낸 위대한 국민 영웅이다.

5 1900년대에 그는 학교를 설립함으로써 젊은이들을 교육시키는 것을 도왔다.

6 1919년에 3.1 운동이 나라 전체에 걸쳐 퍼져나갔을 때, 그는 중국 상하이로 이동했다.

7 그곳에서 그는 대한민국 임시정부에 합류했고 나중에는 그것의 대표자가 되었다.

8 기념관 안에 있는 전시관은 김구의 삶에 관한 많은 것들을 보여준다.

9 우리는 전시관을 둘러보면서 한인애국단의 단원들 사진 앞에 섰다.

10 김구는 일본에 맞서 싸우기 위해 1931년에 비밀 조직을 형성했다.

11 이봉창과 윤봉길이 그 집단에 속해 있었다.

12 전시관의 한 곳에서, 우리는 김구와 윤봉길의 사진 아래에 있는 시계 두 개를 보았다.

13 In 1932, Kim Koo _____ a _____ to _____ Japanese _____ in a park in Shanghai.

    A. kill   B. generals   C. made   D. plan

14 As the leader of the Korean Patriotic Organization, he _____ Yun to _____ _____ the _____.

    A. carry   B. directed   C. mission   D. out

15 When Yun _____ for the mission, he told Kim, "Sir, you are wearing a very old watch. Mine is new, but I won't _____ it _____. Please take my watch, and _____ me have yours."

    A. anymore   B. left   C. let   D. need

16 Kim Koo always _____ Yun's watch in his jacket _____ that he would not _____ Yun's _____.

    A. forget   B. carried   C. so   D. sacrifice

17 After _____ the _____ of the museum, we moved to the _____ of the three _____, Lee Bongchang, Yun Bonggil, and Baek Jeonggi.

    A. tombs   B. completing   C. heroes   D. tour

18 Their _____ had _____ in Japan, but after Korea's _____ Kim Koo _____ them to Hyochang Park.

    A. independence   B. been   C. brought   D. bodies

19 _____ doing so, he showed his _____ love and _____ for the _____ of the three heroes.

    A. respect   B. deep   C. by   D. sacrifice

20 _____ I left Hyochang Park, I _____ about Kim Koo's _____ in My Wish that I had read in the _____ hall.

    A. exhibition   B. thought   C. as   D. words

21 It _____ _____ _____ *Baekbeomilji*.

    A. written   B. was   C. in

22 If God asks me _____ my _____ is, I would _____ _____, "It is Korea's Independence."

    A. clearly   B. what   C. say   D. wish

23 If he asks me what my _____ wish is, I _____ say, "It is the _____ of my _____."

    A. independence   B. second   C. would   D. country

24 If he asks me _____ my third wish is, I would say _____, "It is the _____ _____ of my country." That is my answer.

    A. complete   B. what   C. loudly   D. independence

13 1932년에 김구는 상해에 있는 한 공원에서 일본 장군들을 암살하기 위한 계획을 세웠다.

14 한인 애국단의 지도자로서 그는 윤봉길이 임무를 수행하도록 지시했다.

15 윤봉길이 임무를 위해 떠날 때, 그는 김구에게 말했다. "선생님, 당신은 매우 낡은 시계를 차고 계시는군요. 제 것은 새것이나, 저는 그것이 더 이상 필요하지 않을 것입니다. 부디 제 시계를 가져가시고, 제가 선생님 것을 가지도록 해주십시오."

16 김구는 윤봉길의 희생을 잊지 않기 위해서 윤봉길의 시계를 항상 상의에 넣고 다녔다.

17 기념관 관람을 마치고, 우리는 이봉창, 윤봉길, 그리고 백정기 의사들이 묻힌 삼의사의 묘로 이동했다.

18 그들의 시신은 일본에 있다가 독립이 되고 나서 김구가 그들의 시신을 효창 공원으로 가져왔다.

19 그는 그렇게 함으로써 삼의사들의 희생에 대한 그의 깊은 사랑과 경의를 보여 주었다.

20 내가 효창 공원을 떠날 때, 나는 전시관에서 읽었던 「나의 소원」에 있는 김구의 말을 생각했다.

21 그것은 「백범일지」에 쓰여 있었다.

22 만약 신이 나의 소원이 무엇이냐고 묻는다면, "그것은 대한 독립이오."라고 명확하게 말할 것이다.

23 만약에 그가 나의 두 번째 소원이 무엇이냐고 묻는다면, 나는 "그것은 내 나라의 독립이오."라고 말할 것이다.

24 만약 그가 나의 세 번째 소원이 무엇이냐고 묻는다면, "그것은 내 나라의 완전한 독립이오."라고 큰 소리로 말할 것이다. 그것이 나의 대답이다.

※ 다음 우리말과 일치하도록 빈칸에 알맞은 말을 쓰시오.

My Wish

1 Last week _____ _____ _____ went to Hyochang Park.

2 We _____ the Kim Koo Museum _____ _____ _____ .

3 _____ the _____ of the museum, we saw a _____ _____ of Kim Koo.

4 Kim Koo is _____ _____ _____ _____ who _____ most of his life _____ for the _____ of Korea _____ _____ _____ .

5 In the 1900s, he _____ _____ young people _____ _____ schools.

6 _____ 1919, _____ _____ _____ had spread _____ the country, he _____ _____ Shanghai, China.

7 There he _____ the Government of the Republic of Korea and _____ _____ _____ _____ .

8 _____ _____ _____ in the museum _____ a lot of things about Kim Koo's life.

9 _____ _____ _____ the hall, we _____ _____ a photo of the Korean _____ _____ members.

10 Kim Koo _____ the _____ _____ in 1931 _____ _____ _____ Japan.

11 Lee Bongchang and Yun Bonggil _____ _____ the group.

12 _____ one place in the hall, we _____ _____ _____ _____ a photo of Kim Koo and Yun Bonggil.

나의 소원

1 지난주에 우리 역사 동아리는 효창 공원에 갔다.

2 우리는 공원 안에 있는 김구 기념 관을 방문했다.

3 기념관 입구에서 우리는 하얀색 의 김구 조각상을 보았다.

4 김구는 일본 통치로부터 대한의 독립을 위해 싸우는 데 그의 삶 대부분을 보낸 위대한 국민 영웅 이다.

5 1900년대에 그는 학교를 설립 함으로써 젊은이들을 교육시키는 것을 도왔다.

6 1919년에 3.1 운동이 나라 전 체에 걸쳐 퍼져나갔을 때, 그는 중국 상하이로 이동했다.

7 그곳에서 그는 대한민국 임시정 부에 합류했고 나중에는 그것의 대표자가 되었다.

8 기념관 안에 있는 전시관은 김구 의 삶에 관한 많은 것들을 보여 준다.

9 우리는 전시관을 둘러보면서 한인 애국단의 단원들 사진 앞에 섰다.

10 김구는 일본에 맞서 싸우기 위해 1931년에 비밀 조직을 형성했다.

11 이봉창과 윤봉길이 그 집단에 속 해 있었다.

12 전시관의 한 곳에서, 우리는 김구 와 윤봉길의 사진 아래에 있는 시 계 두 개를 보았다.

13 _____ 1932, Kim Koo _____ _____ _____
kill _____ _____ in a park in Shanghai.

14 As the leader of the Korean _____ _____, he _____ Yun
_____ _____ _____ the mission.

15 When Yun _____ _____ the mission, he told Kim,
"Sir, you are _____ _____ _____ _____ _____.
_____ is new, but I _____ need _____ _____. Please
_____ my watch, and _____ me _____ yours."

16 Kim Koo _____ _____ Yun's watch in his jacket _____
_____ he _____ _____ _____ Yun's _____.

17 After _____ the tour of the museum, we _____ _____
the _____ of the _____ _____, Lee Bongchang, Yun
Bonggil, and Baek Jeonggi.

18 Their bodies _____ _____ in Japan, but _____ Korea's
_____ Kim Koo brought _____ to Hyochang Park.

19 _____ _____ _____, he showed his _____ _____
and respect _____ _____ _____ of the three heroes.

20 _____ I _____ Hyochang Park, I _____ about Kim
Koo's _____ in My Wish _____ I _____ _____ in
the _____.

21 _____ was _____ _____ *Baekbeomilji*.

22 If God asks me _____ _____ _____, I would
say _____, "It is _____ _____."

23 If he asks me _____ _____ _____ _____ is, I would
say, "It is the _____ of my country."

24 If he _____ _____ _____ _____ _____ _____
_____, I would say _____, "It is the _____ _____ of
my country." That is my answer.

---

13 1932년에 김구는 상해에 있는 한 공원에서 일본 장군들을 암살하기 위한 계획을 세웠다.

14 한인 애국단의 지도자로서 그는 윤봉길이 임무를 수행하도록 지시했다.

15 윤봉길이 임무를 위해 떠날 때, 그는 김구에게 말했다. "선생님, 당신은 매우 낡은 시계를 차고 계시는군요. 제 것은 새것이나, 저는 그것이 더 이상 필요하지 않을 것입니다. 부디 제 시계를 가져가시고, 제가 선생님 것을 가지도록 해주십시오."

16 김구는 윤봉길의 희생을 잊지 않기 위해서 윤봉길의 시계를 항상 상의에 넣고 다녔다.

17 기념관 관람을 마치고, 우리는 이봉창, 윤봉길, 그리고 백정기 의사들이 묻힌 삼의사의 묘로 이동했다.

18 그들의 시신은 일본에 있다가 독립이 되고 나서 김구가 그들의 시신을 효창 공원으로 가져왔다.

19 그는 그렇게 함으로써 삼의사들의 희생에 대한 그의 깊은 사랑과 경의를 보여 주었다.

20 내가 효창 공원을 떠날 때, 나는 전시관에서 읽었던 「나의 소원」에 있는 김구의 말을 생각했다.

21 그것은 「백범일지」에 쓰여 있었다.

22 만약 신이 나의 소원이 무엇이냐고 묻는다면, "그것은 대한 독립이오."라고 명확하게 말할 것이다.

23 만약에 그가 나의 두 번째 소원이 무엇이냐고 묻는다면, 나는 "그것은 내 나라의 독립이오."라고 말할 것이다.

24 만약 그가 나의 세 번째 소원이 무엇이냐고 묻는다면, "그것은 내 나라의 완전한 독립이오."라고 큰 소리로 말할 것이다. 그것이 나의 대답이다.

※ 다음 문장을 우리말로 쓰시오.

1 Last week my history club went to Hyochang Park.

➡ _____

2 We visited the Kim Koo Museum inside the park.

➡ _____

3 At the entrance of the museum, we saw a white statue of Kim Koo.

➡ _____

4 Kim Koo is a great national hero who spent most of his life fighting for the independence of Korea from Japanese rule.

➡ _____

5 In the 1900s, he helped educate young people by building schools.

➡ _____

6 In 1919, when the independence movement had spread throughout the country, he moved to Shanghai, China.

➡ _____

7 There he joined the Government of the Republic of Korea and later became its president.

➡ _____

8 The exhibition hall in the museum shows a lot of things about Kim Koo's life.

➡ _____

9 While looking around the hall, we stopped at a photo of the Korean Patriotic Organization's members.

➡ _____

10 Kim Koo formed the secret organization in 1931 to fight against Japan.

➡ _____

11 Lee Bongchang and Yun Bonggil belonged to the group.

➡ _____

12 At one place in the hall, we saw two watches under a photo of Kim Koo and Yun Bonggil.

➡ _____

13 In 1932, Kim Koo made a plan to kill Japanese generals in a park in Shanghai.

➡ _____

14 As the leader of the Korean Patriotic Organization, he directed Yun to carry out the mission.

➡ _____

15 When Yun left for the mission, he told Kim, "Sir, you are wearing a very old watch. Mine is new, but I won't need it anymore. Please take my watch, and let me have yours."

➡ _____

_____

_____

16 Kim Koo always carried Yun's watch in his jacket so that he would not forget Yun's sacrifice.

➡ _____

17 After completing the tour of the museum, we moved to the tombs of the three heroes, Lee Bongchang, Yun Bonggil, and Baek Jeonggi.

➡ _____

18 Their bodies had been in Japan, but after Korea's independence Kim Koo brought them to Hyochang Park.

➡ _____

19 By doing so, he showed his deep love and respect for the sacrifice of the three heroes.

➡ _____

20 As I left Hyochang Park, I thought about Kim Koo's words in My Wish that I had read in the exhibition hall.

➡ _____

21 It was written in *Baekbeomilji*.

➡ _____

22 If God asks me what my wish is, I would say clearly, "It is Korea's independence."

➡ _____

23 If he asks me what my second wish is, I would say, "It is the independence of my country."

➡ _____

24 If he asks me what my third wish is, I would say loudly, "It is the complete independence of my country." That is my answer.

➡ _____

_____

※ 다음 괄호 안의 단어들을 우리말에 맞도록 바르게 배열하시오.

My wish

1 (week / last / history / my / went / club / Hyochang / to / Park.)
➡ _____

2 (visited / we / Kim / the / Koo / inside / Museum / park. / the)
➡ _____

3 (the / at / of / entrance / museum, / the / saw / we / white / a / statue / Kim / of / Koo.)
➡ _____

4 (Koo / Kim / a / is / national / great / who / hero / most / spent / his / of / fighting / life / the / for / of / independence / from / Korea / rule. / Japanese)
➡ _____

5 (the / in / 1900s, / helped / he / young / educate / people / by / schools. / building)
➡ _____

6 (1919, / in / the / when / movement / independence / spread / had / the / throughout / contry, / he / to / moved / China. / Shanghai,)
➡ _____

7 (he / there / the / joined / Government / the / of / Republic / Korea / of / and / became / later / president. / its)
➡ _____

8 (exhibition / the / in / hall / museum / the / shows / lot / a / of / things / about / Koo's / life. / Kim)
➡ _____
_____

9 (looking / while / the / around / hall, / the / stopped / we / a / at / photo / of / Korean / the / Patriotic / members. / Organization)
➡ _____
_____

10 (Koo / Kim / the / formed / secret / in / organization / 1931 / fight / to / Japan. / against)
➡ _____

11 (Bongchang / Lee / and / Bonggil / Yun / to / belonged / group. / the)
➡ _____

12 (one / at / in / place / hall, / the / saw / we / watches / two / a / under / photo / Kim / of / Koo / and / Bonggil. / Yun)
➡ _____

나의 소원

1 지난주에 우리 역사 동아리는 효창 공원에 갔다.

2 우리는 공원 안에 있는 김구 기념관을 방문했다.

3 기념관 입구에서 우리는 하얀색의 김구 조각상을 보았다.

4 김구는 일본 통치로부터 대한의 독립을 위해 싸우는 데 그의 삶 대부분을 보낸 위대한 국민 영웅이다.

5 1900년대에 그는 학교를 설립함으로써 젊은이들을 교육시키는 것을 도왔다.

6 1919년에 3.1 운동이 나라 전체에 걸쳐 퍼져나갔을 때, 그는 중국 상하이로 이동했다.

7 그곳에서 그는 대한민국 임시정부에 합류했고 나중에는 그것의 대표자가 되었다.

8 기념관 안에 있는 전시관은 김구의 삶에 관한 많은 것들을 보여준다.

9 우리는 전시관을 둘러보면서 한인 애국단의 단원들 사진 앞에 섰다.

10 김구는 일본에 맞서 싸우기 위해 1931년에 비밀 조직을 형성했다.

11 이봉창과 윤봉길이 그 집단에 속해 있었다.

12 전시관의 한 곳에서, 우리는 김구와 윤봉길의 사진 아래에 있는 시계 두 개를 보았다.

13 (1932, / in / Koo / Kim / a / made / plan / kill / to / generals / Japanese / in / park / a / Shanghai. / in)
➡ _____

14 (the / as / of / leader / Korean / the / Organization, / Patriotic / directed / he / to / Yun / out / carry / mission. / the)
➡ _____

15 (Yun / when / for / left / mission, / the / told / he / you / Kim, / "Sir, / wearing / are / very / a / watch. / old // is / mine / new, / I / but / need / it / won't / anymore. // take / please / watch, / my / and / me / let / yours." / have)
➡ _____
_____

16 (Koo / Kim / carried / always / watch / Yun's / in / jacket / his / that / so / would / he / forget / not / sacrifice. / Yun's)
➡ _____

17 (completing / after / tour / the / the / of / museum, / moved / we / the / to / tombs / the / of / heroes, / three / Bongchang, / Lee / Bonggil, / Yun / and / Jeonggi. / Baek)
➡ _____

18 (bodies / their / been / had / Japan, / in / after / but / independence / Korea's / Koo / Kim / them / brought / Hyochang / to / Park.)
➡ _____

19 (doing / by / so, / showed / he / deep / his / and / love / for / respect / sacrifice / the / the / of / heroes. / three)
➡ _____

20 (I / as / left / Park, / Hyochang / thought / I / Kim / about / words / Koo's / in / Wish / My / that / had / I / read / the / in / hall. / exhibition)
➡ _____

21 (was / it / written / *Baekbeomilji.* / in)
➡ _____

22 (God / if / me / asks / my / what / is, / wish / would / I / clearly, / say / is / "it / Independence." / Korea's)
➡ _____

23 (he / if / asks / what / me / my / wish / second / is, / would / I / say, / is / "it / independence / the / of / country." / my)
➡ _____

24 (he / if / me / asks / my / what / wish / third / is, / would / I / loudly, / say / is / "it / complete / the / of / independence / country." / my // is / that / answer. / my)
➡ _____
_____

13 1932년에 김구는 상해에 있는 한 공원에서 일본 장군들을 암살하기 위한 계획을 세웠다.

14 한인 애국단의 지도자로서 그는 윤봉길이 임무를 수행하도록 지시했다.

15 윤봉길이 임무를 위해 떠날 때, 그는 김구에게 말했다. "선생님, 당신은 매우 낡은 시계를 차고 계시는군요. 제 것은 새것이나, 저는 그것이 더 이상 필요하지 않을 것입니다. 부디 제 시계를 가져가시고, 제가 선생님 것을 가지도록 해주십시오."

16 김구는 윤봉길의 희생을 잊지 않기 위해서 윤봉길의 시계를 항상 상의에 넣고 다녔다.

17 기념관 관람을 마치고, 우리는 이봉창, 윤봉길, 그리고 백정기 의사들이 묻힌 삼의사의 묘로 이동했다.

18 그들의 시신은 일본에 있다가 독립이 되고 나서 김구가 그들의 시신을 효창 공원으로 가져왔다.

19 그는 그렇게 함으로써 삼의사들의 희생에 대한 그의 깊은 사랑과 경의를 보여 주었다.

20 내가 효창 공원을 떠날 때, 나는 전시관에서 읽었던 「나의 소원」에 있는 김구의 말을 생각했다.

21 그것은 『백범일지』에 쓰여 있었다.

22 만약 신이 나의 소원이 무엇이냐고 묻는다면, "그것은 대한 독립이오."라고 명확하게 말할 것이다.

23 만약에 그가 나의 두 번째 소원이 무엇이냐고 묻는다면, 나는 "그것은 내 나라의 독립이오."라고 말할 것이다.

24 만약 그가 나의 세 번째 소원이 무엇이냐고 묻는다면, "그것은 내 나라의 완전한 독립이오."라고 큰 소리로 말할 것이다. 그것이 나의 대답이다.

※ 다음 우리말을 영어로 쓰시오.

1 지난주에 우리 역사 동아리는 효창 공원에 갔다.

➡ _____

2 우리는 공원 안에 있는 김구 기념관을 방문했다.

➡ _____

3 기념관 입구에서 우리는 하얀색의 김구 조각상을 보았다.

➡ _____

4 김구는 일본 통치로부터 대한의 독립을 위해 싸우는 데 그의 삶 대부분을 보낸 위대한 국민 영웅이다.

➡ _____
_____

5 1900년대에 그는 학교를 설립함으로써 젊은이들을 교육시키는 것을 도왔다.

➡ _____

6 1919년에 3.1 운동이 나라 전체에 걸쳐 퍼져나갔을 때, 그는 중국 상하이로 이동했다.

➡ _____
_____

7 그곳에서 그는 대한민국 임시정부에 합류했고 나중에는 그것의 대표자가 되었다.

➡ _____

8 기념관 안에 있는 전시관은 김구의 삶에 관한 많은 것들을 보여 준다.

➡ _____

9 우리는 전시관을 둘러보면서 한인 애국단의 단원들 사진 앞에 섰다.

➡ _____

10 김구는 일본에 맞서 싸우기 위해 1931년에 비밀 조직을 형성했다.

➡ _____

11 이봉창과 윤봉길이 그 집단에 속해 있었다.

➡ _____

12 전시관의 한 곳에서, 우리는 김구와 윤봉길의 사진 아래에 있는 시계 두 개를 보았다.

➡ _____

13 1932년에 김구는 상해에 있는 한 공원에서 일본 장군들을 암살하기 위한 계획을 세웠다.

➡ _____

14 한인 애국단의 지도자로서 그는 윤봉길이 임무를 수행하도록 지시했다.

➡ _____

15 윤봉길이 임무를 위해 떠날 때, 그는 김구에게 말했다. "선생님, 당신은 매우 낡은 시계를 차고 계시는군요. 제 것은 새것이나, 저는 그것이 더 이상 필요하지 않을 것입니다. 부디 제 시계를 가져가시고, 제가 선생님 것을 가지도록 해주십시오."

➡ _____

_____

16 김구는 윤봉길의 희생을 잊지 않기 위해서 윤봉길의 시계를 항상 상의에 넣고 다녔다.

➡ _____

17 기념관 관람을 마치고, 우리는 이봉창, 윤봉길, 그리고 백정기 의사들이 묻힌 삼의사의 묘로 이동했다.

➡ _____

_____

18 그들의 시신은 일본에 있다가 독립이 되고 나서 김구가 그들의 시신을 효창 공원으로 가져왔다.

➡ _____

_____

19 그는 그렇게 함으로써 삼의사들의 희생에 대한 그의 깊은 사랑과 경의를 보여 주었다.

➡ _____

20 내가 효창 공원을 떠날 때, 나는 전시관에서 읽었던 「나의 소원」에 있는 김구의 말을 생각했다.

➡ _____

21 그것은 「백범일지」에 쓰여 있었다.

➡ _____

22 만약 신이 나의 소원이 무엇이냐고 묻는다면, "그것은 대한 독립이오."라고 명확하게 말할 것이다.

➡ _____

23 만약에 그가 나의 두 번째 소원이 무엇이냐고 묻는다면, 나는 "그것은 내 나라의 독립이오."라고 말할 것이다.

➡ _____

24 만약 그가 나의 세 번째 소원이 무엇이냐고 묻는다면, "그것은 내 나라의 완전한 독립이오."라고 큰 소리로 말할 것이다. 그것이 나의 대답이다.

➡ _____

_____

구석구석 지문 Test

※ 다음 우리말과 일치하도록 빈칸에 알맞은 말을 쓰시오.

Real Life Talk Step 3

1. My group members _____ An Junggeun _____ we _____
   _____ _____ his _____ _____ the country.

2. You _____ _____ _____ _____ him _____
   the An Junggeun Museum or An Junggeun Park.

1. 우리 그룹은 안중근을 선택했는데, 우리 나라를 위한 희생에 깊은 인상을 받았기 때문입니다.
2. 여러분은 안중근 기념관이나 안중근 공원을 방문함으로써 그에 관하여 더 많은 것을 알 수 있습니다.

Enjoy Writing

Dosan An Changho

1. An Changho _____ _____ _____ 1878.

2. _____ he was _____ _____ _____, he _____ _____ Seoul and _____ _____ school _____.

3. In 1902, he _____ _____ America _____ _____ he could _____ _____ _____.

4. In America, An _____ _____ _____ _____ _____ of the Korean people there and _____ _____ _____ _____ _____ _____.

5. After he _____ _____ _____ Korea, he _____ the New Korean Society in 1907 _____ _____ _____ _____ _____ _____.

6. He also joined the _____ _____ _____ _____ _____ in Shanghai in 1919.

7. After that, he _____ _____ _____ _____ schools _____ _____ people _____ he _____ _____ 1938.

도산 안창호
1. 안창호는 1878년에 태어났다.
2. 그가 십 대였을 때, 그는 서울로 이사를 하고 그곳에서 학교를 다녔다.
3. 1902년에 그는 더 나은 교육을 받기 위해서 미국으로 떠났다.
4. 안창호는 미국에서 한국인들의 삶을 개선하는 것을 도왔고, 존경받는 지도자가 되었다.
5. 그가 한국으로 돌아오고 나서, 그는 대한의 독립을 위해 싸우고자 1907년에 신민회를 설립했다.
6. 그는 또한 1919년에 상해의 대한민국 임시정부에 합류했다.
7. 그 후에, 그는 1938년에 죽을 때까지 사람들을 교육하기 위해 많은 학교들을 세웠다.

Project Step 1

1. A: I want _____ _____ Bulguksa _____ _____. You know Bulguksa, _____ _____?

2. B: Yes, I do. It's _____ _____ _____ Gyeongju.

3. C: Yes. It's _____ _____ _____ _____ _____ _____ _____ in Korea.

4. D: It also _____ _____ _____ _____ _____ the Dabotop.

1. A: 나는 외국인에게 불국사를 소개하고 싶어. 너는 불국사를 알고 있지, 그렇지 않니?
2. B: 응, 알고 있어. 그것은 경주에 있는 절이야.
3. C: 응. 그것은 한국에서 가장 아름다운 절 중 하나야.
4. D: 그것은 또한 다보탑과 같은 많은 문화재들을 보유하고 있어.

※ 다음 우리말을 영어로 쓰시오.

1. 우리 그룹은 안중근을 선택했는데, 우리 나라를 위한 희생에 깊은 인상을 받았기 때문입니다.

➡ _____

_____

2. 여러분은 안중근 기념관이나 안중근 공원을 방문함으로써 그에 관하여 더 많은 것을 알 수 있습니다.

➡ _____

Dosan An Changho

1. 안창호는 1878년에 태어났다.

➡ _____

2. 그가 십 대였을 때, 그는 서울로 이사를 하고 그곳에서 학교를 다녔다.

➡ _____

3. 1902년에 그는 더 나은 교육을 받기 위해서 미국으로 떠났다.

➡ _____

4. 안창호는 미국에서 한국인들의 삶을 개선하는 것을 도왔고, 존경받는 지도자가 되었다.

➡ _____

5. 그가 한국으로 돌아오고 나서, 그는 대한의 독립을 위해 싸우고자 1907년에 신민회를 설립했다.

➡ _____

_____

6. 그는 또한 1919년에 상해의 대한민국 임시정부에 합류했다.

➡ _____

7. 그 후에, 그는 1938년에 죽을 때까지 사람들을 교육하기 위해 많은 학교들을 세웠다.

➡ _____

1. A: 나는 외국인에게 불국사를 소개하고 싶어. 너는 불국사를 알고 있지, 그렇지 않니?

➡ _____

2. B: 응, 알고 있어. 그것은 경주에 있는 절이야.

➡ _____

3. C: 응. 그것은 한국에서 가장 아름다운 절 중 하나야.

➡ _____

4. D: 그것은 또한 다보탑과 같은 많은 문화재들을 보유하고 있어.

➡ _____

MEMO

MEMO

MEMO

영어 기출 문제집

1학기

정답 및 해설

시사 | 박준언

중 3

영어 기출 문제집

적중100

1학기

정답 및 해설

시사 | 박준언

중 3

Future Dreams, Future Jobs

시험대비 실력평가 p.08

01 ④　　　02 florist　　　03 ②　　　04 ③
05 analyze, strength, weakness　　　06 ⑤
07 repair　　　08 ④

01 '학교에 다니다'와 '결혼식에 참석하다'는 의미를 가지는 'attend'가 적절하다.

02 꽃으로 아름다운 것들을 창조하는 사람이라는 의미로 florist(플로리스트)가 적절하다.

03 '조직의 일원이 되다'는 의미로 '~에 속하다'는 belong to가 적절하다.

04 '국가, 조직 또는 개인의 유용하거나 가치 있는 소유물 또는 자질'의 의미로 'resource(자원)'가 적절하다.

05 analyze: 분석하다, strength: 강점, weakness: 약점

06 (A) 아이들의 그림이 교실 벽을 장식한다. (B) 아름다운 꽃으로 집을 장식하는 것은 아주 재미있다.

07 유의어 관계. 고치다 : 다루다

08 (A) 음악 감독으로서, '나는 배우들을 대상으로 오디션을 실시하고'가 적절하다. (B) 오디션을 본 다음 '배역에 맞는 배우를 고른 뒤에'라는 말이 적절하므로 'cast'가 와야 한다.

서술형 시험대비 p.09

01 (1) reduce, calm　(2) among　(3) belong to
　　(4) field
02 (A) something colorful　(B) highly recommend
03 (1) analyst　(2) recorded　(3) During, performance
04 (1) collect, 모으다　(2) personality, 성격
　　(3) greenery, 화초, 푸른 잎
05 conduct

01 (1) 그녀는 그들이 스트레스를 완화하고 평온해지도록(calm) 도와줘. (2) 너는 이 목록에 있는 것들 중에서(among) 무엇에 가장 관심이 있니? (3) 대부분의 사람들은 여섯 가지 성격 유형 중 한 가지에 속해(belong to). 현실적인 타입도 그 중 하나야. (4) 나는 해양 과학자입니다. 해양 과학은 거대한 분야(field)입니다.

02 (A) something은 형용사가 뒤에서 수식을 한다. 다채로운: colorful (B) '매우, 대단히'의 의미로 부사 highly를 사용한다.

03 (1) analyst: 분석가 (2) record: 녹화하다. 명사 games를 꾸며주며 수동의 의미('녹화된')로 과거분사 recorded가 적절하다. (3) '~ 동안에'의 의미로 'the+명사'가 뒤에 있기 때문에 전치사 during이 적절하다. performance: 공연

04 (1) 물건을 가져가서 함께 모으다 (2) 당신이 어떤 사람인지, 행동하고 느끼고 생각하는 방식으로 보여 지는 것 (3) 특히 잘려서 장식으로 사용되는 녹색 식물이나 가지

05 • 오케스트라를 지휘하려면, 여러분은 머릿속에서 음악을 들을 수 있어야 합니다. • 경찰관들은 1년에 네 번 인천에서 학교 폭력 예방 캠페인을 실시합니다.

교과서
Conversation

핵심 Check p.10~11

1 ①, ②, ④　2 ⑤

교과서 대화문 익히기

Check(√) True or False p.12~13

1 T　2 T　3 T　4 F　5 F　6 T　7 T　8 F

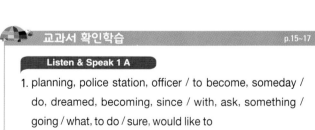

교과서 확인학습 p.15~17

Listen & Speak 1 A

1. planning, police station, officer / to become, someday / do, dreamed, becoming, since / with, ask, something / going / what, to do / sure, would like to

2. wrong / animator, drawing, enough / Being, a, artist / animator / a lot of, practice drawing / quite sure that, if

Listen & Speak 1 B

interested, technology, Which, right / sure, developer in writing. Which job, be right for / quite sure, be a good job for

Listen & Speak 2 A

1. glad, what you do / guide, information, visit / else / popular culture, traditional / It seems, knowing, happy with

2. role model / be like / does, do / how to stretch / reduce, calm themselves / It seems that, to keep both, and

Listen & Speak 2 B

program writer, become / writing, helpful
social worker, help me become / seems, reading books to kids, be helpful

Real Life Talk

most interested, among / working / it seems to me that, belong to, realistic / mean / belong to, personality types. Realistic, types / interesting, What kind of, recommend / and so on / to be / I'm quite sure

Communication Task Step 2

3 Ss, 2 As, 1 E / seems to, belong to / Jobs that, recommended / have always wanted / sounds, quite sure that you could

Wrap Up 1

doing / recipe, cook / to cook, chef / make / taking, to think of, creative / I'm quite sure

---

시험대비 기본평가   p.18

01 It seems, that   02 ③   03 ⑤
04 ②

01 'It seems to me that 주어+동사 ~.'는 '~인 것 같다'라는 의미로 자신의 의견이나 생각을 나타내는 표현이다.

02 어떤 직업이 맞는지 묻는 말에 '나는 ~라고 확신해.'라는 의미로 확실성을 표현하는 말이 적절하다.

03 라디오 방송 작가가 되고 싶어 하는 A에게 도움이 되는 말로 ⑤가 적절하다.

04 'I'm sure (that) ~.'은 '나는 ~을 확신해.'라는 의미로 확실성 정도를 표현하는 말이다.

시험대비 실력평가   p.19~20

01 ③   02 ①   03 ④   04 ③
05 In my opinion   06 ⑤
07 Being an animator is not just about being a good artist.
08 ②   09 ⑤   10 ③

01 전치사 of 뒤에 동사가 올 때는 동명사를 사용해야 한다. become을 becoming으로 고쳐야 한다.

---

02 ① Matt가 이번 주말에 삼촌을 만날 것인지는 대화에서 언급되어 있지 않다.

03 동물에 관심이 있어서 어떤 직업이 나에게 맞는지 묻는 말에 → (C) 애완동물 미용사가 적합한 직업이라 말하고 → (B) 애완동물 미용사가 무엇인지 묻고 → (A) 직업을 설명한다. → 마지막으로 (D) 멋지다고 답하는 것이 적절하다.

04 A가 패션 디자이너가 되고 싶다는 말에 B가 패션쇼에 가는 것이 도움이 될 것 같다고 했으므로 빈칸에는 '내가 그것이 되는 데 뭐가 도움이 될까?'라는 말이 적절하다.

05 의견을 말하는 표현으로 'It seems to me ~' 대신 'In my opinion, ~'을 사용할 수 있다.

06 ⑤번은 '나는 기술에 관심이 있어. 어떤 직업이 나에게 맞을까?'라는 물음에 '네가 훌륭한 축구 선수가 될 수 있을 것이라고 꽤 확신한다.'라는 대답은 어색하다.

07 주어 자리에 동사 be를 동명사 Being으로 바꾸고, 동사 is를 추가한다. 전치사 about 뒤에도 동명사 being을 추가하여 문장을 완성한다.

08 'It seems to me that ~.'은 '~처럼 보인다, ~인 것 같다'라는 의미로 자신의 의견이나 생각을 나타내는 표현이다.

09 현실적인 타입이고, 항상 축구선수가 되기를 원하는 Jessie의 말에 '멋지다'라고 말한 다음 훌륭한 축구선수가 될 수 있을 거라고 확신하지 못한다고 말하는 것은 어색하다.

10 ③ 보라가 Jessie에게 어떤 직업을 제안했는지는 대화에 언급되어 있지 않다.

서술형 시험대비   p.21

01 I have dreamed of becoming a police officer since I was ten.

02 I'm (quite) sure (that) he would like to meet you.

03 (A) Could you please tell me what you do?
   (B) What else do you do?
   (C) It seems to me knowing a lot about China is very important.

04 (A) What does she do?   (B) It seems to me that

01 '10살 때부터'는 'since I was ten'을 쓰고, 주절에는 현재완료 'have dreamed'를 쓴다. '~이 되는 것을 꿈꾸다'는 'dream of'와 동명사 being을 사용한다.

02 확실성의 정도를 나타내는 말은 'I'm (quite) sure (that) 주어+동사'를 이용한다.

3

Grammar <small>교과서</small>

핵심 Check   p.22~23

1 (1) which   (2) that

2 (1) Peter had his legs broken several times.

  (2) I will have my hair cut this Saturday.

시험대비 기본평가   p.24

01 (1) watched → watch

  (2) injure → injured   (3) which → that

  (4) encourage → encourages

02 ④   **03** ④

04 It is those books that[which] Barbara has always wanted to buy.

01 (1) 소녀가 다른 학생을 관찰하는 것이므로, 수동의 과거분사 watched는 부적절하다. 동사원형 watch를 써야 한다. (2) 다리를 부상당한 것이므로 수동의 과거분사 injured로 고쳐야 한다. (3) 'It ~ that' 강조구문으로 부사구 last Friday를 강조한다. (4) 삼촌이 격려하는 것이므로 현재시제, 3인칭 단수 주어에 맞는 동사형을 써야 한다.

02 the taxi를 강조하면, that 뒤에는 불완전한 문장이 와야 하는데, 구조가 완전하다. 내용상 Frank가 Nancy에게 청혼을 한 장소를 강조하는 문장이 되어야 하기 때문에 It was in the taxi that Frank proposed to Nancy.가 적절하다.

03 목적보어 자리에 동사원형이 왔으므로, 사역동사 had가 적절하다.

04 목적어를 강조하는 것이므로, 'It ~ that' 강조구문을 사용한다. 강조되는 대상이 복수라 하더라도 be동사는 is/was만 가능하며, 주절의 문장이 현재완료 시제이므로, 강조구문의 시제도 is로 하는 것에 유의한다.

시험대비 실력평가   p.25~27

01 ②   **02** ③   **03** ①

04 ③   **05** it was Poppy that tore the letter

06 ⓑ gain → to gain,   ⓒ to take → take,

  ⓓ performing → (to) perform, ⓕ stops → to stop

07 ③   **08** ②   **09** ①   **10** ⑤

11 ④

12 Laura had Tom help her husband to repair the washing machine.

13 It is James who is responsible for taking care of

plants.   **14** ⑤   **15** ②   **16** ③

17 ③, ⑤   **18** break → broken

01 'It is[was] ~ that' 강조구문의 강조 대상은 문장 내의 명사(주어, 목적어)와 부사(구/절) 뿐이다.

02 ③의 that은 진주어로 쓰였다. 나머지는 모두 'It ~ that' 강조 구문의 that이다.

03 'have/has/had+목적어+목적보어' 형태에서 목적어의 능동/수동에 따라 목적보어 자리에 동사원형 또는 과거분사를 쓴다. 집이 '칠해지는' 것이므로, 과거분사 painted가 적절하다.

04 자동차가 '수리되는' 것이므로 fixed가 적절하다.

05 과거시제 동사 tore 형태에 유의하여, 'It is[was] ~ that' 강조 구문을 글자 수에 맞게 쓴다.

06 ⓑ order+목적어+to부정사 ⓒ let+목적어+원형부정사 ⓓ help+목적어+(to)부정사 ⓕ get+목적어+to부정사 등의 형태로 쓰는 것이 적절하다. the addict: 중독자

07 ③은 가주어 It과 진주어 명사절을 이끄는 접속사 that이 쓰였다. 나머지는 모두 'It ~ that' 강조 구문이다.

08 ②는 가주어 It과 진주어 명사절을 이끄는 접속사 that이 쓰였다. 나머지는 모두 'It ~ that' 강조 구문이다.

09 ①번 문장은 '그는 아들의 사고에 의해서도 마음이 바뀌지 않았다'는 내용이며, 전치사 by와 문맥을 통해 수동임을 알 수 있다. change를 changed로 고치는 것이 적절하다.

10 (A), (C)는 사역동사 have, make 뒤의 목적보어 자리이므로 원형부정사를, (B), (D)는 order, expect이므로 목적보어로 to부정사를 쓰는 것이 적절하다.

11 ④의 allow는 목적보어 자리에 to부정사를 사용한다. ① to wash → wash, ② eat → to eat, ③ to use → use, ⑤ help → to help

12 사역동사 'have+목적어+동사원형'과 'help+목적어+(to) V' 형태를 적절하게 활용하여 영작한다.

13 내용상 아버지가 기르는 화초에 대한 책임을 맡고 있는 사람에 대한 강조 문장이므로 'It ~ who' 강조 구문을 사용한다. 전치사 for 뒤의 동명사 taking의 형태에 주의한다.

14 ⑤번 문장의 that은 접속사로 쓰였다. 나머지는 모두 'It ~ that' 강조 구문의 that이다.

15 'It ~ that' 강조구문에서는 강조되는 명사의 성격에 따라 that을 who 또는 which로 대체할 수 있다. ②는 진주어 명사절을 이끄는 접속사 that이며 다른 단어로 대체 불가하다.

16 옳은 문장은 ⓒ, ⓔ, ⓖ 3개이다. ⓐ fix → fixed, ⓑ clean → to clean, ⓓ 'It ~ that' 강조구문에서는 형용사를 강조할 수 없다. ⓕ pick → to pick ⓗ do → done

17 사역동사 'have+목적어+원형/과거분사' 형태를 적절하게 활용한 문장을 선택한다. ①은 우리말과 일치하지 않으며, ②도 내용 뿐 아니라 어법상 be taken 뒤에 by가 와야 한다. ④는 to take

의 to를 삭제하는 것이 적절하다.

18 '시합 중 그 축구 선수의 다리가 부러졌다'라는 의미가 정확하게 표현되려면, 수동의 과거분사가 목적보어 자리에 와야 한다. break를 broken으로 고치는 것이 적절하다.

01 (A) It is John that[who] is going to buy the masks at a party this Friday.

(B) It is the masks that[which] John is going to buy at a party this Friday.

(C) It is at a party that John is going to buy the masks this Friday.

(D) It is this Friday that John is going to buy the masks at a party.

02 had me help him to make

03 (1) the Hongdae street → on(in) the Hongdae street

(2) He rescued the injured carefully.

(3) Bush was chairman of the council.

(4) the playground → on[in] the playground

(5) who → that[which]

04 (1) clean　(2) come[coming]　(3) cry[crying]

(4) go　(5) to look

05 on March 14, 1879 that Einstein was

06 (1) check → checked　(2) sing → to sing

(3) meet → to meet　(4) playing → play

(5) was → was 삭제　(6) looks → look

07 (1) The teacher had Susan clean her desk.

(2) The tie made his father look much younger.

(3) Allow her to enjoy the film.

08 (1) 답변 불가

(2) It was Alicia that[who] had John's phone repaired.

(3) It was two weeks ago that Alicia had John's phone repaired.

(4) 답변 불가

(5) It was at the repair shop that John's phone was repaired two weeks ago.

01 강조하는 대상에 따라 알맞게 강조하는 대상이 사람일 때는 who, 사물일 때는 which를 써도 좋다. 'It ~ that' 강조 구문'으로 표현한다.

02 '시키다'의 의미를 갖는 사역동사 have를 시제에 맞게 had로 사용하는 것에 유의하여, 단어들을 배열한다.

03 (1) '부사구'로 장소를 강조하는 것이므로 전치사를 써야 한다.
(2) 태도를 나타내는 '양태 부사'는 'It ~ that' 강조 구문의 강조

대상이 될 수 없다. (3) '주격보어'도 'It ~ that' 강조 구문의 강조 대상이 될 수 없다. (4) '부사구'로서 장소를 강조하는 것이므로 전치사를 써야 한다. (5) 강조 대상이 사람이 아니므로 who는 쓸 수 없다. which 또는 that이 적절하다.

04 (1)~(4)는 사역/지각동사 (5)는 일반 5형식 동사이다. (5)의 목적보어 자리에는 to look의 형태가 적절하다.

05 '1879년 3월 14일이 Einstein이 태어난 날'이라는 문장을 '부사구'를 강조하는 'It ~ that 강조 구문'으로 표현해야 한다. 전치사 on과 함께 쓰는 것에 유의하여 영작한다.

06 (1) '짐 검사를 당하는 것'이니까 수동의 표현이 필요하다. 'have+목적어+과거분사' 형태가 적절하다. (2) get+목적어+to V (3) allow+목적어+to V (4) let+목적어+원형동사 (5) break one's legs 다리가 부러지다 (6) make+목적어+원형동사

07 (1) 사역동사 had + 목적어 + 동사원형. (2) 사역동사 made + 목적어 + 동사원형. (3) 일반 5형식 동사 allow 뒤에 나오는 목적보어 자리에는 to 부정사를 쓰는 것이 적절하다.

08 (1) 사역동사 'have +목적어+ p.p.' 형태에서는 행위자를 파악할 수 없다. 일반적으로 제3자가 행위자이므로, 보기의 문장만으로는 누가 전화기를 수리했는지 답변할 수 없다. (4) 주어진 문장만으로는 수리 시점(2주 전)만을 알 수 있고, 수리 기간은 파악할 수 없으므로 답변 불가임. (2), (3), (5)번은 'It ~ that' 강조 구문에 맞춰 적절히 영작한다.

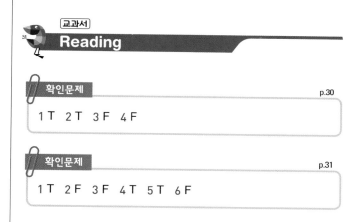

Reading

1 T　2 T　3 F　4 F

1 T　2 F　3 F　4 T　5 T　6 F

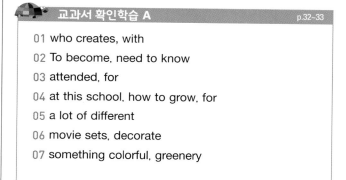

01 who creates, with

02 To become, need to know

03 attended, for

04 at this school, how to grow, for

05 a lot of different

06 movie sets, decorate

07 something colorful, greenery

5

08 highly recommend

09 sport data analyst

10 doesn't it   11 a lot of fun

12 to watch recorded games, run, to collect

13 analyze, to show

14 understands, do better

15 Since, have been

16 baseball games all the time

17 because watching baseball games

18 As, a musical theater

19 audition, look for

20 selecting the cast, for each scene

21 put, together

22 During, conduct

23 my responsibility, each

24 direct, to keep, together

25 Conducting, directing, waving

26 a big field   27 includes, living in them

28 have studied, living

29 the growth ring, that

30 By looking

31 I get from, is used to understand, manage

32 because, the best use

교과서 확인학습 B
 p.34~35

1 Hi, I am Tom. A florist is someone who creates beautiful things with flowers.

2 To become a florist, you need to know many things about flowers.

3 I attended a high school for florists and gardeners.

4 It was at this school that I learned how to grow and care for different types of flowers.

5 These days, florists can do a lot of different things.

6 I design movie sets sometimes and I decorate shops with flowers.

7 I am happy when I create something colorful with fresh flowers and greenery.

8 If you like plants and the arts, I highly recommend you become a florist.

9 I am Emma. I am a sport data analyst.

10 It sounds like a difficult job, doesn't it?

11 In fact, it is a lot of fun. I work for a baseball team.

12 My job is to watch recorded games and run a computer program to collect data.

---

13 Then, I analyze the data to show my team's strengths and weaknesses.

14 If the team understands their strengths and weaknesses, they can do better next time.

15 Since I was young, I have been a big fan of baseball.

16 Now, in my work, I watch baseball games all the time.

17 This is a perfect job for me because watching baseball games is my hobby!

18 Hi, I am Chris. As a director of a musical theater, I do a lot of things.

19 I audition the actors and I look for good, strong voices.

20 After selecting the cast, I teach them the songs for each scene.

21 Then, I put the cast and orchestra together for practic

22 During the performance, I am in the orchestra area and conduct.

23 It's my responsibility to have each song played the same way every time.

24 I direct the musicians and the singers to keep the show together.

25 Conducting and directing is not just about waving my arms around!

26 My name is Yeji. I am an ocean scientist. Ocean science is a big field.

27 It includes studies of the oceans and the creatures living in them.

28 Among other things, I have studied many kinds of fish living in the seas near Korea.

29 It is the growth ring in a fish that interests me.

30 By looking at it, I can find out when and where the fish was born.

31 All the information I get from fish is used to understand sea resources and manage the oceans better."

32 My job is important because it makes the best use of nature possible.

시험대비 실력평가
 p.36~39

01 ②   02 ⑤

03 A florist is someone who creates beautiful things with flowers.

04 ③   05 ③

06 They can do better next time if the team understands their strengths and weaknesses.

07 played   08 ③

09 (After selecting the cast,) He teaches them the songs for each scene.

10 cast   11 ⑤   12 ④

13 the oceans, the creatures living in them

14 It can tell Yeji when and where the fish was born.

15 ②, ③   16 ③

17 He learned how to grow and care for different types of flowers at a school for florists and gardeners.

18 doesn't it 19 ②   20 ④

21 She does it in order to collect data.

22 conducts 23 ③

24 His responsibility is to have each song played the same way every time.

25 ④   26 ④   27 ④

01 (A)는 '오늘날'이라는 의미이다. 따라서 ②번이 적절하다. ①, ③, ⑤ 가끔 ④ 거의 ~하지 않는

02 Tom은 플로리스트와 정원사들을 양성하는 학교에 다녔다고 하였으므로 ⑤번이 글의 내용과 일치한다.

03 플로리스트는 꽃으로 아름다운 것들을 창조하는 사람이라고 하였다.

04 야구 경기를 보는 것이 자신의 취미이기 때문에 완벽한 직업이라고 말하는 것이 적절하다.

05 자료를 수집한 후 분석한다고 하였다.

06 팀이 자신들의 강점과 약점을 알면 다음번에 더 잘할 수 있다고 하였다.

07 각각의 노래가 연주되도록 하는 것이므로 과거분사 형태를 쓰는 것이 적절하다.

08 ③ 공연 중에 지휘한다고 하였다.

09 배역에 맞는 배우를 고른 뒤에, Chris는 그들에게 각 장면을 위한 노래를 가르친다고 하였다.

10 어떤 영화나 연극에 출연하는 사람들은 '출연자들(배역진)'이다.

11 to understand와 병렬 관계이므로 manage라고 쓰는 것이 적절하다.

12 빈칸 (A)에는 By가 들어간다. ① pay attention to: ~에 주의를 기울이다 ② look forward to: ~을 기대하다 ③ depend on: ~에 의존하다 ④ go by: 지나가다, 흐르다 ⑤ take away: ~을 없애주다

13 해양 과학자들은 바다뿐만 아니라 바다에 사는 생명체를 연구한다고 하였다.

14 물고기의 나이테로 물고기가 언제 어디에서 태어났는지를 알 수 있다고 하였다.

15 사람을 선행사로 받는 주격 관계대명사 who가 쓰이며, who를 대신하여 that을 써도 무방하다.

16 항상 같은 일을 하는 것이 아니라 여러 가지 일을 한다고 하였다.

17 Tom은 플로리스트와 정원사들을 위한 학교에서 갖가지 종류의 꽃을 키우고 관리하는 방법을 배웠다고 하였다. 'It was at a high school for florists and gardeners that he learned how to grow and care for different types of flowers.'라고 답해도 좋다.

18 일반동사의 부가의문문이고, 주어가 it이므로 doesn't it이라고 쓰는 것이 적절하다.

19 어려운 직업처럼 들리지만 [B] 사실 매우 재미있다고 말하며 녹화된 경기를 보고 자료를 수집한다고 말함 [A] 수집한 자료를 분석하여 팀에게 보여주는 일을 한다고 설명. 어릴 때부터 야구의 열혈 팬이었고 [C] 지금 일하는 내내 야구를 보므로 자신에게 완벽한 직업이라고 함.

20 어렸을 때부터 야구의 열혈 팬이었던 Emma는 자신의 직업에 만족하고 있다는 것을 글을 통해 알 수 있다.

21 Emma는 자료를 수집하기 위하여 컴퓨터 프로그램을 실행한다고 하였다.

22 오케스트라나 합창단 앞에 서서 공연을 지시하는 것은 '지휘하다'이다.

23 Chris는 배역에 맞는 배우를 고르고 그들에게 각 장면을 위한 노래를 가르친다고 하였다. 따라서 ③번이 일치한다.

24 각각의 노래가 매번 동일하게 연주되도록 만드는 것이 Chris의 책임이라고 하였다.

25 주어진 문장의 it이 가리키는 것은 the growth ring in a fish 이다.

26 예지의 작업은 자연을 가장 잘 활용할 수 있게 한다는 점에서 중요하다고 하였다.

27 ① includes ② creatures ③ resources ④ attention ⑤ manage

서술형 시험대비   p.40~41

01 creates

02 He attended a high school for florists and gardeners.

03 We need to know many things about flowers to become a florist.

04 He feels happy when he creates something colorful with fresh flowers and greenery.

05 strengths and weaknesses

06 She watches recorded games and runs a computer program to collect data. Then, she analyzes the data to show her team's strengths and weaknesses.

07 Her hobby is watching baseball games.

08 analyst

09 waving his arms around

10 He is in the orchestra area during the performance.

11 He directs the musicians and the singers.

12 It is the actors that I audition.

13 It is the growth ring in a fish that interests Yeji.

14 It's because her job makes the best use of nature possible.

15 As an ocean scientist, she has studied many kinds of fish living in the seas near Korea.

16 We should look at the growth ring in a fish.

01 주격 관계대명사의 선행사가 someone이므로 단수 동사를 쓰는 것이 적절하다.

02 Tom은 플로리스트와 정원사들을 위한 학교를 다녔다고 하였다.

03 플로리스트가 되기 위해서 여러분은 꽃에 관해 많은 것을 알 필요가 있다고 하였다.

04 그는 싱싱한 꽃과 화초로 다채로운 무언가를 창조해 낼 때 행복하다고 하였다.

05 팀이 자신들의 강점과 약점을 이해하면 다음번에 더 잘할 수 있다는 의미이다.

06 스포츠 데이터 분석가로서 Emma는 녹화된 경기를 보고 자료를 수집하기 위해 컴퓨터 프로그램을 실행한 후 팀의 강점과 약점을 보여주기 위해서 자료를 분석하는 일을 한다고 하였다.

07 Emma는 자신의 취미가 야구 경기를 보는 것이라고 하였다.

08 어떠한 주제를 분석하여 그것에 관한 의견을 주는 사람은 '분석가'이다.

09 Chris에 따르면 지휘하고 감독하는 것은 단지 그의 팔을 흔드는 것 이상을 의미한다.

10 Chris는 공연 동안에 오케스트라 석에 있다고 하였다.

11 공연을 제대로 진행하기 위해 그는 연주자들과 가수들을 감독한다고 하였다.

12 Chris는 배우들을 대상으로 오디션을 실시한다고 하였다. 따라서 강조하는 대상을 the actors로 하여 답할 수 있다.

13 'The growth ring in a fish interests Yeji.'라고 답해도 좋다.

14 그녀의 직업은 자연을 가장 잘 활용할 수 있게 한다는 점에서 중요하다고 하였다.

15 예지는 해양 과학자로서 한국 주변의 바다에 살고 있는 많은 종류의 물고기를 연구해 왔다고 하였다.

16 물고기가 언제 어디서 태어났는지 알고 싶으면 물고기 안에 있는 나이테를 보면 된다고 하였다.

p.43~47

영역별 핵심문제

01 select　02 ⑤　03 ③　04 ①

05 (c)reatures　06 ④　07 ②

08 it seems to me that you belong to the realistic type.

09 She is most interested in working outside and playing sports.

10 ③

11 quite sure you could be a good chef.　12 ①

13 ⑤　14 ④　15 ④　16 ④

17 ③　18 ⑤　19 ②　20 ②

21 will have your computer fixed today.　22 ⑤

23 how to grow and care for different types of flowers　24 ④　25 ⑤　26 ②

27 ③　28 ②　29 ④

30 She works for a baseball team.

01 유의어 관계다. 매우, 대단히 = 고르다, 선택하다

02 (A)의 앞 문장에 전 세계의 요리를 좋아하고 요리를 잘할 수 있으며 음식을 맛있고 아름답게 만들 수 있다는 말을 하고 있고 그에 대한 결과로 요리사가 되고 싶다고 했기 때문에 의미상 '이러한 이유로'가 적절하다. (B)는 '내 꿈을 이루기 위해'가 의미상 적절하다.

03 어떤 것 또는 어떤 사람을 처리해야 할 일이나 의무

04 무언가를 다른 것의 일부로 포함하거나 다른 것의 일부로 만들다

05 영어 설명은 '독립적으로 움직일 수 있는 크거나 작은 생물'이란 의미로 creature가 적절하다.

06 since가 현재완료와 함께 사용이 될 때는 '~일 때부터'의 의미가 된다.

07 자산의 의견을 나타내는 표현으로 '~처럼 보이다'는 의미로 'It seems to me that ~'을 사용한다.

08 '~인 것 같다'는 의미로 'it seems to me that 주어+동사 ~'를 쓴다.

09 목록에 있는 것 중에서 Jessie가 가장 관심이 있는 것은 무엇인가?

10 Jessie에게 축구 선수를 추천한 것은 보라가 아니라 the things on the list에서 추천한 것이다.

11 확실성 정도를 표현하는 말로 'I'm quite sure+주어+동사' 어순이 적절하고 '나는 네가 좋은 요리사가 될 것이라고 꽤 확신해'라는 의미가 된다.

12 have+목적어+동사원형: ~하게 시키다

13 'It ~ that' 강조 구문으로 표현한다. ②는 cheer 동사의 수일치가 부적절하고, ③은 to cheer가 어법상 적절하다.

14 'have+목적어+과거분사' 문장이다. ⑤번의 break one's leg 도 '다리가 부러지다'라는 뜻이지만, '펜스가 그를 쳤다'는 내용 이 부적절하다.

15 ④는 가주어 It과 진주어 명사절을 이끄는 접속사 that이 쓰인 문장이다. 나머지는 모두 'It ~ that' 강조 구문이 쓰였다.

16 ① fixed → fix ② leaving → leave ③ feels → feel ④ allow의 목적보어 자리에 to부정사는 적절하다. ⑤ break → broken

17 'It ~ that' 강조 구문에서 일어난 해를 가리키는 표현은 연도 앞 에 in을 쓰는 것이 적절하다.

18 <보기>의 have는 'have+목적어+p.p.' 형태로 '목적어가 ~되도 록 시키다'라는 의미이다. 같은 의미로 쓰인 문장은 ⑤번이다. 다 른 문장들의 have는 ① 먹다 ② (특징)으로 ~이 있다 ③ (잡고) 있다 ④ 겪다 등의 의미로 쓰였다.

19 ②는 가주어 It과 진주어 명사절을 이끄는 접속사 that으로 쓰 였다. 나머지는 모두 'It ~ that' 강조 구문의 that이다.

20 'have+목적어+과거분사' 형태이다. to change를 changed로 고치는 것이 적절하다. grief: 슬픔

21 주어진 조건대로 영작할 때, '오늘 네 컴퓨터를 고쳐줄게'라고 해 야 한다. Peter는 컴퓨터를 고칠 줄 모르기 때문에, 누군가 제 3자가 고치도록 해야 하므로, 그에 맞는 표현인 'have+목적어 +p.p.'를 활용한다.

22 '매우' 추천한다는 의미이므로 highly라고 쓰는 것이 적절하다.

23 Tom이 다닌 학교는 다양한 종류의 꽃을 기르고 다루는 방법을 그에게 가르쳐 주었다.

24 누가 Tom이 플로리스트가 되도록 권했는지는 위 글을 읽고 알 수 없다.

25 [C]에서 말하는 these reasons는 주어진 문장에서 언급한 '자 신이 잘하는 것들'을 가리키는 말이다. [C]에서 꿈을 위해 요리 잡지를 보고 [B]에서 또한 프랑스로 가서 다양한 요리 기술을 배우겠다고 말하며 자신의 롤 모델이 아버지라고 언급한다. [A] 아버지에 대한 이야기가 기술되고 있다.

26 자신의 꿈의 직업인 요리사에 관한 글이다.

27 요리사가 되고 싶은 글쓴이의 롤 모델이 아버지라고 하였고, 아 버지는 항상 새로운 조리법에 대해 생각하고 이것을 요리해준다 고 하였으므로 ③번을 유추할 수 있다.

28 스포츠 경기를 보고 컴퓨터 프로그램을 돌려 분석하는 직업으로 ②번이 가장 적절하다.

29 Emma는 어렸을 때부터 야구의 열혈 팬이었고 야구 경기를 보 는 것이 자신의 취미라고 하였으므로 ④번이 글의 내용과 일치 한다.

30 Emma는 야구팀을 위해서 일한다고 하였다.

단원별 예상문제　　　　　　　　　　　　　　p.48~51

01 lead　　　　　02 ③

03 It seems to me knowing a lot about China is very important. 04 ⑤

05 Read a lot of books and practice drawing every day.　　　　06 ①　　　　　07 ④

08 I'm quite sure (that) you could become a (great) soccer player.

09 Do you want to become a police officer?

10 (1) ⓐ　(2) ⓑ　(3) ⓐ　(4) ⓑ　(5) ⓐ

11 It seems, both, and, healthy　　　　　12 ④

13 ③　　　　　　　14 ⑤

15 (1) ⓐ It was the newlyweds that bought a table at the mall 2 weeks ago.

　　(2) ⓑ It was a table that the newlyweds bought at the mall 2 weeks ago.

　　(3) ⓒ It was at the mall that the newlyweds bought a table 2 weeks ago.

　　(4) ⓓ It was 2 weeks ago that the newlyweds bought a table at the mall.

16 ④　　　　　17 ②

18 He looks for good, strong voices.

19 He directs the musicians and the singers to keep the show together.　　　20 ③　　　21 ⑤

22 the oceans　　　　　23 information from fish

---

01 반의어 관계다. 약함 - 강함 : 따르다 - 이끌다

02 영화, 연극, 쇼 등의 한 부분에 적합하다는 것을 보여주기 위해 짧은 공연을 한다.

03 'In my opinion, 주어+동사 ~'는 의견을 말할 때 사용하는 표 현으로 'It seems to me (that)+주어+동사 ~'로 바꾸어 쓸 수 있다.

05 지수에게 많은 책을 읽고, 매일 그리기 연습을 하라고 조언하고 있다.

06 enough는 형용사를 뒤에서 수식하므로 good enough로 바꾸 어야 한다.

07 Jessie의 '무슨 의미야?'라는 질문에 대한 보라의 대답으로 보아 '너는 현실적인 타입에 속하는 것 같아.'라는 말이 적절하다.

08 확실성 정도를 나타내는 표현은 'I'm quite sure (that) 주어+ 동사'를 이용한다.

09 'You do?'의 do는 대동사로 앞 문장의 become a police officer를 대신하는 말이다. 구어체에서 일반동사 의문문의 Do 가 생략되어 'You want to ~?' 형태로 사용하기도 한다.

10 (2), (4) 문장들은 접속사 that이 이끄는 진주어 명사절과 형용 사 보어(2), 명사보어(4)로 이뤄진 문장이다. (1) 부사구를 강조 (3) 부사절을 강조 (5) 의문사를 강조하는 'It ~ that' 강조 구문 이다.

9

11 '~인 것 같다'는 'It seems that ~'을 이용하고, 'A와 B 둘 다'는 'both A and B' 구문을 사용한다. '건강하게'는 우리말로 부사로 해석되지만 'keep+목적어+목적보어' 구문으로 목적보어 자리에는 형용사 healthy를 사용해야 한다.

12 ④ 글의 내용상 나의 컴퓨터가 shop에서 수리되었으므로, '컴퓨터를 수리한 것은 삼촌이다'라는 내용의 문장은 부적절하다.

13 'have+목적어+p.p.' 형태의 문장들이다. 각각 ① '우산을 도둑맞다' ② '아들을 전학보내다' ④ '구매품들을 포장시키다' ⑤ '돈을 인출하다'를 뜻하며, ③번 '신발을 닦다'라는 의미로 쓰려면, shone을 shined로 쓰는 것이 적절하다.

14 ⑤ 'have+목적어+동사원형'이 쓰였다. ① moving → moved ② to wait → wait ③ going → go ④ washed → (to) wash 로 고치는 것이 적절하다.

16 (A)는 자격을 나타내어 '~로서'라고 해석되는 전치사이다. ① ~ 때문에, ~이므로 ② ~만큼 ③ ~하는 동안에 ④ ~로서 ⑤ ~ 때문에

17 the cast는 Chris가 오디션을 실시하여 고른 배우들을 의미한다. 이들에게 노래를 가르친 후 배우와 오케스트라를 함께 연습시킨다는 흐름이 자연스럽다.

18 Chris는 훌륭하고 강한 목소리를 찾아낸다고 하였다.

19 Chris는 공연을 제대로 진행하기 위해 연주자들과 가수들을 감독한다고 하였다.

20 (A) '한국 주변의 바다에 살고 있는'이 fish를 수식하므로 현재분사 형태, (B) by Ving: V함으로써, on Ving: V하자마자 (C) 핵심 주어가 all the information이므로 단수 동사를 쓰는 것이 적절하다.

21 예지가 물고기에 대해 얻은 정보는 바다의 지원을 이해하고 바다를 더 잘 관리하기 위해 사용된다고 하였다.

22 바다를 가리키는 말이다.

23 예지는 물고기로부터 정보를 얻어서 바다 자원을 이해한다고 하였다.

07 First, she will read magazines about cooking. Second, she will go to France to learn various cooking skills.

08 He always thinks of new recipes and then cooks these new dishes for his family.

09 recorded

10 Her hobby is watching baseball games.

11 She watches baseball games all the time in her work.

01 (A) '~에 관심이 있다'는 'be interested in'을 사용한다. (B) 확실성 정도는 'I'm quite sure that ~'을 사용한다.

02 수미의 꿈은 요리사가 되는 것이다. 요리 수업을 듣고 새롭고 창조적인 요리를 생각해 내기 위해 노력하는 것이 그녀의 꿈을 이루는 데 중요한 것 같다.

03 확실성 정도를 표현하는 말은 'I'm quite sure (that)+주어+동사'나 'I have no doubt that+주어+동사'를 사용할 수 있다.

04 기자의 질문이 '수상에 가장 크게 기여한 것'을 묻는 것이므로, 부모님 때문이라는 내용으로 'because of my parents'를 'it ~ that' 구문으로 강조하는 문장을 쓰는 것이 적절하다.

05 사역동사 'have+목적어+원형[과거분사]' 형태를 적절하게 활용하도록 한다.

06 글쓴이는 자라서 요리사가 되기를 원한다.

07 글쓴이는 꿈을 이루기 위해 요리 잡지를 읽고, 다양한 요리 기술을 배우기 위하여 프랑스로 갈 것이라고 하였다.

08 아버지는 항상 새로운 조리법에 대해 생각하고 그것을 요리해 준다고 하였다.

09 녹화된 경기라는 의미이므로 과거분사를 쓰는 것이 적절하다.

10 그녀의 취미는 야구 경기를 보는 것이라고 하였다.

11 그녀는 일하는 중에 내내 야구를 본다고 하였다.

서술형 실전문제 p.52~53

01 A: I'm interested in technology
   B: I'm quite sure that

02 dream, It seems, taking a cooking, trying to think of new and creative dishes, achieve

03 I have no doubt that you can be a good animator if you try hard.

04 was because of my parents that I received this award

05 (1) Her father had Sally wash Toto.
   (2) Her father had Toto washed by Sally.

06 She wants to be a chef (when she grows up).

창의사고력 서술형 문제 p.54

|모범답안|

01 A: I'm interested in art.
   B: I'm quite sure that a designer

02 (1) |모범답안| I had my phone repaired yesterday.
   (2) |모범답안| Sophia will have her car checked by a mechanic at the repair shop tomorrow.

03 bags from around, making things, what I made look beautiful, it is a bag designer that, read fashion magazines, go to France to learn to design bags

01 ①　　02 ⑤　　03 run　　04 ③

05 ④

06 That's a person who works at a pet hair salon.

07 ③

08 a farmer, a police officer, a soccer player, and so on

09 ②

10 I'm quite sure that you can be a good animator if you try hard.

11 (1) It is for three days that Lucy has been reading the novel.

(2) It is Austin who wrote the novel.

12 (1) Mom had me put the unused things in the boxes.

(2) I will have the boxes donated to charity.

13 (1) Mom had me brush my teeth for myself.

(2) It is my dog Angel that is washing so many dishes.

14 ③　　15 ②　　16 ③　　17 ④

18 ④

19 He conducts during the performance.

20 my responsibility to have each song played

21 ③　　22 ⑤

01 ①번은 'analyst(분석가)'에 관한 설명이다.

02 '직업에 만족하나요?'라는 A의 말에 B가 '내 생각으로는, 패션 쇼에 가는 것이 도움이 될 거야.'라고 말하는 것은 자연스럽지 못하다.

03 유의어 관계다. 실행하다 : 고치다

04 사람이나 사물을 어떤 상태나 장소로 데려오다[가져오다]

05 '애완동물 미용사가 너에게 좋은 직업이 될 거라고 생각한다.'는 B의 대답으로 보아 (A)에는 자신에게 맞는 직업의 종류를 물어 보는 것이 자연스럽다.

06 '애완동물 미용사는 무엇이니?'라는 A의 질문에 대한 답으로 '그 것은 애완동물 미용실에서 일하는 사람이다'라는 답이 적절하다. 주격 관계대명사 who를 이용하여 선행사 a person을 수식한다.

07 belong to는 자동사이므로 수동태를 사용할 수 없다.

08 Q: 현실적인 타입의 사람들에게 그들이 추천하는 직업은 무엇 인가?

09 빈칸 다음에 좋은 이야기를 만들기 위해 책을 많이 읽고, 그림 그리는 것을 매일 연습하라고 조언하고 있으므로 빈칸에는 만화 영화 제작자가 되기 위해 조언을 구하는 말이 적절하다.

10 '~을 꽤 확신해'는 'I'm quite sure that+주어+동사' 구문을 이 용하고, '노력한다면'은 'if+주어+동사'를 이용한다.

11 내용을 정확히 이해하고, 조건에 맞게 질문에 답하도록 한다. (1) 일요일에 시작해서 화요일이므로 '3일 동안'이다. (2) who 를 쓰는 것이 조건이므로 that을 쓰지 않는 것에 유의한다.

12 시제와 능동/수동에 유의하여, 'have+목적어+원형/과거분사' 형 태로 주어진 단어를 배열한다.

13 (1) 혼자 힘으로: for myself (2) '그릇을 닦고 있는'이라는 우 리말로 보아 현재진행시제로 영작하는 것이 적절하다.

14 주어진 문장과 ③번은 사역동사 have로서 '시키다'라는 의미로 쓰였다. 각 문장에 쓰인 have의 의미는 ①, ② '갖고 있다' ④ '먹다' ⑤ '경험하다' 등이다.

15 ②번 이후의 문장에서 말하는 at this school은 주어진 문장의 a high school for florists and gardeners이다.

16 글의 내용상 '식물과 예술'을 좋아한다면 플로리스트가 될 것을 강력히 추천한다는 말이 가장 적절하다.

17 색종이로 꽃을 장식하는 것은 위 글에 나와 있지 않다.

18 Tom이 어디에서 일하는지는 위 글을 읽고 알 수 없다.

19 Chris는 공연 중에 지휘를 한다고 하였다.

20 노래가 연주되도록 하는 것이므로 사역동사 have의 목적격 보 어로 과거분사 played를 쓰는 것이 적절하다.

21 (B)는 전치사 about의 목적어로 쓰인 동명사이다. 모두 명사를 수식하는 현재분사이지만 ③번은 '~하는 것'으로 해석되는 동명 사이다.

22 자신의 꿈에 관하여 이야기하고 있으므로 아버지가 항상 새로운 요리법에 관해 생각한다는 것은 글의 흐름상 어색하다.

Are You a Digital Citizen?

시험대비 실력평가   p.62

01 ④   02 (a)ddiction
03 stay away from   04 ②   05 ⑤
06 ③   07 death   08 ④

01 학생들의 수가 올해 감소되었다. 설탕을 먹는 것을 그만두었을 때 나의 체중이 줄었다.

02 비디오 게임이 중독으로 이어지지 않게 조심해라.

03 stay away from: ~을 멀리하다, ~에서 떨어져 있다

04 전화를 걸거나 편지나 이메일 등을 보냄으로써 누군가와 연락하다: contact(연락하다)

05 또 다른 것을 대표하는 것으로 여겨지는 것: 상징(symbol)

06 (A) 나는 벤치에 앉아 잠시 동안 책을 읽었다. (B) 나의 집이 너무 작기 때문에 손님의 수를 제한해야 한다.

07 반의어 관계다. 장점-단점 : 출생-죽음

08 • 중독과 싸우기 위해, 중국의 인터넷 중독 치료 캠프가 빠르게 성장하고 있다. • 해독 다이어트는 당신의 몸에 있는 독소를 제거하고 살을 빼는 데 빠르고 쉬운 방법으로써 점점 인기가 많아지고 있다.

서술형 시험대비   p.63

01 (1) form   (2) such as   (3) refreshed   (4) necessary
02 uncomfortable
03 (1) addicted   (2) supposed   (3) comment
    (4) password
04 (1) digital, 디지털의   (2) mistake, 실수
    (3) detox, 해독   (4) conversation, 대화
05 post(ed)

01 (1) 새로운 단어를 만들기 위해 글자를 재배열하세요. (2) 나는 비빔밥이나 불고기와 같은 한국 음식을 좋아한다. (3) 푹 잔 후에, 나는 상쾌함을 느꼈다. (4) 우리가 매일 많은 물은 마시는 것은 필요하다. colorful (B) '매우, 대단히'의 의미로 부사 highly를 사용한다.

02 '편안하고 쾌적하게 느끼지 않거나, 편안하고 쾌적하지 못하도록 하는'의 의미로 '불편한(uncomfortable)'이 적절하다.

03 (1) be addicted to: ~에 중독되다 (2) be supposed to+동사원형: ~하기로 되어 있다 (3) comment: 논평 (4) password: 비밀번호

04 (1) 다수의 작은 신호로 사진, 소리 등을 저장하거나 그것을 숫자로 보여주는 (2) 원하지 않거나 의도하지 않은 결과를 생성하는 행동, 결정 또는 판단 (3) 건강에 좋지 않거나 해로운 음식, 음료, 약을 일정 기간 동안 몸에 섭취하지 않는 기간 (4) 생각, 감정, 아이디어가 표현되거나, 질문과 답변이 되는 두 명 또는 그 이상의 사람들 사이의 이야기

05 • 다양한 한국 음식에 대한 요리법이 서울관광 웹 사이트에 게재될 예정이다. • 나는 많은 사진을 찍고 그것을 인스타그램에 게시했어.

교과서 Conversation

핵심 Check   p.64~65

1 ④   **2** ⑤

교과서 대화문 익히기

Check(√) True or False   p.66

1 T   2 F   3 T   4 T

교과서 확인학습   p.68~69

Listen & Speak 1 A

1. tired / until, less than / Playing, good for / can't stop, addicted / were, would set, limit

2. spend, on / almost, can't help it / If I were you, suggest doing / Outdoor / a lot of, such as / suggest

Listen & Speak 2 A

1. posting, that, took / if, post / looks good / not supposed to, without asking / right away

2. let's / On / download, for free / supposed to download, against / Why don't we, instead

Real Life Talk

posted, on, posted / figured out, password / What should / were, change / should / easy to guess / birth date / In fact, (You')re not supposed to use, personal information / change, stronger one posting / take / took, blog / (you)'re not supposed to post / Why not / owner, right

시험대비 기본평가   p.70

01 If I were you
02 ④
03 ③
04 ⑤

01 'If I were you, I would ~.'는 충고할 때 사용하는 표현으로 '내가 너라면 ~할 것이다[~할 텐데]'의 의미다.

02 오랜 기간 동안 동일한 비밀번호를 사용하는 상대방에게 '오랜 기간 동안 동일한 비밀번호를 사용해서는 안 된다'는 말이 적절하다. 'be not supposed to'를 사용하는 것이 옳다.

03 빈칸에는 상대에게 '스마트폰 화면 잠금을 설정하라'는 충고의 표현이 적절하다.

04 'You're not supposed to ~.'는 '~해서는 안 된다'라는 의미로 불허를 나타내는 표현이다.

시험대비 실력평가   p.71~72

01 ④
02 ③
03 It's against the law.
04 ⑤
05 are not supposed to
06 ②
07 ③
08 ⑤
09 ④
10 ①

01 스마트폰에 너무 많은 시간을 보낸다는 엄마의 말에 → (D) 친구들이 SNS에 모여서 어쩔 수 없다는 이유를 말하고 → (B) 야외 활동을 해보라는 엄마의 충고가 나오고 → (A) 되묻는 말에 대해 → 마지막으로 (C) 되묻는 말에 확인해 주는 말이 오는 순서가 자연스럽다.

02 '낯선 사람이 계속 문자를 보낸다.'는 A의 말에 '내가 너라면 그 번호를 차단할 거야.'라는 대답이 적절하다.

03 '~에 반대하여, ~에 거슬러'의 의미를 가지는 'against'를 추가하여 문장을 완성한다.

04 ⑤ '누군가 네 SNS에 이상한 것을 올렸어.'라는 말에 '넌 어떻게 해야 하니?'라는 물음은 어색하다.

05 '~해서는 안 된다'라는 의미로 불허를 나타낼 때 'should not, must not, be not supposed to' 등을 사용한다.

06 'If I were you, I would ~.'는 충고할 때 사용하는 표현이다.

07 Jenny가 Peter에게 어떤 종류의 게임을 제안하는지는 대화에 언급되어 있지 않다.

08 '~에 중독되다'는 의미로 수동 형태인 'be addicted to'를 사용한다.

09 블로그 주인만이 사진을 사용할 권리가 있다고 말하는 것으로 보아 불허의 표현으로 'you're not supposed to post'가 적절하다.

10 소희는 멋진 사진이 있는 식당을 방문한 것이 아니라 방문한 식당의 사진을 가지고 있다.

서술형 시험대비   p.73

01 If I were you, I would change my password.
02 He used his birth date.
03 (A) Did you ask Sarah if you could post them online?
   (B) You're not supposed to post someone's pictures without asking.
   (C) I'll call Sarah and ask her right away.
04 (A) You're not supposed to download movies from that website

01 'If I were you, I would ~.'는 충고할 때 사용하는 표현으로 '내가 너라면 ~할 것이다[~할 텐데]'로 해석한다.

02 질문: 비밀번호를 만들 때 세호는 무엇을 사용했는가?

Grammar

핵심 Check   p.74~75

1 (1) of (2) for
2 If Paul knew it, he would change the password.

시험대비 기본평가   p.76

01 (1) have → had   (2) will → would
   (3) has → had   (4) will → would
02 ③
03 ④
04 It is not easy for you to live without a smartphone.

01 문제에서 모든 문장이 가정법 과거 문장이므로, if절의 동사를 과거로, 주절의 조동사도 과거형으로 고치는 것이 적절하다.

02 to부정사가 진주어가 되는 구문에서 to부정사의 의미상의 주어는 전치사 'for 또는 of+목적격'의 형태로 표현한다. of를 쓰는 경우는 to부정사의 '의미상의 주어에 대해 성격이나 태도'를 나타내는 형용사가 있을 때이다.

03 주절에 조동사의 과거형이 나왔으므로, 가정법 문장이다. 내용상 be동사의 과거형이 필요한데, 가정법 과거에서 be동사의 과거형은 주로 were를 쓴다.

04 to부정사의 의미상의 주어를 표현할 때 전치사 for를 쓴다. 일반적으로 '가주어-진주어' 구문에서 동명사 주어는 진주어로 잘 쓰지 않으며, 문제의 조건에서 to부정사를 이용하라고 한 것에 유의한다.

시험대비 실력평가   p.77~79

01 ②   02 ④   03 ④   04 ③
05 ④
06 If I were you, I would suggest doing outdoor activities to your friends.
07 It is easy for Smith to ride a bike.
08 If there were no televisions, it would not be easy for us to watch the news.
09 ④   10 ④   11 ⑤
12 If Laura had enough time, she could stay longer in Seoul.washing machine.
13 It was careless of her to leave the window open.
14 ④   15 ③   16 ④   17 ②
18 took → had taken

01 honest는 사람의 성품에 관한 형용사이다. 이때 의미상의 주어는 for가 아니라 of를 쓴다.

02 to부정사의 의미상의 주어는 전치사 for를 사용하는데, 사람의 성격이나 태도를 나타낼 때는 of를 쓴다. ④ 'Charles가 선생님께 그런 질문들을 한 것은 무례했다.'는 내용이므로 of를 써야 하며, 다른 문장들은 모두 for를 쓴다.

03 ④ 가정법 문장이라면 won't를 wouldn't로, 직설법 문장이라면 had를 has로 쓰는 것이 적절하다.

04 가정법 과거로서 직설법 현재 시제와 적절하게 전환된 문장은 ③번뿐이다. ①은 가정법 과거완료가 필요하고, ②와 ⑤는 가정법 전환이 이상한 문장이며, ④는 직설법의 인과 관계가 어색하게 표현되었다.

05 to부정사의 의미상의 주어를 표현할 때 알맞은 전치사를 고르는 문제이다. ⓐ, ⓓ, ⓕ에는 사람의 성격이나 태도에 관한 형용사가 있으므로 전치사 of를 쓰는 것이 적절하며, 나머지는 모두 for를 쓴다. *orphanage: 고아원

06 가정법 과거 시제의 문장이다. If I were you로 시작하고 주절에 조동사의 과거형 would를 쓰되, suggest 뒤에 동명사가 목적어로 온다는 사실에 유의하여 배열한다.

07 가주어 It과 진주어 to부정사구를 이용할 때, 의미상의 주어 Smith를 전치사 for로 받는 것에 유의하여 배열한다.

08 가정법 과거와 '가주어-진주어'가 혼합된 문장이다. '~가 없다면'이라는 표현은 'If there were no ~'로 나타내는 것이 적절

하고, 가주어 it과 진주어 to watch the news를 활용하여 조동사 과거형 would를 적절하게 배열한다.

09 ④번의 It은 비인칭 주어로서 날씨, 요일, 계절, 명암 등에 사용된다. 나머지는 모두 가주어 it으로 사용되었다.

10 가정법 과거 형태의 문장들이다. If절에는 동사의 과거형을, 주절에는 조동사의 과거형을 쓰는 것이 적절하다.

11 ⑤ 성격을 나타내는 형용사를 받을 때는 to부정사의 의미상의 주어에 of를 사용한다. '당신이 그의 불우한 어린 시절 경험을 언급한 것은 매우 잔인했다' ① of → for, ② for → of, ③ of → for, ④ my → me(전치사 뒤에는 목적격)

12 내용상 가정법의 형태로 문장이 구성된다. have동사의 과거형과 조동사 can의 과거형을 사용하되, long의 비교급을 쓰는 것에 유의하여 영작한다.

13 대화의 내용상 여동생 수진이가 추운 날씨에 창문을 열어놓아서, 화초가 얼어 죽은 것에 대해 '그녀가 창문을 열어 둔 것은 부주의했다'라는 문장을 만드는 것이 적절하다. 단어를 모두 배열할 때, 의미상의 주어 자리의 for는 of로 바꾼다.

14 ④ 가정법 과거완료 문장이다. If절에 'had+p.p' 형태, 주절에는 '조동사 과거+have+p.p' 형태가 온다. 'would not be'를 'would not have been'으로 고치는 것이 적절하다.

15 '~가 없다면'이라는 가정법 표현은 'If there were no ~'로 나타내며, Without 또는 'If it were not for ~'로 대체할 수 있다. 'If it were not for'는 if를 생략해서 'Were it not for ~'로 표현 가능하다.

16 옳은 문장은 ⓒ, ⓔ, ⓖ, ⓗ 4개이다. ⓐ using → to use, ⓑ for → of, ⓓ of → for ⓕ importantly → important

17 ②는 시간, 요일, 날짜, 날씨, 무게, 거리, 금액, 명암 등을 표현할 때 쓰는 '비인칭 주어' it이다. 나머지는 모두 to부정사구를 진주어로 하는 '가주어-진주어' 구문으로 쓰였다.

18 '택시 대신 지하철을 탔더라면 많은 시간을 절약할 수 있었을 텐데.'라는 의미의 가정법 과거완료 문장이다. 가정법 과거로도 고칠 수 있지만, 단어 하나만 찾아 고치는 문제이므로 took을 had taken으로 고치는 것이 적절하다.

서술형 시험대비   p.80~81

01 (1) didn't have smartphones, we would play outside more
(2) it would be more difficult for us to check
(3) necessary for you to manage your digital footprint
(4) very wise of us to use digital devices efficiently
02 (1) If it were not for   (2) If there were no
(3) Were it not for   (4) As there is
03 it didn't rain, I could go for a walk with my dog

04 exercised regularly, he could be

05 (1) very dangerous for even adults to swim in the sea

  (2) foolish of you to try to cross the valley

  (3) fun for Minseo to play cards with her family yesterday

06 (1) have → had (2) be → have been

  (3) was → were (4) am → were[was]

  (5) it not → it were not

07 (1) sitting → sit (2) your → you (3) of → for

  (4) for → of (5) checked → to check

08 (1) If there were another me, I could make him share my work.

  (2) If I were you, I would reduce my time on smartphone by half.

  (3) If we didn't have televisions, it would not be easy for us to watch the music shows.

  (4) If Sally were[was] in Hawaii, she would be happy.

01 가정법과 '가주어-진주어' 구문, to부정사의 의미상의 주어 등에 유의하여, 주어진 단어들을 적절히 배열한다.

02 '돈이 없으면, 물건을 쉽게 거래할 수 없다'는 내용으로 직설법으로 표현하면, '돈이 있어서 물건을 쉽게 거래할 수 있다'가 된다. 가정법 과거를 전제로, 'Without = If it were not for = Were it not for'를 기억해 두는 것이 좋다.

03 직설법으로 표현하면, '비가 오기 때문에 산책을 할 수 없다'는 것이다. 글자 수와 어법에 맞게 do를 didn't로, can을 could로 변형하는 것에 유의하여, 단어를 적절히 배열한다.

04 'David이 규칙적으로 운동을 하지 않기 때문에 건강이 좋지 않다.'라는 직설법 문장을 가정법으로 표현하면, 'David이 규칙적으로 운동을 하면, 건강이 좋을 것이다.'가 된다. If절에 과거동사, 주절에 조동사 과거형에 유의하여 영작한다.

05 (1) '어른들조차'를 의미상의 주어로 표현할 때는 for even adults로 쓰는 것에 유의한다. (2) '어리석다'는 사람의 성질을 나타내므로 전치사 of를 쓴다. (3) 같은 의미로 'Minseo had fun playing cards with her family yesterday.' 형태로도 표현이 가능하다.

06 문제에서 모든 문장이 가정법이라고 했으므로, (1) if절 동사를 과거시제로 고치는 것이 적절하다. (2) 내용상 시제가 '가정법 과거완료'이므로, 주절을 '조동사+have+p.p'로 고쳐야 한다. (3) 가정법 과거의 be동사는 were가 일반적이며, 현대 영어에서는 주어가 1, 3인칭 단수일 때는 was도 쓸 수 있다. (4) if절의 be동사를 과거로 고친다. (5) '~가 없다면'이라는 가정법 표현은 'If it were not for'로 쓴다.

07 '가주어-진주어' 구문에서 to부정사의 의미상의 주어와 그에 맞

는 전치사의 활용에 유의하여, 어색한 단어를 하나만 찾아서 적절하게 고치도록 한다.

08 직설법 현재 문장을 가정법으로 바꿀 때, 종속절에는 동사의 과거형을, 주절에는 '조동사의 과거형+동사원형'을 쓰는 것에 유의하여, 문장을 전환한다. (3)에서 'it is easy'는 가정법으로 바꾸면 조동사 would를 활용하고, 내용이 반대가 되므로 'it would not be easy'로 바뀌는 것에 유의한다.

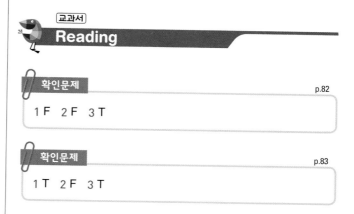

교과서 Reading

확인문제 p.82

1 F 2 F 3 T

확인문제 p.83

1 T 2 F 3 T

교과서 확인학습 A p.84~85

01 When, in the morning, what

02 read, on

03 Imagine, is, near, How

04 check items, that are

05 Are, addicted

06 Without, feel uncomfortable

07 take, into   08 enjoyable to

09 while studying

10 reduce, I spend

11 right after, an alert

12 next to, while 13 What, score, check, half

14 have, with   15 causes you to spend, on

16 focus on, have a pain

17 for you to start

18 means staying away from, for

19 help, freedom from, noisy

20 focus, on, feel refreshed, creative ideas

21 help, spend

22 Living, however, is

23 necessary for you, for

24 need to follow

25 form, create rules, using

26 turn off, while 27 take, into

28 keep, out of the bedroom, them

29 More Time for , spend more time playing

30 Fewer, fewer, on

31 I were, would, by half

32 I were, would, off

33 had, would be, too much

34 With, wise

1 Hi, students! When you wake up in the morning, what is the first thing you do?

2 Do you read SNS postings on your smartphone?

3 Imagine your smartphone is not near you. How do you feel?

4 Students, please check items on the list that are true for you.

5 Are you addicted to your smartphone?

6 Without my smartphone, I feel uncomfortable.

7 I take my smartphone into the bathroom.

8 It is more enjoyable to spend time on my smartphone than with friends.

9 I often check SNS postings while studying.

10 I try to reduce the time I spend on my smartphone, but I fail.

11 I check my smartphone right after I hear the sound of an alert.

12 I have my smartphone next to me while I'm eating.

13 What is your score? Did you check more than half?

14 If so, you may have a problem with smartphone addiction.

15 Smartphone addiction causes you to spend too much time on your smartphone.

16 Also, you cannot focus on your studies and may have a pain in your neck.

17 Then now is the time for you to start digital detox.

18 Digital detox means staying away from digital devices, such as smartphones and computers, for a while.

19 Digital detox will help you a lot. You can enjoy freedom from the noisy digital world.

20 You can focus more on your work. Sometimes you can feel refreshed and have new, creative ideas.

21 Digital detox will also help you spend more time with others.

22 Living without a smartphone, however, is not easy.

23 So, it is necessary for you to set some rules for using your smartphone.

24 You then need to follow the rules.

25 Now, please form groups and, in your group, create rules for using your smartphone.

26 We will turn off our smartphones while studying.

27 We will not take our smartphones into the bathroom.

28 We will keep our smartphones out of the bedroom and not use them at night.

29 More Time for Outside Activities – We will spend more time playing outside without our smartphones.

30 Fewer SNS Messages – We will post fewer SNS messages on our smartphones.

31 If I were you, I would reduce my time on my smartphone by half.

32 If I were you, I would turn off all alerts.

33 You did a good job, students! If we had no smartphones, our lives would be more difficult, but too much use of a smartphone is dangerous.

34 With digital detox, you can become a wise smartphone user.

01 ④

02 about whether or not you are addicted to your smartphone

03 ①, ④   04 to spend   05 ⑤   06 detox

07 ⑤   08 ④   09 ③

10 Rules for Using   11 ④

12 They will not take their smartphones into the bathroom.

13 ⑤

14 what is the first thing you do?

15 ④   16 ④   17 ③   18 ②

19 ③

20 Smartphone addiction causes us to spend too much time on our smartphones.

21 had   22 ④

23 They want to turn off all alerts.

01 (A)와 (B)에는 '~하는 동안에'라는 의미의 접속사 while이 적절하다. 주절의 주어와 종속절의 주어가 같은 경우, 종속절의 주어와 be동사를 생략하여 (A)와 같이 나타낼 수 있다.

02 목록은 스마트폰에 중독되었는지 여부에 관한 것이다.

03 ① reduce의 유의어 ② uncomfortable의 반의어 ③ true의 반의어 ④ next to의 유의어 ⑤ spend의 반의어

04 cause는 to부정사를 목적격 보어로 취하는 동사이다. 따라서 to spend라고 쓰는 것이 적절하다.

05 스마트폰에 중독된 사람들을 위한 해결책으로 디지털 디톡스를 제시하고 있다.

06 '사람들이 무언가에 중독된 것을 멈추게 하기 위하여 그들에게 주어지는 치료'는 'detox(해독)'이다.

07 디지털 디톡스의 장점에 관해 언급하다가 스마트폰 없이 사는 것이 어렵다고 글의 흐름을 전환하고 있으므로 however가 적절하다.

08 빈칸 (B)에는 to부정사의 의미상의 주어가 들어간다. 앞서 나온 형용사가 사람의 성질을 나타내는 형용사가 아니므로 'for+목적격'을 쓴다.

09 디지털 디톡스의 장점은 시끄러운 디지털 세상으로부터 자유를 즐기고, 일에 조금 더 집중하고, 생기를 되찾으며, 새롭고 창의적인 생각을 갖게 하고, 다른 사람과 더 많은 시간을 보낼 수 있는 것이라고 하였다.

10 위 글은 학생들이 자신의 스마트폰 사용에 대한 몇 가지 규칙에 관한 것이다.

11 글의 흐름상 스마트폰 없이 밖에서 노는 데 더 많은 시간을 쓸 것이라고 말하는 것이 적절하다. with → without

12 예림, 용민, 호진이는 그들의 스마트폰을 화장실로 가져가지 않을 것이라고 하였다.

13 빈칸 (A)에는 전치사 on이 들어가 'spend+시간+on+N: N에 시간을 쓰다'는 의미를 완성한다. ① be interested in: ~에 흥미가 있다 ② get to: ~에 도착하다 ③ stay with: ~와 함께 머물다 ④ take a picture of: ~의 사진을 찍다 ⑤ depend on: ~에 의존하다, ~에 달려 있다

14 'the first thing'과 'you do' 사이에는 목적격 관계대명사 that 혹은 which가 생략되어 있다. '당신이 하는 첫 번째의 것'이라는 의미로 'the first thing you do'라고 쓸 수 있다.

15 반 이상에 체크했다면 스마트폰 중독 문제를 갖고 있을지도 모르는 것이라고 하였다.

16 친구들과 보내는 시간보다 스마트폰을 하면서 보내는 시간이 더 즐거운 것이 스마트폰 중독 사항에 해당한다.

17 스마트폰 없이 사는 것은 쉽지 않으므로 스마트폰 사용에 대한 몇 가지 규칙을 정할 필요가 있다는 연결이 자연스러우므로, 결과를 이끄는 so가 가장 적절하다.

18 스마트폰 중독이 야기할 수 있는 문제 제시 - [B] 또 다른 문제 제시와 디지털 디톡스의 개념 설명 - [A] 디지털 디톡스의 장점 - [C] 하지만 스마트폰 없이 사는 것이 쉬운 것은 아님

19 디지털 디톡스란 스마트폰과 컴퓨터 같은 디지털 장치들로부터 잠시 동안 떨어져 있는 것을 의미한다.

20 스마트폰 중독은 우리가 스마트폰에 너무 많은 시간을 보내게 한다고 하였다.

21 주절로 미루어 보아 가정법 과거 문장임을 알 수 있다. 따라서 had가 적절하다.

22 매일 디지털 디톡스를 하겠다는 계획은 없다.

23 지호, 소희, 유민은 모든 알림을 끄기를 원한다.

서술형 시험대비 p.92~93

01 I try to reduce the time I spend on my smartphone, but I fail.

02 comfortable → uncomfortable, far from → next to

03 If you checked more than half

04 I check my smartphone

05 You cannot focus on your studies and may have a pain in your neck.

06 We need to start digital detox.

07 We can enjoy freedom from the noisy digital world.

08 We need to follow the rules.

09 It is necessary for us to set some rules for using our smartphone.

10 our smartphones

11 They will turn off their smartphones while studying.

12 spend more time playing outside

13 The writer thinks that it is dangerous.

14 take my smartphone into

01 스마트폰에 중독되었는지 확인하기 위한 항목이므로, 스마트폰 사용 시간을 줄이려고 노력하지만 실패한다고 말하는 것이 글의 흐름상 적절하다.

02 스마트폰 중독은 스마트폰이 없으면 불안함을 느끼고, 식사 중에 스마트폰을 옆에 가지고 있는 것이다. far from: ~로부터 먼

03 '반 이상에 체크했다면'이란 의미이다.

04 알림소리를 듣자마자 스마트폰을 확인하는 것이 항목에 있었다. immediately: 즉시

05 스마트폰 중독은 스마트폰에 너무 많은 시간을 소비하게 하는 것에 더해서, 공부에 집중할 수 없고 목에 통증을 느낄 수 있다.

06 다른 사람들과 더 많은 시간을 보낼 수 있으려면 디지털 디톡스를 시작해야 한다.

07 시끄러운 디지털 세상으로부터 자유를 즐길 수 있도록 하는 것이 디지털 디톡스라고 하였다.

08 규칙을 정한 후 그것들을 따라야 한다고 하였다.

09 몇 가지 규칙을 정할 필요가 있다고 하였다.

10 '우리의 스마트폰'을 가리키는 말이다.

11 공부하는 동안 스마트폰을 끌 것이라고 하였다.

12 호성, 민수와 함께 지나는 스마트폰 없이 밖에서 노는 데 더 많은 시간을 쓸 것이라고 하였다. 따라서 '스마트폰으로 노는 대신에'로 표현할 수 있다.

13 글쓴이는 지나친 스마트폰 사용이 위험하다고 생각한다.

14 호진이는 디지털 디톡스의 방법으로 화장실에 스마트폰을 가져 가지 않겠다고 하였다

영역별 핵심문제
p.95~99

01 conversation   02 ⑤   03 ③
04 ①   05 copyright   06 were, would not post
07 If I were you, I would put aside the smartphone.
08 Because only the blog owner has the right to use them.
09 He is not supposed to use his personal information.
10 ⑤   11 ③   12 ①   13 ⑤
14 ④   15 ④   16 ①   17 ④
18 (A) If I hadn't been lazy, I could have won the race.
   (B) If I hadn't played at that time, I wouldn't be hungry now.
   (C) If I had worked hard on it, the house would have stood strong.
19 ②   20 ③   21 ④
22 digital detox
23 Digital detox means staying away from digital devices, such as smartphones and computers, for a while.   24 ④   25 ④
26 use them at night
27 (A) advantages   (B) disadvantages
28 ③   29 ④

01 유의어 관계다. 제한하다 – 대화

02 (A)는 젊은이를 위해 더 많은 일자리를 만들기(create)를 원한다는 의미가 적절하다. (B)는 그의 사랑스런 딸과 공원에서 즐거운(enjoyable) 오후를 보냈다는 의미가 적절하다.

03 무언가, 특히 해로운 것을 하는 것이나 사용하는 것을 중단하지 못하는 것: 중독(addiction)

04 어떤 사람이 유리한 결과를 얻는 데 도움이 될 만한 것: 장점, 유리함(advantage)

05 저작권은 창작자가 그나 그녀의 문학과 예술 작품에 가지고 있는 권리이다.

06 'be not supposed to+동사원형'은 '~해서는 안 된다'는 불허의 의미로, 'If I were you, I would not+동사원형'을 사용해

서 '내가 너라면 ~하지 않을 텐데.'의 의미로 '~하지 마라'라는 충고의 의미를 나타낼 수 있다.

07 'If I were you, I would ~.'는 충고할 때 사용하는 표현으로 '내가 너라면 ~할 것이다(~할 텐데)'로 해석한다. 'put aside'는 '치우다'라는 의미이다.

08 다른 사람의 블로그에서 가져온 사진을 자신의 블로그에 게시하면 안 되는 이유를 'Because+주어+동사' 어순으로 쓴다.

09 질문: 세호는 비밀번호를 만들 때 무엇을 사용하면 안 되나?

10 '누군가 네 비밀번호를 알아낸 것 같아.'라는 문제에 대해 알맞은 충고는 비밀번호를 바꾸라는 것이 적절하다.

11 보라는 비밀번호를 만들 때 개인 정보를 사용하지 말라고 충고하고 있다.

12 nice(착하다)는 의미상의 주어를 of Peter로 쓴다.

13 가정법 과거에는 동사의 과거형이 온다. 이 경우 비인칭 주어 it과 동사 snowed를 쓸 수 있다는 것에 유의한다.

14 비교급 강조는 much, 의미상의 주어는 for you이다.

15 '과거시제의 직설법 문장'을 가정법으로 고치면 '가정법 과거완료'가 된다. If절에 'had+p.p.', 주절에 '조동사 과거+have+p.p'를 쓰며, 직설법과 반대되도록 not을 활용한다.

16 옳은 문장은 ⓕ, 1개이다. ⓐ to diligent → to be diligent, ⓑ possibly → possible, ⓒ of → for, ⓓ they → them, ⓔ going → go, ⓖ not be → not to be

17 <보기>의 if는 간접의문문의 명사절을 이끄는 접속사로서 '~인지'라는 뜻으로 쓰였다. ④의 if가 보기와 쓰임이 같으며, 이때 쓰인 would도 '과거의 습관'을 의미하는 뜻으로 사용된 것에 유의한다. ④를 제외한 나머지는 모두 가정법 과거시제를 이끄는 종속 접속사로 쓰였다.

18 (B)는 혼합 가정문으로, If절에 'had p.p' 형태가, 주절에 '조동사 과거+동사원형'이 온다. 시간 표현이 동반되는 것에 유의한다. (A)와 (C)는 모두 가정법 과거완료 문장으로, If절의 과거완료와 주절의 표현에 유의하여 영작하도록 한다.

19 ②는 비인칭 주어로서 거리를 나타낸다. 나머지는 모두 '진주어 to부정사구'를 받는 가주어 It이다.

20 주어진 문장은 디지털 디톡스가 여러분을 돕는다는 의미이므로, 구체적으로 어떠한 도움을 주는지 열거하고 있는 ③번이 적절하다.

21 스마트폰 중독 증상으로는 스마트폰에 너무 많은 시간을 소비하고, 공부에 집중할 수 없고, 목에 통증을 느끼는 것이라고 하였다.

22 상쾌함을 느끼는 이유가 시끄러운 디지털 세상으로부터 자유를 즐기기 위해 디지털 디톡스를 시작해서라고 말할 수 있다.

23 디지털 디톡스란 스마트폰과 컴퓨터 같은 디지털 기기들로부터 잠시 동안 떨어져 있는 것을 의미한다고 하였다.

24 (A)는 진주어로 쓰인 to부정사이다. ①, ② 부사적 용법 중 목적 ③ 형용사적 용법 ④ 진주어 ⑤ 부사적 용법 중 형용사 수식

25 스마트폰 사용에 대한 규칙에 관한 글이므로 스마트폰 없이 밖에서 시간을 덜 보내겠다는 것은 어색하며 more가 더 적절하다.

26 밤에 스마트폰을 침실 밖에 두고 사용하지 않을 것이라고 하였으므로, 그들의 스마트폰을 침실로 가져가지 않고 밤에 사용하지 않겠다고 말하는 것이 적절하다.

27 빈칸 (A)와 (B) 이후에 나열된 사항들은 각각 스마트폰의 장점과 단점이다. 따라서 advantages, disadvantages 순서로 쓰는 것이 적절하다.

28 스마트폰이 없다면 우리가 사람들과 연락하는 것이 쉽지 않을 것이라고 하였으므로, ③번에 대한 대답으로 '스마트폰'이라고 답할 수 있다.

29 스마트폰이 없을 때의 장점을 말하고 있는 데 스마트폰 사용의 장점을 말하는 ④번은 글의 흐름상 어색하다.

단원별 예상문제
p.100~103

01 (c)reate 02 ③
03 I have a website we can download it from for free. 04 ① 05 ②
06 more than → less than 07 ⑤ 08 ④
09 If I were you, I would suggest doing outdoor activities to your friends.
10 without asking 11 ③
12 (1) ⓒ (2) ⓑ (3) ⓐ (4) ⓑ (5) ⓐ
13 ③ 14 ③
15 (1) knew your phone number, would call
   (2) were[was] a police officer, would find out
   (3) had seen the accident, would have been
   (4) hadn't joined my club, couldn't have succeeded
16 Are you addicted to your smartphone?
17 ⑤ 18 ③ 19 ② 20 ⑤
21 Smartphone addiction makes us have a pain in our neck.

01 반의어 관계다. 줄이다-늘리다 : 파괴하다-만들다
02 위험한 것을 처리할 대비가 되도록 사람들에게 하는 경고
03 '우리가 그것을 무료로 내려 받을 수 있는'이 '웹 사이트'를 수식하는 구조로 'a website (that/which) we can download it from for free' 어순을 사용한다.
05 컴퓨터 게임에 중독되었다고 말하는 친구에게 해 줄 충고로 게임 시간을 제한하기 위해 일일 계획을 짜라는 말이 적절하다.

06 피곤해 보인다는 말에 4시간 이상 잤다는 말보다는 4시간도 못 잤다는 말이 자연스럽다.
07 생일 날짜를 비밀번호로 사용했다는 말로 보아 개인정보를 사용하지 말라는 충고가 적절하다.
08 SNS의 비밀번호가 누군가에 의해 도용된 것이므로 비밀번호가 추측하기에 쉬웠느냐고 묻는 것이 적절하다. (d)번의 difficult를 easy로 바꾸어야 한다.
09 '내가 너라면'은 가정법 과거형으로 be동사는 'were'를 사용한다. '~할 텐데, ~할 것이다'라는 의미로 주절에는 'would+동사원형'을 사용하고, suggest는 동명사를 목적어로 취하는 동사이다.
11 '~인지 아닌지'의 의미로 동사의 목적어 자리에 사용된 if를 찾는다. ②번은 '~일지라도'의 양보의 의미를 가지는 if이다.
12 (1) 거리를 나타내는 비인칭 주어 (3) 가주어 It, 진주어 to부정사 (2), (4) It ~ that 강조구문 (5) 가주어 It, 진주어 that절
13 가정법 과거 문장들이다. ① makes → made ② 'If there were no smartpones, it would be hard ~'로 고쳐야 한다. ④ will share → would share ⑤ will → would
14 ① for → of ② skating → skate ④ of → for ⑤ he to mastering → him to master
15 (1), (2)는 가정법 과거, (3), (4)는 가정법 과거완료이다. If절 동사의 시제와 주절의 조동사의 과거 뒤의 표현에 유의하여 빈칸에 알맞게 영작한다. (1)의 my를 your로 (4)의 your를 my로 전환하는 것도 주의하고, 특히 (4) B의 대답이 Yes이므로, but 뒤에는 '부정 의미'를 갖는 가정법이 필요하며, 내용상 주절에도 not이 와야 한다.
16 글의 흐름상 '스마트폰에 중독되었어요?'라는 말이 들어가는 것이 자연스럽다.
17 공부에 집중하기 위해서 스마트폰의 알림을 끄는 것은 위 항목에 해당하지 않는다.
18 score는 명사로 쓰여 '(경기, 시합의) 득점, (시험의) 점수, (음악) 악보'라는 의미가 있으며, 동사로 쓰여 '득점하다', '채점하다'라는 의미가 있다. 밑줄 친 (B)는 '점수'라는 의미로 쓰였다. ①, ④ 악보, ② 채점하다, ③ 득점, 점수 ⑤ 득점하다
19 주어진 문장의 now란 스마트폰으로 인한 여러 문제를 가지고 있는 지금을 의미한다. 주어진 문장에서 digital detox를 처음으로 언급하고 이를 설명하는 문장이 뒤이어 나오는 것이 자연스럽다. 따라서 ②번이 적절하다.
20 디지털 티톡스는 학생들이 디지털 세계로부터 자유를 즐길 수 있도록 한다.
21 스마트폰 중독은 우리가 스마트폰에 너무 많은 시간을 소비하게 하고, 공부에 집중할 수 없고, 목에 통증을 느낄 수 있게 한다고 하였다.

01 it's against the law
02 spends, smartphone, get together, SNS, to suggest, outdoor activities
03 You're not supposed to post someone's pictures without asking.
04 I had been in Busan, I could have seen the fireworks festival
05 (1) It was too boring for Sally to stay home on a sunny day.
    (2) It is really careless of you to reach out to a big dog.
06 (A) Living(또는 To live)　(B) to set　(C) to follow
07 We will keep our smartphones out of the bedroom and not use them at night.
08 If I were you, I would turn off all alerts.
09 Too much use of a smartphone is dangerous.
10 They are going to spend more time for outside activities, and post fewer SNS messages.

01 왜 Catherine은 웹 사이트에서 무료로 영화를 다운로드하면 안 되는가?
02 내 아들, Tony는 스마트폰에 너무 많은 시간을 보낸다. 그와 그의 친구들은 거의 매일 SNS에서 만난다. 나는 그에게 친구들과 야외 활동을 하는 것을 제안해 보라고 말했다.
03 'must not, should not'은 '~해서는 안 된다'는 불허, 금지의 표현으로 'be not supposed to'로 바꾸어 쓸 수 있다.
04 내용상 '내가 부산에 있었다면, 불꽃 축제를 볼 수 있었을 텐데'가 빈칸에 적절하다. 가정법 과거완료 시제이므로 'If I had been'을 종속절에, 주절에는 'could have seen'을 쓴다.
05 의미상의 주어에 알맞은 전치사에 유의한다. '부주의하다'에는 전치사 of를 쓴다. 가주어 It과 be동사를 시제에 맞게, 주어진 단어들을 적절히 배열, 글자 수에 맞추어 영작한다.
06 (A) '스마트폰 없이 사는 것'이라는 주어로 to부정사나 동명사를 쓸 수 있다. (B) '규칙을 정하는 것'이라는 의미로 진주어 to부정사를 쓴다. (C) '규칙을 따르는 것'이라는 의미가 적절하며, 동사 need는 to부정사를 목적어로 취한다.
07 스마트폰을 밤에 침실 밖에 두고 사용하지 않을 것이라고 말하는 것이 적절하다.
08 가정법 과거를 활용하여 쓸 수 있다. 가정법 과거는 'If+주어+동사의 과거형, 주어+조동사의 과거형+동사원형'으로 표현한다.
09 스마트폰을 너무 많이 사용하는 것은 위험하다고 하였다.
10 지나, 호성, 민수는 스마트폰을 현명하게 사용하기 위하여 밖에서 노는 데 더 많은 시간을 보내고 SNS 메시지를 더 적게 올릴 것이라고 하였다.

|모범답안|
01 (1) A: Do you use the same password for a long time?
    B: Yes.
    A: You're not supposed to use the same password for a long time.
    (2) A: Do yo u post bad comments online?
    B: Yes.
    A: You're not supposed to post bad comments online.
02 Televisions, televisions, we should spend more time with our family, we would be healthier, it would not be easy for us to watch movies, it would be more difficult for us to check the news

01 ④　　　　02 disadvantage　　　　03 ③
04 ⑤　　　　05 ④
06 I would not[wouldn't] post someone's pictures without asking
07 ②　　　　08 ④　　　　09 ①
10 addicted
11 you're not supposed to post them on your blog
12 (a) (사진을) 찍다　(b) 가져왔다
13 ②
14 (1) It was not possible for the villagers to build the castle in a month.
    (2) It is rude of Thomas not to show respect for the old man.
    (3) It is impossible for the Chinese girl to take drugs on an airplane.
15 (1) would be easy for us to spend more time with our family / would be healthier for us to have more time to exercise
    (2) would not be easy for us to watch shows and dramas / would be difficult for us to check the news
16 ②　　　　17 is, cannot　18 ⑤　　　19 ⑤
20 Then now is the time for you to start digital detox.
21 ④　　　　22 ⑤
23 (C)-(B)-(A)
24 What can be the rules of digital detox?
25 ④

01 ④번은 'intend(의도하다)'에 관한 설명이다. 'create'에 대한 영어 설명은 'to make something new, or invent something'이 되어야 한다.

02 반의어 관계다. 안전한–위험한 : 장점–단점

03 특정한 목적을 위해 만들어진 기계적인 물체

04 '오랜 기간 동안 같은 비밀번호를 사용하니?'라고 묻는 A의 물음에 개인 정보를 사용하면 안 된다는 B의 말은 자연스럽지 않다.

05 대화의 흐름상 'Sarah에게 사진을 올려도 되는지 물어봤니?'라는 말이 오는 것이 자연스럽다.

06 'be not supposed to+동사원형'은 '~해서는 안 된다'라는 의미로 'If I were you'를 사용하여 '내가 너라면 ~하지 않을 텐데'의 의미로 'If I were you, I would not[wouldn't] ~' 형태로 문장을 완성하면 된다.

07 주절의 동사가 'would+동사원형'이므로 if절의 시제는 가정법 과거형이 적절하다. be동사는 'were'를 사용한다.

08 In fact는 앞 문장의 내용을 강조하면서 덧붙여 말하는 기능을 한다. 그래서 '그것은 좋지 않아. 사실 그것은 큰 실수야.'라는 내용으로 ④가 적절하다. 그리고 내용상 'it'은 '생일 날짜를 사용한 것'을 가리키는 인칭대명사이다.

09 '웹 사이트에서 영화를 내려 받지 말고 극장에 가는 게 어때?'라고 말하고 있으므로 대안을 제시하는 'instead'가 적절하다.

10 컴퓨터 게임을 하는 것을 멈출 수가 없다고 말하고 있으므로 '중독되었다'는 의미가 적절하다.

11 '~해서는 안 된다'는 'be not supposed to+동사원형'을 사용한다.

13 ②의 if는 간접의문문 명사절을 이끄는 접속사이며, 나머지는 모두 가정의 조건절을 이끄는 종속접속사이다.

14 to부정사 또는 동명사가 주어인 문장을 '가주어-진주어' 구조로 표현할 때, 일반적으로 'It ~ for+의미상의 주어 +to V' 형태로 쓴다. 사람의 성질이나 태도를 나타내는 형용사가 있을 때는 of를 for 자리에 쓴다. (2)는 무례하다는 뜻이므로, of를 쓰는 것이 적절하며, (1), (3)은 'for+의미상의 주어' 형태로 쓴다.

15 전제 조건 'If there were no televisions'가 가정법 과거 문장이므로 it 뒤의 be동사는 would be이다. we를 의미상 주어로하면 for us, 나머지는 표에 맞추어 적절히 배열한다.

16 <보기>의 would는 가정법의 주절에서 쓰이는 조동사이다. ① would like to = want to ③ 과거의 습관적 행위 ④ will의 과거시제 ⑤ 공손한 질문

17 가정법과거 문장은 직설법 현재 문장으로 바꿔 쓸 수 있다.

18 앞서 나온 형용사가 사람의 성질을 나타내는 것이 아니므로 to부정사의 의미상의 주어로 'for+목적격'이 쓰인다. 모두 for가 쓰이지만 polite는 사람의 성질을 나타내는 형용사이므로 'of+목

적격'으로 의미상의 주어를 표현한다.

19 주어진 문장의 the rules가 가리키는 것은 스마트폰 사용을 위해 만든 규칙인 'to set some rules for using your smartphones'를 의미한다.

20 디지털 디톡스를 시작하는 주체는 '여러분'이므로 to부정사의 의미상 주어로 'for you'를 쓰는 것에 유의한다.

21 다른 사람들과 함께 보낼 시간이 많아진다고 하였다.

22 스마트폰 중독이 야기할 수 있는 문제는 스마트폰에 너무 많은 시간을 보내게 하고, 공부에 집중할 수 없고, 목에 통증을 느끼는 것이라고 하였다.

23 장점에 대해 말하자고 하였으므로 장점을 언급한 (C) → (B) 또 다른 장점을 언급하고 반면 단점도 있다고 말함 → (A) 스마트폰이 없을 경우의 단점에 관해 말함

24 학생들은 디지털 디톡스의 규칙에 관해 이야기하고 있다.

25 스마트폰에 SNS 메시지를 더 적게 올릴 것이라고 말한 그룹은 지나, 호성, 민수의 그룹이다.

Love for My Country

01 ③   02 independence

03 look forward to   04 ②   05 ⑤

06 ③   07 specialist   08 ④

01 처칠의 동상이 의회 건물 밖에 서 있다.

02 다른 나라에 의해 지배되거나 통치되는 것으로부터의 해방[벗어남]: independence(독립)

03 look forward to+동명사: ~하기를 기대하다

04 예술 작품, 그림 또는 기타 흥미로운 것들의 공개적인 전시

05 누군가, 특히 중요한 사람이 묻혀 있는 큰 석조 구조물이나 지하 공간

06 (A) 건물 전체로 불이 빠르게 퍼졌다. (B) 투표는 당신의 애국적인 의무 중 일부다.

07 유의어 관계이다. 바람, 소원 : 전문가

08 나는 독도가 한국에 속한다는 것을 많은 사람들에게 알리고 싶다. '~에 속하다'라는 의미로 'belong to'를 사용한다.

서술형 시험대비   p.117

01 (1) harmony (2) movement (3) kill (4) poem

02 republic

03 (1) entrance (2) president (3) government
(4) Japanese

04 (1) amusement park, 놀이공원
(2) organization, 조직 (3) poem, 시
(4) sacrifice, 희생

05 complete

01 (1) 많은 종교 지도자들은 세상에 평화와 화합을 가져오기 위해 열심히 노력하고 있습니다. (2) 그녀는 저명한 과학자이며 세계 환경 운동의 선구자이다. (3) 가뭄은 작물을 죽일 수도 있다. (4) 그녀의 시는 우리에게 강하고 용감하게 살라고 말합니다.

02 공화국은 국민이나 그들이 선출하는 대표자들에 의해 권력이 유지되는 나라이다.

03 (1) entrance: 입구 (2) president: 대통령 (3) government: 정부 (4) Japanese: 일본의

04 (1) 박람회장 놀이기구, 쇼, 그리고 다른 오락거리가 있는 넓은 야외 공간 (2) 조직화될 목적으로 함께 일하는 사람들의 집단

(3) 깊은 의미를 암시하고 읽을 때 리드미컬하게 들리는 아름다운 단어를 사용하는 한 편의 글 (4) 특정한 목적을 위해 귀중한 어떤 것을 포기하는 것

05 • 몇몇 사람들은 예체능 수업이 완전한 시간 낭비라고 생각한다.
• 때때로, 그는 단지 하나의 작품을 끝내기 위해 20 시간을 보내기도 한다.

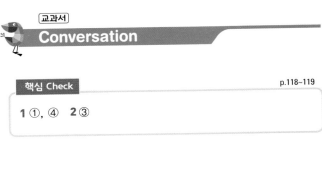

Conversation

핵심 Check   p.118~119

1 ①, ④   2 ③

교과서 대화문 익히기

Check(√) True or False   p.120

1 T   2 F   3 T   4 F

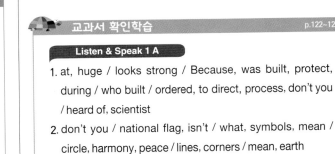

교과서 확인학습   p.122~123

Listen & Speak 1 A

1. at, huge / looks strong / Because, was built, protect, during / who built / ordered, to direct, process, don't you / heard of, scientist

2. don't you / national flag, isn't / what, symbols, mean / circle, harmony, peace / lines, corners / mean, earth

Listen & Speak 2 A

1. planning to go / built / heard, great / treasures that, had taken / must be interesting / looking forward to

2. what did you do / volunteer work / What kind / cleaned, tombs, respect, who / Sounds / planning to go, join / I'm looking forward to

Real Life Talk

reading / Poetry, know, don't you / heard / poems when, under, rule, desire, independence, be felt, poems / to read, poems, learn / In fact, to visit / when / near, Palace, palace / Let's / looking forward to, visit

Wrap Up

put on traditional / for, Germany / there are / shopping / know, don't you / traditional, soup, delicious, healthy, to trying

시험대비 기본평가   p.124

01 looking forward to   02 ⑤   03 ③
04 ②

01 앞으로 하고 싶은 일에 대한 기대를 표현할 때 'I'm looking forward to ~.'나 'I look forward to ~.'의 표현을 사용한다.
02 빈칸 뒤의 부가의문문 형태가 'don't you?'인 것으로 보아 앞의 평서문은 일반동사 긍정문 형태가 오는 것이 적절하고, B가 대답으로 '그것에 관해 들었어.'라고 말하므로 그것에 관해 아는지 확인하는 말이 적절하다.
03 앞으로 하고 싶은 일에 대한 기대를 표현할 때 'be dying to+동사원형'을 사용한다.
04 'You know ~, don't you?'는 알고 있는지 물어보는 표현이다.

시험대비 실력평가   p.125~126

01 ⑤   02 ④   03 ④   04 ③
05 I'm looking forward to making it.
06 ④
07 King Jeongjo ordered Jeong Yakyong to direct the building process.   08 ②, ⑤   09 ③
10 ④

01 'look forward to'에서 to는 전치사이므로 명사나 동명사가 온다. trying이 적절하다.
02 Judy와 Seho는 점심으로 삼계탕을 먹을 것이다.
03 봉사 활동하러 현충원에 갔다는 말에 → (D) 거기(현충원)서 어떤 종류의 봉사 활동을 했는지 묻고 → (B) 묘 주변을 청소했다는 대답을 하고 → (A) 자기도 할 수 있는지 묻는 말에 → 마지막으로 (C) '물론이지.'라고 승낙의 답을 한다.
04 '너는 안중근에 대해 알지, 그렇지 않니?'라는 물음에 '너는 안중근 박물관에 가서 그에 대해 더 많은 정보를 얻을 수 있어.'라고 답하는 것은 어색하다.
05 '~하는 것을 기대하고 있다'라는 의미로 'be dying to+동사원형'은 'look forward to+동명사'로 쓸 수 있다.
06 ④번은 '나는 간송 박물관에 갈 예정이야.'라는 말에 '그러고 싶지만, 그곳을 방문하는 것이 기대가 돼.'라고 말하는 것은 어색하다.
07 '~에게 …하라고 명령[지시]하다'는 'order+목적어+to부정사'

구문을 사용한다. direct를 to direct로 바꾸어 쓴다.
09 'know'의 목적어로 '의문사+주어+동사' 어순의 간접의문문으로 사용해야 한다. 'what the symbols in Taegeukgi mean'이 되어야 한다.
10 각각의 모서리에 4개의 선이 있는 것이 아니라 네 모서리에 검은 선들이 있다.

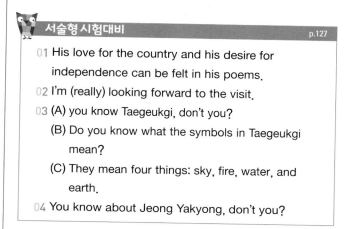

서술형 시험대비   p.127

01 His love for the country and his desire for independence can be felt in his poems.
02 I'm (really) looking forward to the visit.
03 (A) you know Taegeukgi, don't you?
    (B) Do you know what the symbols in Taegeukgi mean?
    (C) They mean four things: sky, fire, water, and earth.
04 You know about Jeong Yakyong, don't you?

01 질문: 윤동주의 시를 통해 무엇이 느껴질 수 있나?
02 기대나 희망을 나타낼 때 'look forward to+명사/동명사'를 사용한다.

교과서
Grammar

핵심 Check   p.128~129

1 (1) had   (2) visited
2 (1) that   (2) so that

시험대비 기본평가   p.130

01 ⑤   02 ③   03 ②
04 (1) that, could[might]   (2) so hot that
    (3) that, he can[may]   (4) so hard that, can't

01 본동사의 시제가 과거이고, 그 이전에 일어난 약속이므로 과거완료시제를 쓴다.
02 'so as to V' 또는 'so that ~ 주어 can'은 '~하기 위해서'라는 뜻이며, 'so 형용사 that 주어 V'는 '너무 ~해서 …하다'라는 의미이다.
03 ① came(과거) 이전에 일어난 일이므로 had gone으로 써야 한다. ③ had found → found, ④ had lived → have lived, ⑤ when은 '시점'을 묻는 의문사이므로 완료시제와 함

23

계 쓸 수 없다.

04 '목적'을 나타내는 'so that'과 '결과'를 나타내는 'so+수식어 +that+can[can't]'를 이해하고, 적용하는 문제이다. that을 기준으로 앞, 뒤 문장에 나타난 동사의 시제를 일치시키는데 유의하여, so that을 활용하도록 한다.

시험대비 실력평가   p.131~133

01 ③   02 ④   03 ⑤   04 ③

05 ⑤   06 ⑤   07 ①

08 has → had   09 ④   10 ⑤   11 ④

12 ①

13 (1) Father Lee Taeseok returned to Sudan in order that he could help poor people there.

(2) Amy practices every day so that she can join our sports club.

(3) Clara left for Paris in order that she could study fashion.

(4) Thames ran fast so that he would not be late for the meeting.

14 (1) squeezed out the pimples so that they would disappear

(2) in order that he could get a full college scholarship

01 과거 시점 이전에 발생한 일이다. has broken → had broken

03 'so that+주어+조동사'가 적절히 사용된 것을 찾는다.

04 ① had not eaten → has not eaten ② 까마귀가 도시로 이주하기 전 정글에 살았다는 문장이므로 The crow had lived in the jungle before it moved to the city.가 옳은 문장이다. ④ 설거지를 끝내야 한다고 요구한 것이므로 had finished → (should) finish ⑤ had read → have read

05 ① in order for → in order that ② not being → would not be ③ so joy that → so joyful that ④ so to → so as to 또는 in order to

06 다른 문장들은 모두 '목적'을 나타내는 표현인데, ⑤의 두 번째 문장은 '결과'를 나타낸다. 보통, '결과'의 so (that)는 앞 문장의 끝에 컴마(쉼표)를 쓴다.

07 <보기>의 had solved는 과거완료시제 중 '완료' 용법으로 쓰였다. ②, ③, ⑤는 '계속' ④는 '경험' 용법이다.

08 과거의 특정 시점 이전에 계속된 일이므로 과거완료시제이다.

09 '일본을 물리치기 위해 군인들은 열심히 훈련했다'라는 문장들로서 모두 '목적'을 나타내는데, ④만 '군인들은 열심히 훈련해서 일본을 물리쳤다'라는 뜻의 '결과'를 나타낸다.

10 ⑤ 'Irene이 전보다 더 열심히 공부했기 위해서 시험에 떨어졌

다'는 이상한 문장이다. (al)though와 같은 '양보'의 접속사로 바꾸는 것이 적절하다.

11 ① has → had ② had picked → has picked 또는 picked ③ have → had ⑤ had been given → had given

12 ② be stay → be 또는 stay로 동사를 하나만 쓴다. ③ in order to that → in order that ④ so that 생략 또는 in order to → I can ⑤ she can → she could *subtitles: 자막

13 '목적'을 나타내는 to부정사 또는 'in order to', 'so as to' 등의 표현은 'so[in order]+that+주어+조동사'로 바꿔 쓸 수 있다.

14 목적'을 나타내는 부사절 'so that', 'in order that' 뒤의 문장 구조에 유의하여, 그림에 맞게 적절히 영작한다. *squeeze out: 짜내다 *pimple: 여드름

서술형 시험대비   p.134~135

01 (1) bought many Korean treasures that some Japanese had taken to Japan

(2) made the Turtle Ship so that he could protect the people

(3) walked slowly so that no one could hear him

02 had searched, had made

03 (1) Could you remind me of the time so that I won't be late for the party? 또는 Could you remind me of the time in order that I won't be late for the party?

(2) Whenever Jane was ill, her mom used to make her a bowl of porridge in order for her to get well.

(3) They are saving money so that they can buy a big house.

(4) Remember my number in order that you can contact me. 또는 Remember my number in order for you to contact me.

(5) The foreigners from Italy went to Gyeongju so that they could see Bulguksa.

(6) Many people joined the New Korean Society in order to support the Independence movement.

04 (1) We need ice and sugar so that we can make patbingsu.

(2) We went to the river so that she could catch some fish.

(3) A firefighter ran into the woods so that she could rescue the koalas.

(4) My grandma exercises every day in order that she can keep healthy.

05 had lived alone in the house for thirty-three years until the official visited him last year

06 (1) ⓐ, 내가 그 곳에 도착했을 때, Peter는 이미 뉴욕으로 떠나 버렸다.

　(2) ⓓ, 작년까지 William은 14년간 부산에서 살았다.

　(3) ⓓ, 콘서트가 시작되기 전까지 그들은 그 가수를 거의 하루 동안 기다렸다.

　(4) ⓑ, Maria는 이번 겨울에 한국에 올 때까지 눈을 본 적이 없었다.

　(5) ⓐ, 내가 공항에 도착했을 무렵 탑승 수속이 이미 끝났다.

　(6) ⓒ, 우리가 집에 왔을 때, 누군가가 창문을 깬 것을 알게 되었다.

　(7) ⓑ, 나는 전에 그 사람을 만난 적이 없어서 그 사람을 알아보지 못했다.

　(8) ⓐ, 그 부부가 깨었을 때, 누군가가 구두 만들기를 끝내놓았다.

01 (1) 과거의 특정 시점 이전에 일어난 일은 '과거완료시제'로 사용하는 것에 유의한다. (2), (3) '목적'을 나타내는 부사절에 'so that 주어 could'를 사용한다.

02 과거의 어느 특정 시점을 기준으로 먼저 일어난 일을 과거완료시제로 표현한다. Before, After가 있을 때, 시간의 전후관계가 명확하므로 과거시제도 쓸 수 있으나, 문제에서 완료시제로 쓸 것을 요구했음에 유의한다.

03 (1) so order that → so that 또는 in order that (2) of her → for her (3) so which → so that (4) in order for you can → in order for you to 또는 in order that you can (5) can → could (6) so order to → in order to

04 주어진 단어들 중 동사의 수와 시제에 유의하여, 'so that' 또는 'in order that'으로 적절한 문장을 영작한다. (3) 소방대원은, 괄호에 주어진 단어가 she이므로 여성임에 유의한다.

05 과거의 어느 특정 시점을 기준으로 그 전부터 시작된 동작이나 상태는 과거완료시제로 표현한다. 작년에 공무원이 방문한 과거의 시점을 기준으로 노인이 혼자 산 것이므로 'had lived alone'을 쓰는 것이 적절하다.

06 과거완료시제는 완료, 경험, 결과, 계속 등의 용법으로 구분할 수 있으며, 해석을 정확하게 하는 것이 중요하다.

Reading

확인문제
p.136

1 F　2 F　3 T　4 T

확인문제
p.137

1 F　2 T　3 F　4 F　5 T

교과서 확인학습 A
p.138~139

01 my history club
02 visited, inside the park
03 At, entrance
04 a great national hero, spent, from
05 helped educate, by building
06 In, when the independence movement, moved to
07 joined, became its president
08 The exhibition hall, shows
09 looking around, stopped at, Patriotic Organization's
10 formed, organization, to fight against
11 belonged to
12 At, saw two watches
13 In, made a plan to
14 Patriotic Organization, directed, to carry
15 left for, wearing a very old watch, Mine, it, take, let, have
16 always carried, so that, forget, sacrifice
17 completing, moved to, tombs
18 had been, independence, them
19 By doing so, for the sacrifice
20 As, left, words, that, had read
21 It, written in
22 what my wish is, Korea's Independence
23 what my second wish, independence
24 asks me what my third wish is, complete independence

교과서 확인학습 B
p.140~141

1 Last week my history club went to Hyochang Park.

2 We visited the Kim Koo Museum inside the park.

3 At the entrance of the museum, we saw a white statue of Kim Koo.

4 Kim Koo is a great national hero who spent most of his life fighting for the independence of Korea from Japanese rule.

5 In the 1900s, he helped educate young people by building schools.

6 In 1919, when the independence movement had spread throughout the country, he moved to Shanghai, China.

7 There he joined the Government of the Republic of Korea and later became its president.

8 The exhibition hall in the museum shows a lot of things about Kim Koo's life.

9 While looking around the hall, we stopped at a photo of the Korean Patriotic Organization's members.

10 Kim Koo formed the secret organization in 1931 to fight against Japan.

11 Lee Bongchang and Yun Bonggil belonged to the group.

12 At one place in the hall, we saw two watches under a photo of Kim Koo and Yun Bonggil.

13 In 1932, Kim Koo made a plan to kill Japanese generals in a park in Shanghai.

14 As the leader of the Korean Patriotic Organization, he directed Yun to carry out the mission.

15 When Yun left for the mission, he told Kim, "Sir, you are wearing a very old watch. Mine is new, but I won't need it anymore. Please take my watch, and let me have yours."

16 Kim Koo always carried Yun's watch in his jacket so that he would not forget Yun's sacrifice.

17 After completing the tour of the museum, we moved to the tombs of the three heroes, Lee Bongchang, Yun Bonggil, and Baek Jeonggi.

18 Their bodies had been in Japan, but after Korea's independence Kim Koo brought them to Hyochang Park.

19 By doing so, he showed his deep love and respect for the sacrifice of the three heroes.

20 As I left Hyochang Park, I thought about Kim Koo's words in My Wish that I had read in the exhibition hall.

21 It was written in *Baekbeomilji*.

22 If God asks me what my wish is, I would say clearly, "It is Korea's Independence."

23 If he asks me what my second wish is, I would say, "It is the independence of my country."

24 If he asks me what my third wish is, I would say loudly, "It is the complete independence of my country." That is my answer.

시험대비 실력평가

p.142~145

01 ②　　　　02 ④

03 It is at the entrance of the museum.

04 He moved to Shanghai in 1919.

05 ②, ④

06 He planned to kill the Japanese generals in a park in Shanghai.

07 ④　　　08 ⑤　　　09 ①, ③　　　10 ⑤

11 Kim Koo's firm wish for the complete independence of Korea was written in *Baekbeomilji*.

12 visit the Kim Koo Museum inside the park

13 ④

14 He fought for the independence of Korea from Japanese rule.

15 ④　　　　16 exhibition　17 ②

18 There were two watches.

19 ③　　　20 ⑤　　　21 my watch　22 ④

23 ③　　　24 ⑤

25 They are written in *Baekbeomilji*.

01 동명사와 함께 쓰이면서 '~함으로써'라는 의미를 완성하는 전치사 by가 적절하다.

02 김구 선생은 학교를 설립함으로써 젊은이들을 교육시키는 것을 도왔다. ③ 그는 생의 대부분을 일본을 위해 싸우느라 보낸 것이 아니라 일본에 대항해서 싸우느라 보냈다.

03 기념관 입구에 김구 선생의 동상이 있다고 하였다.

04 김구가 중국 상해로 이동한 때는 1919년이라고 하였다.

05 기념관 안에 있는 전시관에는 한인 애국단 멤버의 사진, 김구와 윤봉길의 사진 아래에 있는 두 개의 시계가 있다고 하였다.

06 김구는 상해에 있는 한 공원에서 일본 장군들을 죽일 계획을 하였다.

07 김구가 일본에 맞서 싸우기 위해 1931년에 만든 것은 비밀 조직이었다.

08 윤봉길의 희생을 잊지 않기 위해서 김구는 그의 시계를 항상 가지고 다녔다.

09 선행사가 Kim Koo's words in My Wish이므로 which나 that을 쓰는 것이 적절하다.

10 (B)의 대명사 Their가 가리키는 것은 (C)의 이봉창, 윤봉길, 백정기이며, 독립 이후 이들의 시신을 일본에서 효창공원으로 모셔왔다. (A)에서 말하는 By doing so는 김구의 이러한 행동을 의미하는 말이다.

11 백범일지에는 한국의 독립에 대한 김구의 단호한 소망이 적혀있다고 하였다.

12 역사 동아리는 효창 공원 안에 있는 김구 기념관을 방문하기 위하여 그 공원으로 갔다.

13 효창공원 입구에는 하얀색의 김구 조각상이 있다고 하였다.

14 김구는 일본 통치로부터 한국의 독립을 위해 싸웠다고 하였다.

15 역사 동아리가 어떻게 효창 공원으로 갔는지는 위 글을 읽고 답할 수 없다.

16 사진, 조각 혹은 다른 흥미로운 물건들이 전시되는 공개 행사는 '전시회(exhibition)'이다.

17 '전시관을 둘러보던 중'이라는 말이므로 around라고 쓰는 것이 적절하다.

18 김구와 윤봉길 사진 아래에는 두 개의 시계가 있었다고 하였다.

19 모두 김구를 가리키는 말이지만 ③번은 윤봉길을 가리키는 말이다.

20 (A)는 '~로서'라고 해석되는 전치사로 자격을 나타낼 때 쓰인다.
① 전치사(~처럼) ② 부사(~만큼 …한) ③ 접속사(~이기 때문에) ④ 접속사(~이듯이) ⑤ 전치사(~로서)

21 자신의 시계를 가리키는 말이다.

22 글의 흐름상 나라의 완전한 독립을 의미하는 것이므로 'complete'이라고 쓰는 것이 적절하다. *complement: 보충[보족]물

23 나의 소원'에 따르면 김구가 가장 바란 것은 한국의 독립이었다.

24 세 영웅의 시신을 일본에서 한국으로 모셔온 사람은 김구이다.

25 김구의 말이 쓰여 있는 책은 '백범일지'이다.

서술형 시험대비 p.146~147

01 Shanghai, China

02 They went to Hyochang Park last week.

03 A white statue of Kim Koo was (at the entrance of the museum).

04 It was in Shanghai, China.

05 national hero, the independence of Korea

06 The writer saw a photo of the Korean Patriotic Organization's members.

07 It was because he tried to fight against Japan.

08 belonged to the secret group

09 His plan was to kill Japanese generals in a park in Shanghai.

10 exchanged watches

11 It was because he would not forget Yun's sacrifice.

12 They moved to the tombs of the three heroes, Lee Bongchang, Yun Bonggil, and Baek Jeonggi.

13 **일본에 있던 삼의사의 시신을 독립 이후에 효창 공원으로 모셔온 것**

14 The writer read it in the exhibition hall.

15 It(=His third wish) was the complete independence of his country.

01 중국 상해를 가리키는 말이다.

02 글쓴이의 역사 동아리가 지난주에 간 곳은 효창공원이다.

03 기념관 입구에는 하얀색의 김구의 조각상이 있다고 하였다.

04 위 글의 내용에 따르면 대한민국 임시 정부는 중국 상하이에 있었다.

05 김구는 일본 통치로부터 한국의 독립을 위해 싸우는 데 그의 삶 대부분을 보낸 위대한 국민 영웅이다.

06 글쓴이는 한인 애국단 단원들의 사진을 보았다고 하였다.

07 김구가 비밀 조직을 만든 이유는 일본에 맞서 싸우기 위해서라고 하였다.

08 대답으로 미루어 보아 김구가 만든 비밀 조직에 누가 속해 있었는지를 묻는 말을 쓰는 것이 적절하다.

09 김구의 계획은 상해에 있는 한 공원에서 일본 장군들을 암살하는 것이었다.

10 윤봉길은 김구가 지시한 임무를 수행하기 위해 떠나기 전 그와 함께 시계를 교환하였다. exchange: 교환하다

11 윤봉길의 희생을 잊지 않기 위하여 그의 시계를 항상 가지고 다녔다.

12 기념관 관람을 마치고 이봉창, 윤봉길, 백정기 의사들이 묻힌 삼의사의 묘로 이동했다.

13 세 사람의 시신은 일본에 있었지만, 독립 이후에 김구가 그들을 효창 공원으로 모셔온 것을 의미한다.

14 글쓴이는 전시관에서 '나의 소원'을 읽었다고 하였다.

15 김구의 세 번째 소원은 나라의 완전한 독립이라고 하였다.

영역별 핵심문제 p.149~153

01 entrance 02 ⑤ 03 ③ 04 ①

05 (e)xhibition 06 ④

07 He bought many Korean treasures that some Japanese had taken to Japan.

08 You know, don't 09 ②

10 They are planning to visit the Yun Dongju Museum.

11 ③ 12 ⑤ 13 ④ 14 ③

15 (1) so that they can show
(2) so that they could see the *Mona Lisa*

16 (1) had killed (2) had been (3) made
(4) had gone (5) had pulled

17 (1) The rabbit regretted that she had slept in the middle of the race.
(2) The ant reminded the grasshopper that he had played in the summer.

18 ①

19 He built schools in order to help educate young people.

20 ⑤   21 ③   22 found → founded

23 ④   24 ④

25 He formed the Korean Patriotic Organization in 1931.

26 ⑤

01 반의어 관계이다. 독립-의존 : 출구-입구

02 (A) 나는 UN과 같은 국제 조직에서 일하고 싶다. (B) 희생 없는 사랑은 없다.

03 보통 기둥 끝에 붙어 있고 국가나 협회를 대표하는 천 조각: flag(깃발)

04 특정한 결과를 위해 차례로 일어나는 일련의 일들: process(과정)

05 박물관은 피카소 작품을 전시하고 있다.

06 'desire'는 '바람, 갈망'의 뜻이다.

07 대화의 내용상 전형필이 한 훌륭한 일에 대한 글로, 주격인 he를 주어로 시작하여 동사는 bought를 사용하고 목적어로는 many Korean treasures가 오는 것이 적절하다. 그 다음 many Korean treasures를 수식하는 목적격 관계대명사절로 '주어+동사' 어순으로 영작한다.

08 상대방이 알고 있는지 확인하는 표현으로 'You know ~, don't you?'를 사용한다.

09 주어진 문장이 '정말? 난 그걸 몰랐어.'라고 말하고 있으므로 'that'은 앞 문장에 언급된 윤동주의 나라에 대한 사랑과 독립에 대한 염원이 시에서 느껴진다는 것을 가리킨다.

10 질문: 그들은 다음 주 토요일에 무엇을 할 예정인가?

11 보라가 Andy에게 윤동주의 시를 많이 읽어 보라고 제안하는 내용은 대화에서 언급되어 있지 않다.

12 so that 뒤에는 절을 써야 한다. for her to get을 she could get으로 고치는 것이 적절하다. 아니면, so that for her를 삭제해도 무방하다.

13 과거완료시제가 사용된 문장들이다. begin의 과거분사형은 began이 아니라 begun이다.

14 not은 to부정사 앞에 위치해야 한다. in order not for him → in order for him not to

15 (1) 학생들이 좋은 공연을 보여줄 수 있도록 열심히 연습 중이다. (2) 많은 관광객이 모나리자를 보려고 루브르 박물관에 모여들었다.

16 (1), (2), (4), (5) 과거의 어느 특정시점을 기준으로 그 이전에 시작된 일은 과거완료시제로 표현한다. (3) 역사적 사실은 주절의 동사 시제와 상관없이 과거시제를 쓴다.

17 우리말에 맞게 과거완료시제와 주어진 단어들을 적절히 사용하여 배열한다.

18 주어진 문장의 the park는 효창공원을 의미한다. 공원 안에 있는 김구 기념관을 방문했다는 말이 나온 후 기념관 입구에서 김구 선생의 동상을 보았다고 말하는 것이 자연스럽다.

19 젊은이들을 교육시키는 데 도우려고 학교를 설립했다고 하였다.

20 김구는 중국 상해에서 대한민국 임시 정부에 가입하였다.

21 '존경받는 지도자'라는 의미가 자연스럽다. 따라서 과거분사 respected를 쓰는 것이 적절하다.

22 안창호는 1907년 신민회(the New Korean Society)를 설립하였다. find-found-found(발견하다), found-founded-founded(설립하다).

23 안창호가 몇 개의 학교를 설립했는지는 위 글을 읽고 답할 수 없다.

24 모두 '많은(= many)'이라는 의미로 쓰일 수 있지만 'the number of'는 '~의 수'라는 의미이다.

25 김구가 한인 애국단을 조직한 때는 1931년이다.

26 김구는 한인 애국단의 지도자로서 윤봉길에게 일본 장군들을 암살하도록 지시하였다.

단원별 예상문제   p.154~157

01 shallow   02 ③

03 I felt great respect for the people who died for the country. 04 ①   05 ④

06 harmony

07 You know about Yun Dongju, don't you?

08 ⑤

09 It's a museum built by Gansong Jeon Hyeongpil. 또는 It's a museum which[that] was built by Gansong Jeon Hyeongpil.

10 ⑤

11 (1) not to forget (2) so as not to forget (3) in order that

12 ①, ⑤   13 ④   14 ②

15 He built schools to help educate young people.

16 ③   17 ②

18 He built a lot of schools to educate people (until he died in 1938).   19 ④   20 ②

21 상해에 있는 한 공원에서 일본 장군들을 암살하는 것

01 반의어 관계이다. 완전한 - 불완전한 : 깊은 - 얕은

02 왕이나 여왕이 쓰는 금으로 만들어지고 보석으로 장식된 원형 장식물: crown(왕관)

03 '주어(I)+동사(felt)+목적어(respect)'를 먼저 쓰고, 우리말 해석의 '나라를 위해 돌아가신'이 'the people'을 수식하는 구조로

'for the people who died for the country'의 어순을 사용하여 문장을 완성한다.

04 Soyeon이 봉사활동을 한 곳은 박물관이 아니라 현충원이다.

05 대화의 내용상 태극기의 상징이 무엇을 의미하는지 묻는 말이 적절하다.

06 사람들이 평화롭고 서로 동의하거나 일이 옳거나 적절해 보이는 상황.

07 'You know ~, don't you?'는 알고 있는지 물어보는 표현이다.

08 주어인 '나라에 대한 그의 사랑과 독립에 대한 염원'이 느껴질 수 있는 것이므로 수동인 'can be felt'가 적절하다.

09 'It is ~'로 문장의 주어, 동사가 있기 때문에 동사 'was built'를 사용할 수 없다. museum을 수식하는 과거분사 built만 남겨두고 was는 생략해야 한다. 또는 관계대명사를 첨가하여 'which[that] was built'로 고칠 수 있다.

10 모든 빈칸에 들어갈 단어는 so이다. ⑤는 '너무 ~해서 …하다'라는 '결과'를 나타내는 상관접속사 'so ~ that'이다. 나머지는 모두 '목적'을 뜻하는 'so that'이다.

11 목적을 나타내는 'so that'과 같은 의미의 표현들로 'in order that', 'so as to', 'in order to' 등을 활용하도록 한다.

12 과거 이전에 발생한 일은 과거완료시제로 표현한다. ② has overworked → had overworked ③ has been → had been ④번 문장은 내용의 인과관계상 사건의 발생 순서를 바로잡아야 한다. '내가 경기장에 도착했을 때, 1피리어드가 시작되었다.'는 내용이므로 The first period had begun when I arrived at the court.로 하는 것이 적절하다.

13 (a)+(C): Vicky는 그의 아들이 위대한 음악가가 될 수 있게 매일 그에게 클래식 음악을 들려준다. (b)+(D): Kate는 금메달을 따기 위해 지난 4년간 하루 500개씩 슛 연습을 해왔다. (c)+(A): Taylor는 벌금을 물지 않기 위해 연체된 모든 책들을 도서관에 반납했다. (d)+(B): Clara는 건강해지기 위해 정크푸드 섭취를 중단했다.

14 spend+시간+Ving: V하느라 시간을 쓰다

15 1900년대에 김구는 젊은 사람들을 교육하는 데 도움이 되기 위하여 학교를 설립하였다.

16 효창 공원 안에는 김구 기념관이 있다고 하였다.

17 ②번 앞 문장에서는 안창호가 10대 때 서울로 갔다고 하였고, ②번 뒤 문장에서는 안창호의 미국 활동에 대해 이야기하고 있으므로, 안창호가 미국으로 이주했다는 내용은 ②번에 들어가는 것이 적절하다.

18 안창호는 1938년 그가 죽을 때까지 사람들을 교육시키기 위하여 많은 학교를 설립하였다.

19 안창호는 한국으로 돌아와 1907년에 신민회를 설립하였다.

20 (A)는 a plan을 수식하는 형용사로 쓰인 to부정사이다. ①, ④ 부사적 용법 중 목적(~하기 위해서) ② any chance를 수식하는 형용사 ③ 명사적 용법으로 쓰인 진주어 ⑤ 부사적 용법 중 판단의 이유

21 'to kill Japanese generals in a park in Shanghai'를 의미한다.

서술형 실전문제　　　　　p.158~159

01 was built to protect, directed, building process
02 ⓐ allowed, ⓑ to use, ⓒ completed, ⓓ had burnt, ⓔ disappointed, (A) so that, ⓕ like
03 ④ I found out that she had lost her bag.
04 (1) so that it could warm my body
　　(2) which my uncle had bought
　　(3) in order to show
05 in order to / to
06 He founded it to fight for Korea's independence.
07 미국에 있는 한국인들의 삶을 향상시키는 것을 도왔다.
08 My Wish
09 They are in Hyochang Park.
10 desire, love

01 수원 화성은 전쟁 동안 사람들을 보호하기 위해 지어졌다. 정약용이 건설 과정을 감독했다.

02 ⓐ when이 이끄는 부사절이 과거시제이므로 과거동사 allowed, ⓑ 'allow+목적어+목적격보어(to부정사)', ⓒ 30분 전이 과거 시점이므로 과거동사 completed, ⓓ 과거 이전의 시점이므로 had burnt, ⓔ 실망하게 된 것이므로 disappointed ⓕ 조동사 뒤에 동사원형이 나와야 하므로 like, (A)에는 '그가 나를 좋아하도록'의 뜻이 되어야 하므로 2 단어는 'so that'이 적절하다.

03 내가 알아낸 것과 그녀가 가방을 잃어버린 것의 전후 관계를 정리하면, '나는 그녀가 가방을 잃어버린 것을 알아냈다'가 된다. 그에 적절하게 과거완료시제를 사용한다.

04 (1), (3) <보기>의 단어들을 사용하고, 중복 없이 문맥에 맞게 영작해야 하므로, '목적'의 의미를 표현할 때, 'so that 부사절'과 'in order to 부사구'를 어디에 쓰는 것이 좋을지 결정하는 것에 유의한다. (2) 과거완료시제를 적절히 사용한다.

05 so that은 목적을 이끄는 부사절 접속사이다. 따라서 '~하기 위해서'라고 해석되는 in order to 혹은 to부정사 구문으로 대체할 수 있으며, in order to를 대신하여 so as to를 써도 무방하다.

06 안창호가 신민회를 설립한 이유는 한국의 독립을 위해 싸우기 위함이었다.

29

07 미국으로 간 안창호는 미국에 거주하는 한국인들의 삶을 향상시키는 것을 도왔다고 하였다.

08 백범일지에 쓰여 있는 '나의 소원'을 가리키는 말이다.

09 이봉창, 윤봉길, 백정기 삼의사의 묘는 효창 공원에 있음을 알 수 있다.

10 '나의 소원'에 있는 김구의 말은 한국의 독립에 대한 그의 열망과 조국에 대한 그의 사랑을 느끼게 한다.

창의사고력 서술형 문제
p.160

|모범답안|

01 (1) A: You know Dokdo is windy and foggy, don't you?
B: Yes, I heard about it.
(2) A: You know that there is a rock on Dokdo that looks like Korea, don't you?
B: Yes, I heard about it.

02 (1) He shouted so that a passing ship could rescue him.
(2) He used a telescope so that he could better look at the birds.

03 in 1889, who fought against Japanese rule. gathered and trained soldiers, where his soldiers earned one of their greatest victories against Japan

02 어법과 그림에 어울리는 내용으로 적절하게 영작한다.

단원별 모의고사
p.161~165

01 ⑤   02 rule[govern]   03 ①
04 ④   05 ②, ④
06 I'm dying to try it.
07 ⑤   08 ④   09 ①
10 (A) the symbols in Taegeukgi
(B) the black lines
11 (1) was built   (2) built   (3) built
12 (a) You know about   (b) I'm looking forward
13 ②   14 ④   15 ④
16 (1) The goddess said that Pinocchio had lied.
(2) Pooh was stung by bees after he had touched the hive.   17 ④   18 ⑤
19 ④   20 ②   21 ③
22 It shows a lot of things about Kim Koo's life.
23 ⓔ-ⓒ-ⓕ-ⓐ-ⓓ-ⓑ
24 He founded the New Korean Society in 1907 (to fight for Korea's independence).

01 ⑤번은 'statue(조각상)'에 관한 설명이다. 'state(상태)'에 대한 영어 설명은 'a condition or way of being that exists at a particular time'이다.

02 유의어 관계이다. 교육하다 : 통치하다

03 사체를 땅에 묻거나 어떤 것을 땅에 묻고 그것을 덮다

04 안중근에 대해 들어본 적이 있는지 묻는 말에 '아니, 없어. 그는 독립 운동가였어.'라고 답하는 것은 자연스럽지 못하다.

05 대화의 흐름상 '삼계탕을 요리하는 법을 아니?'라고 묻는 말은 어색하다.

06 'be dying to+동사원형'을 이용하여 '몹시 ~하고 싶다'는 기대를 나타낼 수 있다.

07 ⑤번의 'to'는 전치사로 명사나 동명사가 와야 한다.

08 보라가 얼마나 많은 시를 읽기를 원하는지는 대화에서 언급되어 있지 않다.

09 (A)는 'heard'의 목적어를 이끄는 명사절 접속사 'that'이 들어가고, (B)는 선행사 'treasures'를 수식하는 관계대명사절을 이끄는 'that'이 적절하다.

11 (1) 수원 화성이 지어졌다는 수동의 의미를 나타내므로 'be+과거분사'가 적절하다. (2) '누가 그것을 지었니?'라는 능동형 과거동사 'built'가 적절하고, (3)은 'a museum'을 수식하는 과거분사 'built'가 적절하다.

12 (a) You know ~, don't you?는 알고 있는지 물어보는 표현이고, (b) 앞으로 하고 싶은 일에 대한 기대를 표현할 때 'be looking forward to ~.'를 사용한다.

13 ② '~하기 위해서'라는 목적의 부사절을 만들 때, so that 또는 in order that 절 뒤에 can[may] 또는 could[might] 등의 조동사를 쓴다. became을 could[might] become으로 고치는 것이 적절하다.

14 자동차가 짙은 모래먼지로 뒤덮인 것은 하루 종일 황사가 온 탓이고, 과거보다 더 앞선 시점의 일이다. 과거완료시제로 쓰는 것이 적절하다.

15 모두 '목적'을 나타내는 부사절 접속사 'so that'인데, ④번만 '결과'의 의미로 쓰였다.

16 (1) 여신은 피노키오가 거짓말을 했다고 말했다. (2) 푸우는 벌집을 건드린 후에 벌들에게 쏘였다. hive: 벌집

17 김구는 1919년에 중국 상하이로 이동했다고 하였으므로 평생을 한국에서 살았다는 것은 위 글의 내용과 맞지 않다.

18 훗날 임시 정부의 주석이 되었다고 하였으므로 임시 정부를 떠난 것(left)이 아니라 가입한 것(joined)이라고 말하는 것이 적절하다.

19 한인 애국단은 김구가 일본에 맞서 싸우기 위해 1931년에 만든 비밀 조직으로, 이봉창과 윤봉길은 이 조직 소속이었다.

20 carry out은 '수행하다'라는 의미이므로 ②번이 적절하다.

21 밑줄 친 (B)는 목숨을 걸고 임무를 수행하려는 윤봉길의 의지를 나타낸다.

22 전시관은 김구의 삶에 관한 많은 것들을 보여 준다고 하였다.

23 안창호는 10대 때 서울에서 공부하였고(ⓔ) 더 나은 교육을 받기 위하여 미국으로 건너갔다(ⓒ). 미국에 거주하는 한국인들의 삶을 향상시켰고 그는 존경받는 지도자가 되었다(ⓕ). 다시 한국으로 돌아온 안창호는(ⓐ), 신민회를 설립하고(ⓓ) 임시 정부에도 가입하였다(ⓑ).

24 안창호는 한국의 독립을 위해 신민회를 설립하였다.

교과서 파헤치기

Lesson 3

01 충분히; 충분한 02 분석하다 03 출석하다, 참석하다
04 인물, 형상, 사람 모양의 장난감
05 진정시키다, 평온하게 하다 06 출연자들
07 성격 08 세부, 세목 09 개발자
10 매우, 대단히 11 플로리스트, 화초 연구가
12 분석가 13 약함, 약점 14 포함하다
15 ~ 중에서 16 자원 17 지휘하다, 처신하다
18 줄이다, 완화하다 19 전문가 20 다루다
21 생물, 생명체 22 추천하다 23 시인
24 수의사 25 우편집배원 26 선택하다, 고르다
27 화초, 푸른 잎 28 힘, 강점 29 마이크
30 오디션을 보다 31 청진기 32 공연
33 정원사 34 현실적인 35 ~함으로써
36 실현되다 37 ~을 보살피다 38 ~에 만족하다
39 (단체, 조직에) 소속하다, 속하다
40 ~을 최대한 활용하다
41 ~처럼 보이다, ~일 것 같다 42 ~을 확신하다
43 ~을 꿈꾸다

01 personality 02 analyze 03 cast
04 strength 05 stethoscope 06 conduct
07 veterinarian 08 weakness 09 detail
10 select 11 gardener 12 specialist
13 developer 14 microphone 15 highly
16 among 17 florist 18 audition
19 greenery 20 analyst 21 handle
22 include 23 calm 24 responsibility
25 realistic 26 traditional 27 recommend
28 performance 29 creature 30 resource
31 reduce 32 someday 33 engineer
34 enough 35 care for 36 belong to
37 dream of ~ 38 be happy with ~
39 come true 40 by -ing 41 It seems that ~
42 I'm sure that ~ 43 make the best use of

1 cast, 출연자들 2 data, 자료 3 collect, 모으다
4 lead, 이끌다 5 belong to, 소속하다, 속하다
6 responsibility, 책임 7 analyst, 분석가
8 bank teller, 은행 창구 직원 9 greenery, 푸른 잎, 화초
10 personality, 성격 11 resource, 자원
12 analyze, 분석하다 13 include, 포함하다
14 audition, 오디션을 보다 15 developer, 개발자
16 care for, 보살피다

Listen & Speak 1 A

1 planning, police station, police officer / to become, someday / do, too, dreamed of becoming, since / with, ask, something / are, going to ask / what, to do to become / sure, would like to
2 wrong / animator, drawing skill, enough / Being an animator, a, artist / do to become, animator / a lot of, to make, practice drawing / quite sure that, if, try hard

Listen & Speak 1 B

• interested, technology, Which, right / sure, developer
• interested in writing. Which job, be right for / quite sure, be a good job for

Listen & Speak 2 A

1 glad to meet, what you do / guide, different places, information, visit / else / popular culture, traditional / It seems, knowing a lot, happy with, my job
2 finish, role model / wrote, be like / does, do / how to stretch, also helps, reduce, calm themselves / It seems that, to keep both, and

Listen & Speak 2 B

• program writer, become / seems to, writing, helpful
• social worker, help me become / seems, reading books to kids, be helpful

Real Life Talk

most interested, among / interested in working / most interested, among / working, playing / it seems to me that, belong to, realistic / mean / belong to, personality types, Realistic, one of, types / interesting, What kind of, recommend / police officer, and so on / to be / I'm quite sure, soccer player

Communication Task Step 2

3 Ss, 2 As, 1 E / seems to, belong to / Jobs that, recommended, librarian, counselor / have always

wanted / sounds, quite sure that you could

are, doing / looking for, recipe / cook often / to cook, chef someday / make, come true / taking, to think of, creative / I'm quite sure, good chef

---

대화문 TEST Step 2   p.08~10

Listen & Speak 1 A

1 B: Anne, I'm planning to visit the police station to see my uncle. He is a police officer.

G: Oh, I want to become a police officer someday.

B: You do? Me, too. I have dreamed of becoming a police officer since I was ten.

G: Can I come with you, Matt? I want to meet your uncle and ask him something.

B: Sure. What are you going to ask?

G: I want to ask him what I need to do to become a police officer.

B: I see. I'm sure he would like to meet you.

2 M: What's wrong, Jisu?

G: I want to be an animator, but my drawing skill is not good enough.

M: Hmm... Being an animator is not just about a good artist.

G: What should I do to become an animator?

M: Read a lot of books to make good stories and practice drawing every day.

G: Okay, I'll do so.

M: I'm quite sure that you can be a good animator if you try hard.

G: Thank you very much.

Listen & Speak 1 B

• A: I'm interested in technology. Which job would be right for me?

B: I'm quite sure that an app developer could be a good job for you.

• A: I'm interested in writing. Which job would be right for me?

B: I'm quite sure that a writer could be a good job for you.

Listen & Speak 2 A

1 G: I'm glad to meet you, Mr. Han. Could you please tell me what you do?

M: Okay. I guide travelers to different places in China and give them information about where they should visit.

G: What else do you do?

M: I tell them about popular culture and traditional food in China.

G: It seems to me knowing a lot about China is very important. Are you happy with your job?

M: Yes. I really love my job.

2 B: Did you finish the report about your role model?

G: Yes, I did. I wrote about my role model, Ms. Shin. I want to be like her.

B: What does she do?

G: She teaches people how to stretch. She also helps them reduce stress and calm themselves.

B: Good. It seems that she helps to keep both their mind and body healthy.

G: Yes, and I think it's great.

Listen & Speak 2 B

• A: I want to be a radio program writer. What would help me become one?

B: It seems to me writing your own stories would be helpful.

• A: I want to be a social worker. What would help me become one?

B: It seems to me reading books to kids at a hospital would be helpful.

Real Life Talk

Bora: What are you most interested in among the things on this list?

Jessie: I'm most interested in working outside and playing sports.

Bora: Well, it seems to me that you belong to the realistic type.

Jessie: What do you mean?

Bora: Most people belong to one of six personality types. Realistic is one of the types.

Jessie: Oh, that's interesting. What kind of jobs do they recommend for realistic types?

Bora: A farmer, a police officer, a soccer player, and so on.

Jessie: Oh, I have always wanted to be a soccer player.

Bora: That's good. I'm quite sure you could become a great soccer player.

Communication Task Step 2

A: I have 3 Ss, 2 As, 1 I, and 1 E.

B: It seems to me that you belong to Type S.

C: Yes. Jobs that are recommended for Type S are teacher, nurse, librarian or counselor.

A: Cool. I have always wanted to be a teacher.

D: That sounds great. I'm quite sure that you could be

a good teacher.

Wrap Up 1

B: Hello, what are you doing, Sumi?

G: I'm looking for a good recipe on the Internet. I need it for my family dinner today.

B: That is nice. Do you cook often?

G: Yes, I try to cook every weekend. I want to be a chef someday.

B: What are you doing to make your dream come true?

G: I'm taking a cooking class. I try to think of new and creative dishes.

B: I'm quite sure you could be a good chef.

본문 TEST Step 1   p.11~13

01 florist, who creates, with
02 To become, need, things
03 attended, for, gardeners
04 how to, care for
05 days, lot of different
06 movie sets, decorate, with
07 something colorful, fresh, greenery
08 If, highly recommend, become
09 sport data analyst
10 sounds like, doesn't it
11 In fact, work for
12 watch recorded, run, collect
13 analyze, show, strengths, weaknesses
14 If, understands, do better
15 Since, have been, big
16 work, watch, all, time
17 perfect, because watching, hobby
18 As, director, theater, lot
19 audition, look for, voices
20 selecting, cast, each scene
21 put, cast, together, practice
22 During, performance, area, conduct
23 responsibility, each, played, way
24 direct, to keep, together
25 Conducting, directing, waving, around
26 scientist, big field
27 includes studies, creatures living
28 Among, have studied, living
29 growth ring, that interests
30 By looking, out, born
31 used to, resources, manage
32 because, the best use

본문 TEST Step 2   p.14~16

01 florist, who creates, with
02 To become, need to know many things
03 attended, for, gardeners
04 at this school, how to grow, care for
05 These days, a lot of different
06 movie sets, decorate, with flowers
07 something colorful with, greenery
08 plants, highly recommend
09 sport data analyst
10 sounds like, doesn't it
11 In fact, a lot of fun
12 to watch recorded games, run, to collect
13 analyze, to show, weaknesses
14 understands, strengths, do better
15 Since, have been
16 baseball games all the time
17 perfect job, because watching baseball games, hobby
18 As, a musical theater, a lot of
19 audition, look for, voices
20 selecting the cast, for each scene
21 put, cast, together
22 During, performance, conduct
23 my responsibility, each, played, same way
24 direct, to keep, together
25 Conducting, directing, waving
26 ocean scientist, a big field
27 includes, oceans, creatures living in them
28 Among, have studied, living
29 the growth ring, that interests
30 By looking, find out, was born
31 I get from, is used to understand, manage, oceans better
32 because, makes the best use of

본문 TEST Step 3   p.17~18

1 안녕하세요. 저는 Tom입니다. 플로리스트란 꽃으로 아름다운 것들을 창조하는 사람입니다.

2 플로리스트가 되기 위해서 여러분은 꽃에 관해 많은 것을 알 필요가 있습니다.

3 나는 플로리스트와 정원사를 양성하는 고등학교에 다녔습니다.

4 제가 다양한 종류의 꽃을 기르고 다루는 방법을 배운 곳이 바로 이 학교에서였습니다.

5 오늘날, 플로리스트는 많은 다양한 일을 할 수 있습니다.

6 나는 때때로 영화 세트장을 디자인하고 꽃으로 상점을

꾸밉니다.

7 나는 싱싱한 꽃과 화초로 다채로운 무언가를 창조해 낼 때 행복합니다.

8 만약 당신이 식물과 예술을 좋아한다면, 나는 당신에게 플로리스트가 될 것을 강력히 추천합니다.

9 나는 Emma입니다. 나는 스포츠 데이터 분석가입니다.

10 어려운 직업처럼 들리죠, 그렇지 않나요?

11 사실, 그것은 매우 재미있습니다. 나는 야구팀을 위해서 일합니다.

12 나의 일은 녹화된 경기를 보고 자료를 수집하기 위해 컴퓨터 프로그램을 실행하는 것입니다.

13 그러고 나서, 나는 내 팀의 강점과 약점을 보여 주기 위해서 그 자료들을 분석합니다.

14 만약 팀이 자신들의 강점과 약점을 이해하면, 그들은 다음번에 더 잘할 수 있습니다.

15 어렸을 때부터, 나는 야구의 열혈 팬이었습니다.

16 지금, 나는 일하는 중에 내내 야구를 봅니다.

17 야구 경기를 보는 것은 나의 취미이기 때문에 이것은 나에게 완벽한 직업입니다!

18 안녕하세요, 나는 Chris입니다. 뮤지컬 극장 감독으로서 나는 많은 것들을 합니다.

19 나는 배우들을 대상으로 오디션을 실시하고, 훌륭하고 강한 목소리를 찾아냅니다.

20 배역에 맞는 배우를 고른 뒤에, 나는 그들에게 각 장면을 위한 노래를 가르칩니다.

21 그러고 나서, 나는 배우와 오케스트라를 함께 연습시킵니다.

22 공연 동안에, 나는 오케스트라 석에 있고 지휘를 합니다.

23 각각의 노래가 매번 동일하게 연주되도록 만드는 것은 나의 책임입니다.

24 나는 공연을 제대로 진행하기 위해 연주자들과 가수들을 감독합니다.

25 지휘하고 감독하는 것은 단지 내 팔을 흔드는 것만이 아닙니다!

26 나는 예지입니다. 나는 해양 과학자입니다. 해양 과학은 거대한 분야입니다.

27 그것은 바다와 그 안에 살고 있는 생물에 관한 연구를 포함합니다.

28 여러 가지 중에서 나는 한국 주변의 바다에 살고 있는 많은 종류의 물고기를 연구해 왔습니다.

29 나의 흥미를 끄는 것은 바로 물고기 안에 있는 나이테입니다.

30 나이테를 살펴봄으로써, 나는 언제 어디서 그 물고기가 태어났는지 알아낼 수 있습니다.

31 내가 물고기에서 얻은 모든 정보는 바다의 자원을 이해하고 바다를 더 잘 관리하기 위해 사용됩니다.

32 내 직업은 자연을 가장 잘 활용할 수 있게 한다는 점에서 중요합니다.

1 Hi, I am Tom. A florist is someone who creates beautiful things with flowers.

2 To become a florist, you need to know many things about flowers.

3 I attended a high school for florists and gardeners.

4 It was at this school that I learned how to grow and care for different types of flowers.

5 These days, florists can do a lot of different things.

6 I design movie sets sometimes and I decorate shops with flowers.

7 I am happy when I create something colorful with fresh flowers and greenery.

8 If you like plants and the arts, I highly recommend you become a florist.

9 I am Emma. I am a sport data analyst.

10 It sounds like a difficult job, doesn't it?

11 In fact, it is a lot of fun. I work for a baseball team.

12 My job is to watch recorded games and run a computer program to collect data.

13 Then, I analyze the data to show my team's strengths and weaknesses.

14 If the team understands their strengths and weaknesses, they can do better next time.

15 Since I was young, I have been a big fan of baseball.

16 Now, in my work, I watch baseball games all the time.

17 This is a perfect job for me because watching baseball games is my hobby!

18 Hi, I am Chris. As a director of a musical theater, I do a lot of things.

19 I audition the actors and I look for good, strong voices.

20 After selecting the cast, I teach them the songs for each scene.

21 Then, I put the cast and orchestra together for practice.

22 During the performance, I am in the orchestra area and conduct.

23 It's my responsibility to have each song played the same way every time.

24 I direct the musicians and the singers to keep the show together.

25 Conducting and directing is not just about waving my arms around!

26 My name is Yeji. I am an ocean scientist. Ocean science is a big field.

27 It includes studies of the oceans and the creatures living in them.

28 Among other things, I have studied many kinds of fish living in the seas near Korea.

29 It is the growth ring in a fish that interests me.

30 By looking at it, I can find out when and where the fish was born.

31 All the information I get from fish is used to understand sea resources and manage the oceans better.

32 My job is important because it makes the best use of nature possible.

구석구석지문 TEST Step 1 p.24

Enjoy Writing C

1. Dream Job
2. around the world, am good at cooking
3. make food look tasty, beautiful
4. For these reasons, that, when, grow up
5. To achieve, about cooking
6. to learn various cooking skills
7. My role model
8. always thinks, recipes
9. have my name remembered, who enjoy my food

Project

1. WANTED
2. like robots
3. it, are looking for
4. to train, fix robots
5. For, visit our website

Project Step 3

1. Are, good at training, fixing
2. so, a good robot specialist
3. For more information, visit

구석구석지문 TEST Step 2 p.25

Enjoy Writing C

1. My Dream Job
2. I like food from around the world and I am good at cooking.
3. I can also make food look tasty and beautiful.
4. For these reasons, it is a chef that I want to be when I grow up.
5. To achieve my dream, I will read magazines about cooking.

6. Also, I will go to France to learn various cooking skills.
7. My role model is my dad.
8. He always thinks of new recipes and then cooks these new dishes for us.
9. I want to have my name remembered by people who enjoy my food.

Project

1. HELP WANTED!!
2. Do you like robots?
3. If your answer is yes, it is you that we are looking for.
4. Please join us to train and fix robots.
5. For more information, visit our website at www.robots.com.

Project Step 3

1. Are you good at training and fixing robots?
2. If so, we're sure that you'll be a good robot specialist.
3. For more information, visit our websites.

단어 TEST Step 1　　　　p.26

01 점수	02 알람소리, 경보	03 출생, 탄생
04 발언, 논평, 비평	05 연락하다	06 장점, 유리함
07 해독	08 불편한	09 중독
10 단점, 약점, 불리한 점		11 즐거운
12 만들다, 형성시키다		13 필요한
14 시끄러운	15 반, 절반	16 위험한
17 줄이다	18 시민	19 게시하다
20 집중하다	21 대신에	22 창의적인
23 실수	24 ~할 작정이다	25 추측하다
26 제한하다	27 인터넷이나 SNS에 올리는 글	
28 상쾌한	29 존중하다, 존경하다	
30 저작권	31 옥외의, 야외의	32 고통
33 제안하다	34 야기하다, 원인이 되다	
35 사실	36 무료로	37 반면에
38 치우다	39 당장	40 설정하다
41 잠시 동안	42 ~에서 떨어져 있다, ~을 멀리하다	
43 알아내다, 계산하다		

단어 TEST Step 2　　　　p.27

01 addiction	02 birth	03 uncomfortable
04 cause	05 limit	06 post
07 block	08 reduce	09 copyright
10 alert	11 refreshed	12 advantage
13 instead	14 respect	15 noisy
16 disadvantage	17 enjoyable	18 mistake
19 focus	20 comment	21 form
22 intend	23 suggest	24 citizen
25 contact	26 necessary	27 half
28 outdoor	29 pain	30 creative
31 dangerous	32 detox	33 password
34 device	35 for a while	36 put aside
37 such as	38 stay away from	
39 in fact	40 put aside	41 for free
42 figure out	43 on the other hand	

단어 TEST Step 3　　　　p.28

1 birth, 출생　2 half, 반, 절반　3 copyright, 저작권
4 symbol, 상징　5 advantage, 장점
6 comment, 논평, 해설, 비평　7 alert, 경고, 알림
8 device, 기기, 장치　9 intend, ~할 작정이다
10 addiction, 중독　11 message, 메시지
12 contact, 연락하다　13 mistake, 실수
14 digital, 디지털 방식을 쓰는　15 detox, 해독
16 conversation, 대화

대화문 TEST Step 1　　　　p.29~30

Listen & Speak 1 A

1. look tired / until late, so, slept for less than / Playing, is not good for your health / can't stop, addicted / were, would set, to limit

2. spend, much time on / get together, almost, can't help it / If I were you, suggest doing outdoor activities / Outdoor / a lot of, such as / right, suggest

Listen & Speak 2 A

1. are, doing / posting, that, took with / if, could post / because, looks good / not supposed to post, without asking / call, right away

2. let's watch / On / download, for free / supposed to download, from, against, law / Why don't we go, instead, Let's

Real Life Talk

posted strange things on, posted them / figured out, password / What should, do / were, change, password / should / easy to guess / used, birth date / In fact, (You')re not supposed to use, personal information, make a password / change, stronger one

Wrap Up

doing, writing, posting / take / took, from, blog / (you')re not supposed to post / Why not / Because, owner, right to use

대화문 TEST Step 2　　　　p.31~32

Listen & Speak 1 A

1. G: You look tired, Peter.

B: I played computer games until late, so last night I slept for less than four hours.

G: Playing computer games too much is not good for your health.

B: I know, Jenny, but I can't stop it. I think I'm addicted to it.

G: If I were you, I would set a daily plan to limit game time.

B: That's a good idea. Thanks.

2. W: Tony, you spend too much time on your smartphone.

B: My friends get together on SNS almost every day, so I can't help it, Mom.

W: If I were you, I would suggest doing outdoor activities to your friends.

B: Outdoor activities?

W: Yes. You can do a lot of great activities such as soccer or skating.

B: All right. I will suggest them today.

Listen & Speak 2 A

1. G: James, what are you doing?

B: I'm posting some of the pictures that I took with Sarah today.

G: Did you ask Sarah if you could post them online?

B: No, but I think it's okay because she looks good in the pictures.

G: You're not supposed to post someone's pictures without asking.

B: Oh, maybe you're right. I'll call Sarah and ask her right away.

2. G: David, let's watch this new movie on the computer.

B: On the computer?

G: Yes. I have a website we can download it from for free.

B: You're not supposed to download movies from that website, Catherine. It's against the law.

G: Really? I didn't know that.

B: Why don't we go to the movie theater, instead?

G: Okay. Let's go.

Real Life Talk

Bora: Seho, look! Somebody posted strange things on your SNS. I don't think you posted them.

Seho: Really? Who did this?

Bora: I think someone figured out your password.

Seho: What should I do?

Bora: If I were you, I would change my password.

Seho: I think I should.

Bora: Is your password easy to guess?

Seho: I used my birth date.

Bora: That is not good. In fact, it is a big mistake. You're not supposed to use your personal information when you make a password.

Seho: Okay, I see. I will change it to a stronger one.

Wrap Up

B: What are you doing, Sohee?

G: I'm writing a posting about the restaurant I visited today.

B: Those are great pictures. Did you take all of them?

G: No. I took the pictures from someone's blog.

B: Then you're not supposed to post them on your blog.

G: Why not?

B: Because only the blog owner has the right to use them.

G: Oh, I see.

본문 TEST Step 1   p.33~34

01 When, wake up, first

02 read, postings on, smartphone

03 Imagine, near, How, feel

04 check items on, true

05 Are, addicted to

06 Without, feel uncomfortable

07 take, into, bathroom

08 more, spend, on, than

09 check, postings while studying

10 try, reduce, on, fail

11 right after, sound, alert

12 next to, while, eating

13 score, more than half

14 so, problem with, addiction

15 addiction causes, spend, time

16 focus, studies, pain, neck

17 for you to start

18 staying away, such, while

19 lot, freedom from, noisy

20 focus, work, refreshed, creative

21 help, spend, with, others

22 Living without, however, easy

23 necessary, set, rules, using

24 need to follow

25 form, create rules, using

26 turn off, while studying

27 take, smartphone into, bathroom

28 keep, out of, use

29 spend, playing outside without

30 post fewer, messages on

31 were, reduce, by half

32 would turn off, alerts

33 lives, difficult, use, dangerous

34 With, become, wise, user

01 When, wake up in the morning, what
02 read, postings on
03 Imagine, is, near, How
04 check items, that are
05 Are, addicted to
06 Without, feel uncomfortable
07 take, into, bathroom
08 more enjoyable to, on, than with
09 check, postings while studying
10 reduce, I spend on, fail
11 right after, an alert   12 next to, while
13 What, score, check more than half
14 have, with, addiction
15 causes you to spend, on
16 Also, focus on, studies, have a pain in, neck
17 for you to start digital detox
18 means staying away from, for
19 help, a lot, freedom from, noisy
20 focus, on, feel refreshed, creative ideas
21 help, spend, with others
22 Living, however, is
23 necessary for you to set, for using
24 need to follow
25 form, create rules for using
26 turn off, while studying   27 take, into
28 keep, out of the bedroom, them
29 More Time for, spend more time playing outside
    without
30 Fewer, post fewer, on
31 I were, would reduce, on, by half
32 I were, would, off
33 had, would be more difficult, too much, dangerous
34 With, wise smartphone user

1 안녕하세요, 학생 여러분! 여러분은 아침에 일어났을 때, 가장 먼저 하는 일이 무엇인가요?
2 스마트폰으로 SNS 게시물을 읽나요?
3 스마트폰이 여러분 근처에 있지 않다고 상상해 보세요. 기분이 어떤가요?
4 학생 여러분, 이 목록에서 여러분에게 맞는 항목들을 표시해 보세요.
5 너는 스마트폰에 중독되었는가?
6 나는 스마트폰이 없으면, 불편함을 느낀다.
7 나는 스마트폰을 화장실에 가져간다.

8 나는 친구들과 함께 시간을 보내는 것보다 스마트폰을 하면서 보내는 시간이 더 즐겁다.
9 나는 공부하면서 SNS 게시물을 종종 확인한다.
10 나는 스마트폰을 사용하는 시간을 줄이려고 노력하지만, 실패한다.
11 나는 알림음을 듣자마자 스마트폰을 확인한다.
12 나는 식사 중에 스마트폰을 옆에 둔다.
13 여러분의 점수는 어떤가요? 절반보다 더 많이 표시했나요?
14 만약 그렇다면, 여러분은 스마트폰 중독의 문제를 가지고 있을지도 모릅니다.
15 스마트폰 중독은 여러분이 스마트폰에 너무 많은 시간을 보내게 만듭니다.
16 또한 여러분은 학업에 집중할 수 없고 목에 통증이 있을지도 모릅니다.
17 그렇다면 지금 여러분은 디지털 디톡스를 시작할 시간입니다.
18 디지털 디톡스는 스마트폰과 컴퓨터 같은 디지털 기기들로부터 잠시 동안 떨어져 있는 것을 의미합니다.
19 디지털 디톡스는 여러분을 많이 도와줄 것입니다. 여러분은 시끄러운 디지털 세계로부터 자유를 즐길 수 있습니다.
20 여러분은 하는 일에 더욱 집중할 수 있습니다. 종종 여러분은 상쾌함을 느끼고 새롭고 창의적인 아이디어를 얻을 수 있습니다.
21 디지털 디톡스는 또한 여러분이 다른 사람들과 더 많은 시간을 보내도록 도와줄 것입니다.
22 하지만 스마트폰 없이 사는 것은 쉽지 않습니다.
23 그러므로 여러분은 스마트폰을 사용하기 위한 몇 가지 규칙을 정할 필요가 있습니다.
24 그리고 나서 여러분은 그 규칙들을 따라야 합니다.
25 자, 조를 형성하고, 여러분의 조에서, 스마트폰을 사용하기 위한 규칙을 만들어 보세요.
26 우리는 공부하는 동안 스마트폰을 끌 것이다.
27 우리는 화장실에 스마트폰을 가져가지 않을 것이다.
28 우리는 밤에 스마트폰을 침실 밖에 두고 사용하지 않을 것이다.
29 야외 활동을 위한 더 많은 시간 – 우리는 스마트폰 없이 밖에서 노는 데 더 많은 시간을 보낼 것이다.
30 SNS는 더 적게 – 우리는 스마트폰에 SNS 메시지를 더 적게 올릴 것이다.
31 만약 내가 너라면, 나는 스마트폰에 쓰는 시간을 절반으로 줄일 것이다.
32 만약 내가 너라면, 모든 알림을 끌 것이다.
33 잘했어요, 학생 여러분! 만약 스마트폰이 없다면 우리의 삶이 더 힘들겠지만, 스마트폰을 너무 많이 사용하는 것은 위험합니다.
34 디지털 디톡스와 함께, 여러분은 현명한 스마트폰 사용자가 될 수 있습니다.

1 Hi, students! When you wake up in the morning, what is the first thing you do?

2 Do you read SNS postings on your smartphone?

3 Imagine your smartphone is not near you. How do you feel?

4 Students, please check items on the list that are true for you.

5 Are you addicted to your smartphone?

6 Without my smartphone, I feel uncomfortable.

7 I take my smartphone into the bathroom.

8 It is more enjoyable to spend time on my smartphone than with friends.

9 I often check SNS postings while studying.

10 I try to reduce the time I spend on my smartphone, but I fail.

11 I check my smartphone right after I hear the sound of an alert.

12 I have my smartphone next to me while I'm eating.

13 What is your score? Did you check more than half?

14 If so, you may have a problem with smartphone addiction.

15 Smartphone addiction causes you to spend too much time on your smartphone.

16 Also, you cannot focus on your studies and may have a pain in your neck.

17 Then now is the time for you to start digital detox.

18 Digital detox means staying away from digital devices, such as smartphones and computers, for a while.

19 Digital detox will help you a lot. You can enjoy freedom from the noisy digital world.

20 You can focus more on your work. Sometimes you can feel refreshed and have new, creative ideas.

21 Digital detox will also help you spend more time with others.

22 Living without a smartphone, however, is not easy.

23 So, it is necessary for you to set some rules for using your smartphone.

24 You then need to follow the rules.

25 Now, please form groups and, in your group, create rules for using your smartphone.

26 We will turn off our smartphones while studying.

27 We will not take our smartphones into the bathroom.

28 We will keep our smartphones out of the bedroom and not use them at night.

29 More Time for Outside Activities – We will spend more time playing outside without our smartphones.

30 Fewer SNS Messages – We will post fewer SNS messages on our smartphones.

31 If I were you, I would reduce my time on my smartphone by half.

32 If I were you, I would turn off all alerts.

33 You did a good job, students! If we had no smartphones, our lives would be more difficult, but too much use of a smartphone is dangerous.

34 With digital detox, you can become a wise smartphone user.

Enjoy Writing C

1. If There Were

2. would be, advantages, disadvantages, if, were

3. let's talk about

4. If, didn't have, would play outside

5. Plus, would be safe from

6. On the other hand, would be, disadvantages

7. If, would not, for us to contact

8. would take, for us to find information

Project 2

1. It, for us to be, citizens

2. If, Internet, SNS, would be more difficult

3. it, for us to use, wisely

4. respect myself, others

5. share my password with

6. use kind words

7. never use bad words

8. don't spend, much time online

Project 3

1. for everyone to become

2. show, what digital citizens do

3. enjoy

Enjoy Writing C

1. If There Were No Smartphones

2. There would be some advantages and some disadvantagesif there were no smartphones.

3. First, let's talk about some advantages.

4. If we didn't have smartphones, we would play outside more often.

5. Plus, we would be safe from neck pain.

6. On the other hand, there would be some disadvantages.

7. If there were no smartphones, it would not be easy for us to contact people.

8. Also, it would take so long for us to find information.

Project 2

1. It is necessary for us to be digital citizens!

2. If there were no Internet or SNS, our lives would be more difficult.

3. So, it is very important for us to use digital devices wisely as a digital citizen.

4. I respect myself and others on SNS.

5. I never share my password with anyone.

6. I use kind words.

7. I never use bad words.

8. I don't spend too much time online.

Project 3

1. It's very important for everyone to become a digital citizen.

2. Our group will show you what digital citizens do.

3. Please enjoy.

Lesson 5

01 매장, 장례식	02 존경, 경의	03 통치, 지배
04 희생; 희생하다	05 바람, 갈망	06 우편 번호
07 비밀. 비밀의	08 장군	09 정부
10 조화	11 교육시키다	12 전문가
13 퍼지다, 퍼뜨리다	14 먹이를 주다, 먹이다	
15 (정치적, 사회적) 운동		16 ~의 도처에, ~ 내내
17 입구	18 보호하다	19 지도자, 리더
20 주된, 주요한	21 임무	22 묘, 무덤
23 조직, 기구	24 궁전	25 보물
26 애국적인	27 안개 낀	28 대통령, 의장
29 독립	30 감독하다. 지휘[총괄]하다	
31 조각상	32 묻다, 매장하다	33 공화국
34 끝내다; 완전한	35 전시회	36 ~에 속하다
37 ~을 입다	38 ~에 관해 듣다	39 ~가 필요하다
40 ~을 수행하다	41 ~처럼 보이다	42 ~하기 위해서
43 ~을 기대하다		

01 bury	02 secret	03 desire
04 respect	05 government	06 rule
07 educate	08 burial	09 foggy
10 general	11 sacrifice	12 poem
13 independence	14 palace	15 main
16 tomb	17 direct	18 treasure
19 feed	20 patriotic	21 statue
22 protect	23 spread	24 zip code
25 entrance	26 complete	27 leader
28 organization	29 specialist	30 harmony
31 exhibition	32 mission	33 republic
34 throughout	35 movement	36 put on
37 belong to	38 carry out	39 look like+명사
40 be in need	41 hear of	
42 so that+주어+동사		
43 look forward to+명사/동명사		

1 treasure, 보물   2 republic, 공화국

3 exhibition, 전시회   4 mission, 임무   5 palace, 궁전

6 organization, 조직   7 bury, 묻다   8 process, 과정

9 sacrifice, 희생   10 statue, 조각상

11 burial, 매장, 장례식　12 tomb, 무덤

13 amusement park, 놀이공원　14 crown, 왕관

15 poem, 시　16 flag, 깃발

Listen & Speak 1 A

1. Look at, huge / looks strong / Because, was built to protect, during / who built / ordered, to direct, process, don't you / heard of, great scientist

2. don't you / national flag, isn't it / what, symbols, mean / Tell me, them / circle, means harmony, peace / lines, corners mean / mean, earth

Listen & Speak 2 A

1. planning to go / museum built by / heard, great things / bought, treasures that, had taken / must be interesting / looking forward to

2. what did you do / to do volunteer work / What kind of / cleaned around, tombs, respect, who died / Sounds, too / planning to go, join / I'm looking forward to

Real Life Talk

reading / Poetry, know, don't you / heard, much / poems when, under, rule, desire, independence, be felt, poems / to read, poems, learn more / In fact, planning to visit / when, going / near, Palace, palace at / Let's meet / looking forward to, visit

Wrap Up

let put on traditional / gifts for, Germany / there are, gift shops / shopping, for lunch / know, don't you / traditional, soup, delicious, make you healthy / looking forward to trying

Listen & Speak 1 A

1. B: Look at Suwon Hawseong. It's huge.

   G: It also looks strong.

   B: Because it was built to protect the people during wars.

   G: Wow. Do you know who built it?

   B: Yes. King Jeongjo ordered Jeong Yakyong to direct the building process. You know about Jeong Yakyong, don't you?

   G: Yes, I've heard of him. He was a great scientist in Joseon.

2. G: Brian, you know Taegeukgi, don't you?

   B: Sure. It's the national flag of Korea, isn't it?

   G: That's right. Do you know what the symbols in Taegeukgi mean?

   B: No, I don't. Tell me about them.

   G: The circle in the middle means harmony and peace.

   B: What do the black lines on the four corners mean?

   G: They mean four things: sky, fire, water, and earth.

Listen & Speak 2 A

1. G: I'm planning to go to the Gansong Museum.

   B: What is the Gansong Museum?

   G: It's a museum built by Gansong Jeon Hyeongpil.

   B: I heard that he did great things for the country.

   G: Yes. He bought many Korean treasures that some Japanese had taken to Japan.

   B: Wow. The museum must be interesting.

   G: Yes. I'm looking forward to it!

2. B: Soyeon, what did you do last weekend?

   G: I went to Hyeonchungwon to do volunteer work.

   B: What kind of volunteer work did you do there?

   G: I cleaned around the tombs. I felt great respect for the people who diedfor the country.

   B: Sounds great. Can I do it, too?

   G: Sure. I'm planning to go there again next Wednesday. Will you join me?

   B: Sure. I'm looking forward to it.

Real Life Talk

Andy: Bora, what are you reading?

Bora: I'm reading *Sky, Wind, Star, and Poetry* by Yun Dongju. You know about Yun Dongju, don't you?

Andy: I've heard his name, but I don't know much about him.

Bora: He wrote many beautiful poems when Korea was under Japanese rule. His love for the country and his desire for independence can be felt in his poems.

Andy: Really? I didn't know that. I want to read his poems and learn more about him.

Bora: Great. In fact, I'm planning to visit the Yun Dongju Museum soon. Do you want to come with me?

Andy: Yes, when are you going?

Bora: Next Saturday. It's near Gyeongbok Palace.

Can you meet me at the palace at 2 p.m.?

Andy: Sure. Let's meet there.

Bora: Great. I'm really looking forward to the visit.

Wrap Up

B: Tomorrow let's put on traditional Korean clothes, hanbok, and go to Insadong.

G: Good, but I want to buy gifts for my friends in Germany tomorrow.

B: In Insadong, there are many gift shops.

G: Great. After shopping, what should we eat for lunch?

B: Hmm. You know Samgyetang, don't you?

G: No. What is it?

B: It's a traditional Korean soup. It's delicious and will make you healthy.

G: Sounds good. I'm looking forward to trying it.

본문 TEST Step 1 p.52~53

01 Last week, went to

02 visited, inside, park

03 entrance, museum, saw, statue

04 national hero, fighting, independence

05 helped educate, by building

06 movement, spread throughout, moved

07 joined, later became, president

08 exhibition, shows, lot, life

09 While looking around, stopped

10 formed, secret, fight against

11 belonged to, group

12 place, hall, watches under

13 made, plan, kill, generals

14 directed, carry out, mission

15 left, need, anymore, let

16 carried, so, forget, sacrifice

17 completing, tour, tombs, heroes

18 bodies, been, independence, brought

19 By, deep, respect, sacrifice

20 As, thought, words, exhibition

21 was written in

22 what, wish, say clearly

23 second, would, independence, country

24 what, loudly, complete independence

본문 TEST Step 2 p.54~55

01 my history club

02 visited, inside the park

03 At, entrance, white statue

04 a great national hero, spent, fighting, independence, from Japanese rule

05 helped educate, by building

06 In, when the independence movement, throughout, moved to

07 joined, later became its president

08 The exhibition hall, shows

09 While looking around, stopped at, Patriotic Organization's

10 formed, secret organization, to fight against

11 belonged to

12 At, saw two watches under

13 In, made a plan to, Japanese generals

14 Patriotic Organization, directed, to carry out

15 left for, wearing a very old watch, Mine, won't, it anymore, take, let, have

16 always carried, so that, would not forget, sacrifice

17 completing, moved to, tombs, three heroes

18 had been, after, independence, them

19 By doing so, deep love, for the sacrifice

20 As, left, thought, words, that, had read, exhibition hall

21 It, written in

22 what my wish is, clearly, Korea's Independence

23 what my second wish, independence

24 asks me what my third wish is, loudly, complete independence

본문 TEST Step 3 p.56~57

1 지난주에 우리 역사 동아리는 효창 공원에 갔다.

2 우리는 공원 안에 있는 김구 기념관을 방문했다.

3 기념관 입구에서 우리는 하얀색의 김구 조각상을 보았다.

4 김구는 일본 통치로부터 대한의 독립을 위해 싸우는 데 그의 삶 대부분을 보낸 위대한 국민 영웅이다.

5 1900년대에 그는 학교를 설립함으로써 젊은이들을 교육시키는 것을 도왔다.

6 1919년에 3.1 운동이 나라 전체에 걸쳐 퍼져나갔을 때, 그는 중국 상하이로 이동했다.

7 그곳에서 그는 대한민국 임시정부에 합류했고 나중에는 그것의 대표자가 되었다.

8 기념관 안에 있는 전시관은 김구의 삶에 관한 많은 것들을 보여준다.

9 우리는 전시관을 둘러보면서 한인 애국단의 단원들 사진 앞에 섰다.

10 김구는 일본에 맞서 싸우기 위해 1931년에 비밀 조직을 형성했다.

11 이봉창과 윤봉길이 그 집단에 속해 있었다.

12 전시관의 한 곳에서, 우리는 김구와 윤봉길의 사진 아래에 있는 시계 두 개를 보았다.

13 1932년에 김구는 상해에 있는 한 공원에서 일본 장군들을 암살하기 위한 계획을 세웠다.

14 한인 애국단의 지도자로서 그는 윤봉길이 임무를 수행하도록 지시했다.

15 윤봉길이 임무를 위해 떠날 때, 그는 김구에게 말했다. "선생님, 당신은 매우 낡은 시계를 차고 계시는군요. 제 것은 새것이나, 저는 그것이 더 이상 필요하지 않을 것입니다. 부디 제 시계를 가져가시고, 제가 선생님 것을 가지도록 해 주십시오."

16 김구는 윤봉길의 희생을 잊지 않기 위해서 윤봉길의 시계를 항상 상의에 넣고 다녔다.

17 기념관 관람을 마치고, 우리는 이봉창, 윤봉길, 그리고 백정기 의사들이 묻힌 삼의사의 묘로 이동했다.

18 그들의 시신은 일본에 있다가 독립이 되고 나서 김구가 그들의 시신을 효창 공원으로 가져왔다.

19 그는 그렇게 함으로써 삼의사들의 희생에 대한 그의 깊은 사랑과 경의를 보여 주었다.

20 내가 효창 공원을 떠날 때, 나는 전시관에서 읽었던 「나의 소원」에 있는 김구의 말을 생각했다.

21 그것은 「백범일지」에 쓰여 있었다.

22 만약 신이 나의 소원이 무엇이냐고 묻는다면, "그것은 대한 독립이오."라고 명확하게 말할 것이다.

23 만약에 그가 나의 두 번째 소원이 무엇이냐고 묻는다면, 나는 "그것은 내 나라의 독립이오."라고 말할 것이다.

24 만약 그가 나의 세 번째 소원이 무엇이냐고 묻는다면, "그것은 내 나라의 완전한 독립이오."라고 큰 소리로 말할 것 이다. 그것이 나의 대답이다.

1 Last week my history club went to Hyochang Park.

2 We visited the Kim Koo Museum inside the park.

3 At the entrance of the museum, we saw a white statue of Kim Koo.

4 Kim Koo is a great national hero who spent most of his life fighting for the independence of Korea from Japanese rule.

5 In the 1900s, he helped educate young people by building schools.

6 In 1919, when the independence movement had spread throughout the country, he moved to Shanghai, China.

7 There he joined the Government of the Republic of Korea and later became its president.

8 The exhibition hall in the museum shows a lot of things about Kim Koo's life.

9 While looking around the hall, we stopped at a photo of the Korean Patriotic Organization's members.

10 Kim Koo formed the secret organization in 1931 to fight against Japan.

11 Lee Bongchang and Yun Bonggil belonged to the group.

12 At one place in the hall, we saw two watches under a photo of Kim Koo and Yun Bonggil.

13 In 1932, Kim Koo made a plan to kill Japanese generals in a park in Shanghai.

14 As the leader of the Korean Patriotic Organization, he directed Yun to carry out the mission.

15 When Yun left for the mission, he told Kim, "Sir, you are wearing a very old watch. Mine is new, but I won't need it anymore. Please take my watch, and let me have yours."

16 Kim Koo always carried Yun's watch in his jacket so that he would not forget Yun's sacrifice.

17 After completing the tour of the museum, we moved to the tombs of the three heroes, Lee Bongchang, Yun Bonggil, and Baek Jeonggi.

18 Their bodies had been in Japan, but after Korea's independence Kim Koo brought them to Hyochang Park.

19 By doing so, he showed his deep love and respect for the sacrifice of the three heroes.

20 As I left Hyochang Park, I thought about Kim Koo's words in My Wish that I had read in the exhibition hall.

21 It was written in *Baekbeomilji*.

22 If God asks me what my wish is, I would say clearly, "It is Korea's Independence."

23 YIf he asks me what my second wish is, I would say, "It is the independence of my country."

24 If he asks me what my third wish is, I would say loudly, "It is the complete independence of my country." That is my answer.

구석구석지문 TEST Step 1

Real Life Talk Step 3

1. chose, because, were impressed by, sacrifice for
2. can learn more about, by visiting

Enjoy Writing

1. was born in
2. When, in his teens, moved to, went to, there
3. left for, so that, get a better education
4. helped improve the lives, became a respected leader
5. had returned to, founded, to fight for Korea's independence
6. Government of the Republic of Korea
7. built a lot of, to educate, until, died in

Project Step 1

1. to introduce, to foreigners, don't you
2. a temple in
3. one of the most beautiful temples
4. has many treasures like

구석구석지문 TEST Step 2

Real Life Talk Step 3

1. My group members chose An Junggeun because we were impressed by his sacrifice for the country.
2. You can learn more about him by visiting the An Junggeun Museum or An Junggeun Park.

Enjoy Writing

1. An Changho was born in 1878.
2. When he was in his teens, he moved to Seoul and went to school there.
3. In 1902, he left for America so that he could get a better education.
4. In America, An helped improve the lives of the Korean people there and became a respected leader.

5. After he had returned to Korea, he founded the New Korean Society in 1907 to fight for Korea's independence.
6. He also joined the Government of the Republic of Korea in Shanghai in 1919.
7. After that, he built a lot of schools to educate people until he died in 1938.

Project Step 1

1. A: I want to introduce Bulguksa to foreigners. You know Bulguksa, don't you?
2. B: Yes, I do. It's a temple in Gyeongju.
3. C: Yes. It's one of the most beautiful temples in Korea.
4. D: It also has many treasures like the Dabotop.

MEMO

MEMO

MEMO